BY JOSEPH WOOD KRUTCH

Comedy and Conscience After the Restoration
Our Changing Morals (with others)
Edgar Allan Poe: A Study in Genius
The Modern Temper
Five Masters
Living Philosophies (with others)
Experience and Art
Was Europe a Success?
America Now (with others)
The American Drama Since 1918
Samuel Johnson
Henry David Thoreau
The Twelve Seasons
The Desert Year
The Best of Two Worlds
Modernism in Modern Drama
The Measure of Man
The Voice of the Desert
The Great Chain of Life
Grand Canyon: Today and All Its Yesterdays
Human Nature and the Human Condition
The Forgotten Peninsula

EDITED BY JOSEPH WOOD KRUTCH

The Plays of William Congreve
Nine Plays by Eugene O'Neill
Marcel Proust's Remembrance of Things Past
Representative American Dramas
The Selected Letters of Thomas Gray
Great American Nature Writing
The Gardener's World
The World of Animals

The World of
lore, legend and literature by great writers to the present.

COMPILED WITH

1961 SIMON AND SCHUSTER : NEW YORK

Animals  *A treasury of*
and naturalists from the 5th century B. C.

ILLUSTRATED WITH DRAWINGS, WOODCUTS, PRINTS AND PAINTINGS.

COMMENTARY BY **Joseph Wood Krutch**

To the memory of my sister, Mary Krutch

The editor wishes to express his thanks for the indispensable aid given by the following libraries and their staffs: The Library of the University of Arizona; the Library of the University of California at Berkeley; the Library of Congress.

The following authors and publishers have given their kind permission to include copyright material in this volume:

Atheneum Publishers for a passage from *The Firmament of Time* by Loren Eiseley; © 1960 by Loren Eiseley.

A. S. Barnes and Company, Inc., for a passage from *The New Crichton* by Samuel Stevens Hood; © 1949 by Samuel Stevens Hood.

Constable & Company Ltd. for a passage from *Beasts and Saints* by Helen Waddell.

Dodd, Mead & Company for a passage from *The Life of the Scorpion* by Jean Henri Fabre; © 1923 by Dodd, Mead & Company, Inc.

Doubleday & Company, Inc., for a passage from *Footnotes on Nature* by John Kieran; © 1947 by John Kieran.

Farrar, Straus & Cudahy, Inc., for "The Tom Cat" from *Creatures Great and Small* by Colette. "Tomcat Past His Prime" is an older translation of "The Tom Cat." No part of the translation contained in the present volume may be reproduced in any form.

Harper & Brothers for a passage from *The World of Night* by Lourus J. and Margery J. Milne, © 1948, 1953, 1956 by Lourus J. Milne and Margery J. Milne; for a passage from *Lives* by Gustav Eckstein, © 1932 by Harper & Brothers; and for a passage from *Arctic Wild* by Lois Crisler, © 1958 by Lois Crisler, © 1956 by The Curtis Publishing Company.

Harvard University Press for a selection from *The Collected Poems of Christopher Smart,* edited by Norman Callan.

Holt, Rinehart and Winston for a passage from *How to Become Extinct* by Will Cuppy; © 1941 by Will Cuppy.

Alfred A. Knopf, Inc., for a passage from *This Simian World* by Clarence Day, © 1920 by Clarence Day; and for a passage from *Essays of a Biologist* by Julian Huxley, © 1923 by Alfred A. Knopf, Inc.

The Macmillan Company for a passage from *The Friendly Arctic* by Vilhjalmur Stefansson; © 1921 by The Macmillan Company.

William Morrow and Company, Inc., for a passage from *The Voice of the Desert* by Joseph Wood Krutch; © 1954, 1955 by Joseph Wood Krutch.

G. P. Putnam's Sons for a passage from *The Book of Beasts* by T. H. White.

Simon and Schuster, Inc., for a passage from *The River of Life* by Rutherford Platt, © 1956 by Rutherford Platt.

The Viking Press, Inc., for a passage from *Sea of Cortez* by John Steinbeck; © 1941 by John Steinbeck and Edward F. Ricketts.

Vineyard Gazette for a passage on the Heath Hen.

The World Publishing Company for a passage from *The Best of McDermott;* © 1959 by The World Publishing Company.

Lewis Wayne Walker for "Elegant Tern vs. Heermann's Gull."

Mrs. Enos A. Mills for a chapter from *Wild Life on the Rockies* by Enos A. Mills.

Dr. William Beebe for a passage from *Edge of the Jungle.*

Contents

🐆 SECTION FIVE

LEGENDS, FANTASIES, AND FICTIONS

﹋ SECTION SIX
FROM ARISTOTLE TO DARWIN TO?

﹋ SECTION SEVEN
DESTRUCTION AND CONSERVATION

&ea; SECTION EIGHT

HEAD AND HEART

Illustrations

The dragon on the jacket and title page is from *A History of Four Footed Beasts* by Edward Topsell, London, 1658 (*courtesy of the New York Public Library*), and the zodiac sign of Leo is from the first German edition of the work of Hyginus, Augsburg, 1491 (*by special permission of the Spencer Collection, New York Public Library*).

The illustrations on page 1 are from *Dialogus Creaturarum*, Stockholm, 1483. (*Courtesy of the New York Public Library.*)

following page 32

ANIMAL STUDIES, by Francesco Castiglione. (*Courtesy of the Metropolitan Museum of Art, Rogers Fund, 1908.*)

ST. JEROME IN HIS STUDY, by Albrecht Dürer. (*Courtesy of the New York Public Library, Prints Division.*)

PEACEABLE KINGDOM, by Edward Hicks. (*Courtesy of the Abby Aldrich Rockefeller Folk Art Collection, Williamsburg, Va.*)

STELA OF HORUS ON THE CROCODILES, Egyptian, 3320–30 B.C. (*Courtesy of the Metropolitan Museum of Art, Rogers Fund.*)

following page 64

JONAH CAST UP BY THE WHALE, illustration from *Jami at-Tawarikh* by Rashid ad-Din, Fadl Allah, Persian, ca. 1400. (*Courtesy of the Metropolitan Museum of Art, Purchase, 1933, Joseph Pulitzer Bequest.*)

FISH and SEA SERPENT, from *Historiae animalium* by Konrad Gesner, Zurich, 1551. (*Courtesy of the New York Public Library.*)

WATER BUFFALO WITH BOY, English Staffordshire ceramic, ca. 1750. (*Courtesy of the Metropolitan Museum of Art, Gift of R. Thornton Wilson, 1941.*)

following page 128

HUNTING SCENE, from MS. of the *Diwan* (Persian) by Jami, 15th century. *(Courtesy of the Metropolitan Museum of Art, Gift of Alexander Smith Cochran, 1913.)*

NATIVE CALIFORNIANS LASSOING A BEAR, by F. O. C. Darley, from *Pittoresque America* by William Collin Brant, New York, 1872. *(Courtesy of the New York Public Library.)*

FAWN, by Pablo Picasso, from Buffon's *Histoire Naturelle,* Paris, 1942. *(Courtesy of the New York Public Library.)*

PORCUPINE, from *A History of Four Footed Beasts* by Edward Topsell, London, 1658. *(Courtesy of the New York Public Library.)*

BOARS, from *Historiae animalium* by Konrad Gesner, Zurich, 1551. *(Courtesy of the New York Public Library.)*

following page 160

TIGER, from *A History of Four Footed Beasts* by Edward Topsell, London, 1658. *(Courtesy of the New York Public Library.)*

RHINOCEROS, by Albrecht Dürer. *(Courtesy of the New York Public Library, Prints Division.)*

FIGURE OF A CYNOCEPHALUS APE, Egyptian ceramic work, XXVI Dynasty, 663–525 B.C. *(Courtesy of the Metropolitan Museum of Art, Carnarvon Collection, Gift of Edward S. Harkness, 1926.)*

LEOPARD, Nigerian bronze, 16th–17th century. *(Courtesy of the Museum of Primitive Art, photograph by Charles Uht.)*

following page 256

WEATHER COCK, French metalwork, 15th century. *(Courtesy of the Metropolitan Museum of Art, Gift of J. Pierpont Morgan, 1916.)*

BULL, by Pablo Picasso, from Buffon's *Histoire Naturelle,* Paris, 1942. *(Courtesy of the New York Public Library, Prints Division.)*

MILKMAID AND COW, English Staffordshire ceramic, 18th century. *(Courtesy of the Metropolitan Museum of Art, Gift of Mrs. Francis P. Garvan, 1941.)*

GOAT AND RAM, drawing of the Italian School, Lombardy, 15th century. *(Courtesy of the Pierpont Morgan Library.)*

Introduction

Man shares the earth with many other living things and he has dealt with them in many different ways. They have furnished him food, done his work, aroused his curiosity, provided him with "sport," stimulated his sense of beauty, and provoked his wonder. They have also usually returned his affection when he has deigned to give it.

No less varied and hardly less inevitable are the conscious or unconscious attitudes he has found himself taking toward them. To many they still are, as to many they have always been, merely useful or useless; hence to be summarily classified as "domestic animals," "game animals," or "vermin." But insofar as man, either primitive or modern, has had any tinge of philosophy he has also asked questions. Why did God bother to create them or, in terms of a different vocabulary, what is their "place in nature"? Were they put on earth merely to serve man's need or pleasure and, as one medieval writer is said to have maintained, were they endowed with life only in order that their flesh should not decay before some human being got around to eating them? Are they, on the other hand, to some degree fellow creatures with some rights and privileges of their own? How much do they resemble and how greatly do they differ from man himself? What conclusions are to be drawn from the likeness and the difference?

For all these reasons a collection of writings about animals is also about the men who have been moved, for one reason or another, to write on that subject. Sometimes consciously and sometimes unconsciously (but always inevitably) the writer implies an answer to one or more of the questions which any concern with an animal must raise, and this is quite as true in the case of one who describes merely how he collected a trophy as in that of the biologist or the mystic.

The present selection from a vast literature has been made with these facts in mind. It is not a source book because it pretends to no completeness and because no item is included merely to illustrate some point, however important. My first test was readability and I hoped to include nothing which did not justify itself on that basis. But I hoped also that every narrative, or description, or exposition would also contribute something to an over-all picture of man's relations with and attitudes toward the animal kingdom. And it is a remarkable fact, illustrated by the chronological arrangement within the different categories, that almost every major attitude and activity which has ever existed still exists today even though, as I believe, there has been a drift in certain directions.

My categories are not inevitable or formally logical; but they seem to me convenient if, as I must confess, not always mutually exclusive. Since in most cases the writers were not deliberately classifying themselves or writing to fit my arrangement it is inevitable that the hunter may be also an explorer, the scientist also a nature lover and the portraitist also a philosopher. There are, I will readily grant, some pieces which might have been appropriately put in either of two or, perhaps, in any one of more than two sections. But none, I hope, is actually out of place or fails to illustrate to some extent the activity or the attitude which is the major subject of the section.

Still another confession I should make: I am not neutral, and this anthology is to some extent "loaded." I have tried to represent fairly the hunter and the sportsman as well as the "objective scientist," but my own sympathies lie with those to whom the animal world is, first of all, something to be loved and learned from rather than merely to be studied or exploited. In defense as well as explanation of my prejudice—if prejudice it is—I take the opportunity of this introduction to trace an historical development and to justify it if I can.

Different as we are from the other creatures with whom we share the earth, one tremendous fact remains: we are all "alive," whatever that most mysterious of adjectives may mean.

This fact may seem too obvious to deserve mention, but let us imagine that the situation were (as it might be) otherwise. Suppose we were the only living creatures; that we nourished ourselves as plants do on dead minerals; or, perhaps, that we were pure lonely spirits, the only sentient creatures in the universe. If that were true, then the whole experience of being human would be vastly different from what it is— more different, I suppose, to some than to others, but different for everybody.

The late distinguished entomologist William Morton Wheeler, whom no cool scientist could accuse of being a mere sentimental "nature lover," once wrote:

Why animals and plants are as they are we shall never know; of how they came to be what they are, our knowledge will always be extremely fragmentary; but that organisms *are* as they are, that apart from members of our own species they are our only companions in an infinite and unsympathetic waste of electrons, planets, nebulae and stars, is a perennial joy and consolation.

If we look at the history of man's thoughts, emotions and behavior, we shall see that throughout all history he has oscillated perpetually between feeling something akin to what Wheeler so clearly states and not feeling anything of the kind.

We know that most primitive men were deeply concerned with the question of their relation to animals and that, on the whole, they tended to emphasize their closeness rather than their remoteness. To animals they often attributed a consciousness much like their own and they made of them ancestors, fellow creatures, or gods. Though they might live by hunting, they often found it desirable to placate their victims and sometimes offered formal apology for killing or eating them. In many cultures, of course, the clan system was based upon the assumption that each group was most closely identified with one animal rather than another.

The Hebraic tradition, on the other hand, tended to go to the other extreme. The reason perhaps was, not any impulse toward cruelty, but simply that the new monotheism was aware how easily deep concern with animals leads to animal gods and to polytheism. Consequently, it tended to insist upon the absolute uniqueness of man; and from that it encouraged the notion that all other living creatures exist only to serve man's needs.

In Genesis, God instructs Adam to this effect and after the flood He is even more explicit to Noah. Here is the verse:

> And the fear of you and the dread of you shall be upon every beast of the earth, and upon every fowl of the air, upon all that moveth upon the earth, and upon all the fishes of the sea; into your hand are they delivered.

God, in other words, is absolutely distinct from man; man absolutely distinct from all other living things. Man is at God's mercy; everything else is at man's.

Though it was not, perhaps, the intention, this verse seems to predict the whole history of man's cruelty to what are, from a different point of view, his fellow creatures. Most animals who have had any contact with man throughout most history have had good reason to go "in the fear of him and in the dread of him."

Early Christianity took a position consistent with Genesis. According to the Catholic Encyclopedia, the doctrine of St. Thomas Aquinas was that man alone has a soul or a *persona* and that, since God is concerned with the soul only, animals have no rights. Cruelty to them is not, per se, sinful. This seemingly harsh doctrine St. Thomas neutralized to some extent by pointing out that though cruelty to animals is not evil per se it leads easily to cruelty to men and is therefore the cause of evil if not evil in itself. But even this corollary has not always been taken into consideration, and theology, as distinguished from the feeling encouraged by the Christian spirit, is anti-humanistic in its attitude toward other living things. Christian feeling, on the other hand, has certainly helped produce a civilization in which the rights of animals are much more likely to be recognized than they ever were before.

Despite all the ambiguities in contemporary attitudes, despite all the differences between individual feelings and behavior, there is no doubt that society, as it expresses itself in laws and customs, has become increasingly "humane," as we call it. Nominally, cruelty to animals is today a crime—either because animals have rights, because we are fellow creatures, or perhaps, as Catholic doctrine has it, because it encourages cruelty to men. Thus the law conforms to our sentiment rather than to any specific doctrine, and it can easily be shown that, historically, sentiment preceded law.

It would probably surprise most people to learn how recently in Anglo-American history were passed any laws at all regulating the treatment of animals. Gardens for bull-baiting and other blood sports were not legally abolished in England until 1835. It was only thirteen years earlier that the very first English law made the inhumane treatment of animals an offense per se. Up to that time, such treatment was an offense only if it could be shown that it depreciated the value of another's property. You could, in other words, torture your dog if it amused you to do so, but were forbidden to beat another man's horse severely enough to damage the man financially. As late as 1794 a judge in England ruled that "in order to convict a man of barbarous treatment of a beast, it should appear that he had malice towards *the possessor*"—that is to say, malice toward the owner of the beast, rather than toward the beast itself.

The change which came about in law and in public attitudes

was no doubt due less to any new doctrine, either theological or other, than to an increased intensity of imagination, an enlargement of sympathy, and a growing tendency to "feel into" or, as the psychologists call it, toward empathy. But so far as the history of our explicit ideas is concerned, the great change was announced by the early students of what we have now learned to call biology.

The classical expression of this new attitude was first put forth fully in English by the first great English student of natural history, John Ray. In addition to many technical contributions to that emerging science, Ray published in 1691 a book widely read for almost a hundred years thereafter, and called, *The Wisdom of God Manifest in the Works of His Creation*. It is, first of all, a defense of, and a plea for, a study of nature as well as the study of books. But in the course of that plea, it reverses the prevalent convictions concerning the all-importance of man only to God and to himself. Reduced to its barest outlines, Ray's two fundamental propositions are:

(1) Animals other than man were not created merely to serve man, but for their own sakes, as well as for his. Or, as he puts it: "If a good man be merciful to his beast then surely a good God takes pleasure that all his creatures enjoy themselves that have life and sense and are capable of enjoying."

(2) God can be known chiefly through His works, and animate nature is the most wonderful of these works. Man's duty, as well as pleasure, is therefore to examine, to study, and to admire them.

"Let us then consider the works of God and observe the operation of His hands. Let us take notice of and admire His infinite goodness and wisdom in the formation of them. No creature in the sublunary world is capable of doing this except man, and yet we have been deficient therein."

Note especially the last sentence. Man is unique, not because he alone is worth God's bothering with, but because he alone is capable of observing, understanding and admiring the infinitely complex world of nature which God created. Notice also that Ray is the humanistic scientist here, in contrast to his recent predecessor Francis Bacon to whom science sometimes seemed to mean chiefly utilitarian technology.

A generation after Ray's book was published, Alexander Pope put the new attitude into epigrammatic form in his *Essay on Man*, one of the most widely read poems ever written. Here is the crucial passage:

> Has God, thou fool! work'd solely for thy good,
> Thy joy, thy pastime, thy attire, thy food? . . .

> Is it for thee the lark ascends and sings?
> Joy tunes his voice, joy elevates his wings.
> Is it for thee the linnet pours his throat?
> Loves of his own and raptures swell the note.
> The bounding steed you pompously bestride,
> Shares with his lord the pleasure and the pride. . . .
>   Know, Nature's children all divide her care;
> The fur that warms a monarch, warm'd a bear.
> While Man exclaims, "See all things for my use!"
> "See man for mine!" replies a pamper'd goose:
> And just as short of reason he must fall,
> Who thinks all made for one, not one for all.

A hundred years before Pope, John Donne had warned that no man is an island, meaning, not joined to other men. Pope adds that mankind itself is not an island, that just as man is involved with all other men, so is mankind involved with all living things.

What this amounts to, if you like, is something parallel to the Copernican revolution in astronomy. The latter removed earth from the central position and made it only a planet revolving around the central sun. Now a student of animate nature removed man from the position in which he had imagined himself as the center and whole meaning of living creation and made him, too, only a major planet. The parallel is not exact. The earth is not even a major planet—to the astronomer it accounts for little in the universe. Man, on the other hand, remains the most remarkable, certainly, of all living creatures. But he is great only among others which are lesser, though not insignificant; which have a meaning that is subservient, but not inconsiderable, compared to his. He is the major planet but he is not the sun itself. And perhaps he owes his pre-eminence less, as he too often thinks, to his ingenuity and his power than to the fact stressed by Ray: He alone is capable of contemplation and thus, to some extent, of grasping the great thing of which he is a part.

Thus what I chose to call the humanistic attitude as opposed to either the theological or the purely scientific was first clearly stated by a biological scientist who was, as is not always the case, a humanist also.

In history, the conflict between humanistic and anti-humanistic biology began almost as soon as the humanistic attitude was clearly defined. The major villain, curiously enough, was that great mathematician and philosopher, Descartes, who possessed one of the most astonishing minds in all history. He was, however, the victim of one great and fatal aberration for, to put it as simply as possible, he maintained that, all appearance to the contrary, men and other living creatures are absolutely and totally different. Animals are only machines. They seem to enjoy or to suffer, but that is only an illusion. They have no souls; they are therefore not even conscious. As many of his enthusiastic disciples believed and as one of them phrased it, "Animals eat without pleasure; they cry without pain; grow without knowing it; they fear nothing; they know nothing." I call this an aberration of a great man. It is hard to believe that hundreds of people not only believed such statements but acted upon them.

Fortunately, not all seventeenth-century scientists were Cartesians. Some protested against the ruling doctrine; even more important, perhaps, were the pure humanists, the poets and essayists who protested directly or indirectly: Pope himself, Dr. Johnson, and, of course, Blake, Cowper and Burns. In fact, the reaction against Cartesianism may be in part responsible for the phenomenal growth of what we call humanitarianism in the eighteenth century. As a result of it, there is an indescribable difference between, say, even Shakespeare and most eighteenth-century writing, in the implied attitude toward living things other than man.

No one would, I suppose, today call himself a Cartesian. But the tendency to move in that direction is always present. In its mildest form it is the tendency to regard animals as so nearly machines that any attempt to consider their mental or emotional life is dismissed as mere sentimentality or anthropomorphism. In its technical aspect, it is the father of behaviorism, the attempt to reduce all animal behavior to instinct and the conditioned reflex. Nor do those to whom this seems at least a useful method always remember the corollary that man also is an animal, therefore also a machine, and hence to be studied as such by biologists and psychologists, to be manipulated by propagandists and advertisers, but never to be considered a sentient, self-directed human creature.

There is today a small but vigorous minority which maintains that if man is to escape the fate with which he is threatened—if he is not to be considered a machine and treated as such—only theology can save him by emphasizing, not his fellowship with all life, but his separateness from the rest of the animal creation. But my own conviction is that such absolute separateness can never be affirmed again for the simple reason that so much of man actually is animal. Mankind, like the individual man, is not an island. All living things are in this together.

Yet the fact remains that man has never before been in a world which he is coming more and more to dominate, where he has so little to do with other living creatures; indeed, he threatens to crowd them off the face of the earth.

Until very recently no one talked about "conservation" because until very recently man had little effect upon the world as a whole except, perhaps, in very limited areas. What needed conservation was man and his civilization. Now it is the other way around. Now the question is, can anything except man be conserved?

To most people conservation means no more than the efficient exploitation of natural resources to produce comfort and wealth. Its premise is the old premise that only man and his utilitarian needs count. During most of American history that premise was workable. There was so much on our continent that it seemed inexhaustible, and the problem was how to tame and to use the wilderness. A generation ago we woke up to the fact that the frontier was disappearing and that there might conceivably be an end to the resources. Hence we began to talk about conservation—usually in the narrow sense—without changing our fundamental premise. By this token, conservation means no more than careful exploitation with some concern for the needs of the future as well as of the present.

Henry Thoreau, while still a student at Harvard, delivered an oration in which he said:

> This curious world which we inhabit is more wonderful than it is convenient; more beautiful than it is useful; it is more to be admired than to be used.

Perhaps Thoreau's "more to be admired than to be used" is an exaggeration—he liked to exaggerate—for we must, of course, use it too. But the exaggeration is a good counterstatement to the prevalent opinion. Just as individual men cannot live successfully unless they live for something more than merely making a living, so, too, we must regard the earth on which we live as something more than merely that which furnishes us with a living. We should gladly assume—whatever words we use—that "Nature's children all divide her care" and that they are all demonstrations of "the wisdom of God."

In this anthology many men describe many of nature's children and reveal at the same time to what extent they find them beautiful as well as useful, to be admired as well as used.

J. W. K.

PROFILES AND PORTRAITS

I went to the animal fair,
The birds and the beast were there.

Old Song

He created in heaven the angels and on earth the worms; nor was He su-
perior in the one case or inferior in the other. If no other hands but his
could create the angels, neither could any other create the worms.

PSEUDO-AUGUSTINE
(4th century A.D.)

What can be compared with the size of the elephant, the fleetness of the
horse, the strength of the aurochs, the cruelty of the tiger, the splendor of
the peacock, the jaws of the shark, the mouth of the crocodile, the poison
of the cobra, the song of the nightingale?

CAROLUS LINNAEUS
Thoughts on Nature Study and Physics

Sporting the lion ramped, and in his paw
Dandled the kid; bears, tigers, ounces, pards
Gambolled before them, the unwieldy elephant
To make them mirth used all his might and wreathed
His lithe proboscis.

JOHN MILTON
Paradise Lost

Behemoth

[The simplest approach to natural history is the word-portrait of an animal in a form that has persisted from Biblical days to the present, sometimes recognizable even to details.

"Hast thou given the horse his strength?" demanded the Hebrew poet. "He paweth in the valley, and rejoiceth in his strength: he goeth on to meet the armed men. He mocketh at fear, and is not affrighted; neither turneth he back from the sword. The quiver rattleth against him, the glittering spear and the shield. He swalloweth the ground with fierceness and rage. . . . He saith among the trumpets, Ha, ha; and he smelleth the battle afar off, the thunder of the captains, and the shouting."

Fifteen hundred years later the monk Bartholomew Anglicanus would write in his encyclopedia: "Horses be joyful in fields, and smell battles, and be comforted with the noise of trumpets to battle and to fighting." Four centuries after that, Buffon, the most worldly of naturalists, strikes the same note: "This noble animal partakes of the fatigues of war, and seems to feel the glory of victory. Equally intrepid as his master, he encounters danger and death with ardour and magnanimity. He delights in the noise and tumult of arms, and annoys the enemy with resolution and alacrity."

Let us begin, then, with the most eloquent of portraits, that of the half-fabulous behemoth. He may have begun as a hippopotamus but soon became, in the imagination of the oriental poet, the symbol of that beastliness which he thought of as the antithesis of both the divine and the human.]

Behold now behemoth, which I made with thee;
He eateth grass as an ox.
Lo now, his strength is in his loins,
And his force is in the navel of his belly.

He moveth his tail like a cedar:
The sinews of his stones are wrapped together.
His bones are as strong pieces of brass;
His bones are like bars of iron.
He is the chief of the ways of God:
He that made him can make his sword to approach unto him.
Surely the mountains bring him forth food,
Where all the beasts of the field play.
He lieth under the shady trees,
In the covert of the reed, and fens.
The shady trees cover him with their shadow;
The willows of the brook compass him about.
Behold, he drinketh up a river, and hasteth not:
He trusteth that he can draw up Jordan into his mouth.
He taketh it with his eyes:
His nose pierceth through snares.

Canst thou draw out leviathan with an hook?
Or his tongue with a cord which thou lettest down?
Canst thou put an hook into his nose?
Or bore his jaw through with a thorn?
Will he make many supplications unto thee?
Will he speak soft words unto thee?
Will he make a covenant with thee?
Wilt thou take him for a servant for ever?
Wilt thou play with him as with a bird?
Or wilt thou bind him for thy maidens?
Shall the companions make a banquet of him?
Shall they part him among the merchants?
Canst thou fill his skin with barbed irons?
Or his head with fish spears?
Lay thine hand upon him,
Remember the battle, do no more.
Behold, the hope of him is in vain:
Shall not one be cast down even at the sight of him?
None is so fierce that dare stir him up:
Who then is able to stand before me?
Who hath prevented me, that I should repay him?
Whatsoever is under the whole heaven is mine.

THE BOOK OF JOB

Medieval Lion

[*Natural history as a science began with the Greeks—as what, indeed, did not? But it died almost as soon as it was born, and for at least a millennium and a half men eagerly devoured in innumerable versions what were known as "bestiaries." Probably they all go back to some lost original, but every copyist and compiler added whatever fact or fancy happened to occur to him. Wherever possible he drew a moral, no matter how farfetched, for he never doubted that every fact was also a symbol. Nevertheless he told the truth as he saw it even though he knew only by hearsay most of the animals whose portraits he tried to draw. One of the best of the bestiaries is to be found in a Latin manuscript of the twelfth century.*]

Leo the Lion, mightiest of beasts, will stand up to anybody.

The word 'beasts' should properly be used about lions, leopards, tigers, wolves, foxes, dogs, monkeys and others which rage about with tooth and claw—with the exception of snakes. They are called Beasts because of the violence with which they rage, and are known as 'wild' (*ferus*) because they are accustomed to freedom by nature and are governed (*ferantur*) by their own wishes. They wander hither and thither, fancy free, and they go wherever they want to go.

The name 'Lion' (*leo*) has been turned into Latin from a Greek root, for it is called '*leon*' in Greek—but this is a muddled name, partly corrupted, since '*leon*' has also been translated as 'king' from Greek into Latin, owing to the fact that he is the Prince of All Animals.

They say that the litters of these creatures come in threes. The short ones with curly manes are peaceful: the tall ones with plain hair are fierce.

The nature of their brows and tail-tufts is an index to their disposition. Their courage is seated in their hearts, while their constancy is in their heads. They fear the creaking of wheels, but are frightened by fires even more so.

A lion, proud in the strength of his own nature, knows not how to mingle his ferocity with all and sundry, but, like the king he is, disdains to have a lot of different wives.

Scientists say that Leo has three principal characteristics.

His first feature is that he loves to saunter on the tops of mountains. Then, if he should happen to be pursued by hunting men, the smell of the hunters reaches up to him, and he disguises his spoor behind him with his tail. Thus the sportsmen cannot track him.

It was in this way that our Saviour (i.e. the Spiritual Lion of the Tribe of Judah, the Rod of Jesse, the Lord of Lords, the Son of God) once hid the spoor of his love in the high places, until, being sent by the Father, he came down into the womb of the Virgin Mary and saved the human race which had perished. Ignorant of the fact that his spoor could be concealed, the Devil (i.e. the hunter of humankind) dared to pursue him with temptations like a mere man. Even the angels themselves who were on high, not recognizing his spoor, said to those who were going up with him when he ascended to his reward: 'Who is this King of Glory?'

The Lion's second feature is, that when he sleeps, he seems to keep his eyes open.

In this very way, Our Lord also, while sleeping in the body, was buried after being crucified—yet his Godhead was awake. As it is said in the *Song of Songs*, 'I am asleep and my heart is awake', or, in the Psalm, 'Behold, he that keepeth Israel shall neither slumber nor sleep.'

The third feature is this, that when a lioness gives birth to her cubs, she brings them forth dead and lays them up lifeless for three days—until their father, coming on the third day, breathes in their faces and makes them alive.

Just so did the Father Omnipotent raise Our Lord Jesus Christ from the dead on the third day. Quoth Jacob: 'He shall sleep like a lion, and the lion's whelp shall be raised.'

So far as their relations with men are concerned, the nature of lions is that they do not get angry unless they are wounded.

Any decent human ought to pay attention to this. For men do get angry when they are not wounded, and they oppress the innocent although the law of Christ bids them to let even the guilty go free.

The compassion of lions, on the contrary, is clear from innumerable examples—for they spare the prostrate; they allow such

The Whale, the Unicorn and the Pussy Cat

[One long step above the bestiaries in literary style and at least one short step forward in the direction of more accurate information is the compendium of universal knowledge De Proprietatibus Rerum written in Latin in the thirteenth century by the English monk Bartholomaeus Anglicus and translated into wonderful English a century later. It would be unfair to expect Bartholomew to know much about the whale or to doubt the existence of the unicorn, but there is keen observation and a touch of empathy in his description of the domestic cat, often to be found in medieval monasteries despite frequent expressions of disapproval by ecclesiastical authorities.]

An Unicorn is a right cruel beast, and hath that name for he hath in the middle of the forehead an horn of four foot long; and that horn is so sharp and so strong, that he throweth down all, or thirleth all that he reseth on. And this beast fighteth oft with the elephant. And the Unicorn is so strong, that he is not taken with might of hunters; but a maid is set there as he shall come, and she openeth her lap, and the Unicorn layeth thereon his head, and leaveth all his fierceness, and sleepeth in that wise, and is taken as a beast without weapon, and slain with darts of hunters. The Unicorn froteth [rubs] and fileth his horn against stones, and sharpeth it, and maketh it ready to fight in that wise. And his colour is bay. There be many kinds of Unicorns, for some be Rhinoceros (q.v.), and some *Monoceron,* and *AEgloceron.* And *Monoceron* is a wild beast, shaped like to the horse in body, and to the hart in head, and in the feet to the elephant, and in the tail to the boar, and hath heavy lowing, and an horn strutting in the middle of the forehead of two cubits long. And in Ind be some one-horned asses, and such an ass is called *Monoceros,* and is less bold and fierce than other Unicorns.

When the Whale hungereth sore, he casteth out of his mouth a vapour, that smelleth as the smell of amber; and fish have liking in that smell, and for the odour and smell of that vapour, they go into the Whale's mouth, and be so deceived and eaten. Also in this fish earthy matter hath more mastery than watery, and therefore he is soon great and fat; and so in age for greatness of body, on his ridge [back bone] powder [dust] and earth is gathered, and so digged together that herbs and small trees and bushes grow thereon; so that that great fish seemeth an island. And if shipmen come unwarily thereby, un- neath [hardly] they scape without peril,—for he throweth so much water out of his mouth upon the ship, that he overturneth it sometime or drowneth it. And also he is so huge in quantity that when he is taken, all the country is the better for the taking. Also he loveth his whelps with a wonder love, and leadeth them about in the sea long time. And if it happeth that his whelps be let with heaps of gravel and by default of water, he taketh much water in his mouth and throweth upon them, and delivereth them in that wise out of peril. And he setteth them alway between himself and the sun on the more sicher [safe] side. And when strong tempest ariseth, while his whelps be tender and young, he swalloweth them up into his womb; and when the tempest is gone, and fair weather come, then he casteth them up whole and sound. Also against the Whale fighteth a fish of serpent's kind, and is venomous, as a crocodile; and then other fish come to the Whale's tail, and if the Whale be overcome, the other fish die. And if the venomous fish may not overcome the Whale, then he throweth out of his jaws into the water a fumous smell most stinking; and the Whale throweth out of his mouth a sweet-smelling smoke, and putteth off the stinking smell, and defendeth and saveth himself and his in that manner wise.

The cat is a full lecherous beast in youth, swift, pliant, and merry, and leapeth and reseth on everything that is to fore him: and is led by a straw, and playeth therewith; and is a right heavy beast in age and full sleepy, and lieth slyly in wait for mice: and is aware where they be more by the smell than by the sight, and hunteth and reseth on them in privy places: and when he taketh a mouse, he playeth therewith, and eateth him after the play. In time of love is hard fighting for wives, and one scratcheth and rendeth the other grievously with biting and with claws. And he maketh a ruthful noise and ghastful, when one proffereth to fight with another: and unneth

is hurt when he is thrown down off an high place. And when he hath
a fair skin, he is as it were proud thereof, and goeth fast about: and
when his skin is burnt, then he bideth at home; and is oft for his
fair skin taken of the skinner, and slain and flayed.

BARTHOLOMAEUS ANGLICUS
[*De Proprietatibus Rerum* (13th century)]

A History of Four-footed Beasts

[English zoology begins with the publication of a huge folio of more than a
thousand pages compendiously described on the title page thus: "The History
of four-footed beasts and serpents: Describing at large their several names,
conditions, kinds, virtues (both natural and medicinal), countries of their
breed, their love and hatred to mankind, and the wonderful work of God in
their creation, preservation and destruction. Interwoven with curious variety
of historical narrations out of scriptures, Fathers, philosophers, physicians,
poets, etc. . . . Collected out of the writings of Conrad Gesner and other
authors by Edward Topsell. Whereunto is now added The Theater of Insects,
of lesser living creatures: as bees, flies, caterpillars, spiders, worms, etc. . . . By
T. Muffet Dr. of Physic." "Never," adds the dedicatory epistle, "was there so
complete a history of the creatures as this since the days of Solomon who
wrote the story of beasts and creeping things."

For once title page and blurb are hardly an exaggeration. Though neither
Topsell nor his master, the Swiss Conrad Gesner, could shake off entirely the
load of medieval pseudo-erudition, they got more fact into their treatises
than the world had ever before seen collected. Moreover it was with Topsell
in mind that Thoreau (who found the official scientists of his day lacking imagination) wrote: "These men had an adequate idea of a beast, or what a beast
should be; . . . and they will describe and will draw you a cat with four
strokes, more beastly or more beast-like to look at than Mr. Ruskin's favorite
artist draws a tiger. They had an adequate idea of the wildness of beasts and of
men."]

Of all earthly creatures an Elephant is the greatest: for in *India* they are nine cubits high, and five cubits broad; in *Africa* fourteen or fifteen full spans, which is about eleven foot high and proportionable in breadth, which caused *AElianus* to write, that one Elephant is as big as three Bugils; and among these the Males are ever greater than the Females. In the Kingdom of *Melinda* in *Africk*, there were two young ones not above six monthes old, whereof the least was as great as the greatest Ox, but his flesh was as much as you shall finde in two Oxen; the other was much greater.

Their colour is for the most part mouse-colour, or black; and there was one all white in *Ethiopia:* The skin looketh pieled and scabby; it is most hard on the back, but softer underneath the belly, having no covering of hair or gristles, nor yet help by his tail to drive away the flies, for that evil doth this beast feel in his great body, but always hath crevices in his skin, which by their favour do invite the little flies to a continual feast, but when by stretching forth they have received the swarmes, by shriking together again, they inclose the flies, and so kill them: so that these crevices in his skin, are unto him in stead of a main, tail, and hair: yet there are some few hairs which grow scattering upon his hide, whereof some have been brought out of *America* into *Germany*, which were two palms long, but not so stiffe as Swines.

Their skin is so hard and stiffe, that a sharpe sword or iron cannot pierce it. Their head is very great, and the head of a man may easily enter into their mouth, as a finger into the mouth of a Dog; but yet their ears and eyes are not equivalent to the residue of their proportion: for they are small like the wings of a Bat or a Dragon, those of the *Ethiopian Sambri* want ears altogether. Their eyes are like the eyes of Swine, but very red; they have teeth of either side four, wherewith they grind their meat like meal, and they have also two other which hang forth beyond the residue, in the males downward, and these are the greater and crooked; but in the females upward and they are the smaller and straight: the one of them they keep alwayes sharp, to revenge injuries, and with the other they root up plants and trees, for their meat; so that nature hath armed both sexes with these for their chiefest defence. . . .

These Ivory teeth have been alway of great estimation among all the Nations that ever knew them, the *Ethiopians* payed for a tribute unto the King of *Persia* every third year twenty of these teeth hung about with gold and Jet-wood. These are sold by weight, and there be many which deceive the world with the bones of Fishes in stead thereof, but the true Ivory is paler and heavier, and falling upon the ground will easily break, whereas the bones of Fishes are more tenacious, light and strong. It is like to the *Chernites* wherein *Darius* was entombed, and the Marble called *Lapis Coraliticus,* Coral stone: like unto this is the *Alagi* stone, and the *Pederos* Jewel. With this Ivory they made images and statues for their Idol gods, as one for *Pallas* in *Athens,* for *Esculapius* in *Epidaurus,* for *Venus* under the name of *Vrania* by *Phidias,* whereupon she was *Elephantina,* for *Apollo* at *Rome:* and therefore *Pausanias* wondereth at the Grecians that spared no cost for the vain worship of their gods, for they brought of the *Indians* and *Ethiopians,* Ivory to make their Images with more pomp and ostentation: besides of Ivory they make the hafts of knives, and also the best combs, and *Solomon* as appeareth 3 Reg. 10 had a throne of Ivory covered all over with gold, for the costs and charge whereof he could not expend lesse then thirty thousand talents.

A bear is of a most venereous and lustful disposition, for night and day the females, with most ardent inflamed desires, do provoke the males to copulation; and for this cause at that time they are most fierce and angry. . . .

The time of their copulation is in the beginning of Winter, although sometime in Summer (but such young ones seldom live) yet most commonly in *February* or *January.* The manner of their copulation is like to a mans, the male moving himself upon the belly of the female, which lyeth on the earth flat upon the back, and either embraceth other with their fore-feet: they remain very long time in that act, inasmuch as if they were very fat at their first entrance, they disjoin not themselves again till they be made lean.

Immediately after they have conceived, they betake themselves to their dens, where they (without meat) grow very fat (especially the males) only by sucking their fore-feet. When they enter into their den, they convey themselves in backwards, that so they may put out their foot-steps from the sight of the hunters. The males give great honor to the females great with young, during the time of their secresie, so that, although they lie together in one cave, yet do they part it by a division or small ditch in the midst, neither of them touching the other. The nature of all of them is, to avoid cold, and therefore in the Winter time do they hide themselves, chusing rather to suffer famine than cold; lying for the most part three or four months together and never see the light, whereby their guts grow so empty, that they are almost closed up and stick together.

When they first enter into their den, they betake themselves to quiet and rest, sleeping without any awaking, for the first fourteen dayes, so that it is thought an easie stroke cannot awake them. But how long the females go with young is not certain, some affirm three months, other but thirty dayes, which is more probable, for wild beasts do not couple themselves being with young (except a Hare and a Linx) and the Bears being (as is already said) very lustful, to the intent that they may no longer want the company of their males, do violently cast their Whelps, and so presently after delivery, do after the manner of Conies betake themselves to their lust, and nourishing their young ones both together: and this is certain, that they never come out of their caves, till their young ones be thirty dayes old at the least; and *Pliny* precisely affirmeth, that they litter the thirtyeth day after their conception; and for this cause, a Bear bringeth forth the least whelp of all other great beasts, for their whelps at their first littering are no bigger than rats, nor longer than ones finger. And whereas it hath been believed and received, that the whelps of Bears at their first littering are without all form and fashion, and nothing but a little congealed blood like a lump of flesh, which afterwards the old one frameth with her tongue to her own likeness, as *Pliny, Solinus, AElianus, Orus, Oppianus,* and *Ovid* have reported, yet is the truth most evidently otherwise, as by the eye-witness of *Joachimus Rheticus,* and other, is disproved: only it is littered blind without eyes, naked without hair, and the hinder legs not perfect, the fore-feet folded up like a fist, and other members deformed by reason of the immoderate humor or moystness in them, which also is one cause, why the Womb of the Bear cannot retain the seed to the perfection of her young ones.

They bring forth sometimes two, and never above five, which the old Bear daily keepeth close to her breast, so warming them with the heat of her body and the breath of her mouth, till they be thirty days old; at what time they come abroad, being in the beginning of *May,* which is the third Month from the Spring. The old ones being almost dazled with long darkness, coming into light again seem to stagger and reel to and fro, and then for the straightness of their guts, by reason of their long fasting do eat the hearb *Arum,* commonly called in English *Wake-Robbin* or *Calves-foot,* being of very sharp and tart taste, which enlargeth their guts, and so being recovered, they remain all the time their young are with them, more fierce and cruel then at other times. And concerning the same *Arum,* called also *Dra-*

cunculus and *Oryx,* there is a pleasant vulgar tale, whereby some have conceived that Bears eat this herb before their lying secret; and by vertue thereof (without meat, or sense of cold) they pass away the whole Winter in Sleep.

There was a certain Cow-herd in the Mountains of *Helvetia,* which coming down a hill with a great Caldron on his back, he saw a Bear eating of a root which he had pulled up with his feet; the Cow-herd stood still till the Bear was gone, and afterward came to the place where the beast had eaten the same, and finding more of the same root, did likewise eat it; he had no sooner tasted thereof, but he had such a desire to sleep, that he could not contain himself, but he must needs lie down in the way and there fell asleep, having covered his head with the Caldron, to keep himself from the vehemency of the cold, and their slept all the Winter time without harm, and never rose again till the Spring time: Which fable if a man will believe, then doubtless this hearb may cause the Bears to be sleepers, not for fourteen days, but for fourscore days together.

This beast [the cat] is wonderful nimble, setting upon her prey like a Lion, by leaping, and therefore she hunteth both Rats, all kind of Mice, and Birds, eating not only them, but also fish, wherewithall she is best pleased. Having taken a mouse, she first playeth with it, and then devoureth it, but her watchful eye is most strange, to see with what pace and soft steps, she taketh birds and flies; and her nature is to hide her own dung or excrement, for she knoweth that the favour and presence thereof, will drive away her sport, the little Mouse being able by that stool, to smell the presence of her mortal foe.

To keep Cats from hunting of Hens, they use to tie a little wilde Rew under their wings, and so likewise from Dove-coates, if they set it in the windowes, they dare not approach unto it for some secret in nature. Some have said that Cats will fight with Serpents, and Toads, and kill them, and perceiving that she is hurt by them; she presently drinketh water and is cured: but I cannot consent unto this opinion: it being true of the Weasell as shall be afterward declared. *Pontzettus* sheweth by experience that Cats and Serpents love one another, for there was (saith he) in a certain Monastery, a Cat nourished by the Monkes, and suddenly the most parts of the Monks which used to play with the Cat fell sick: whereof the Physitians could find no cause, but some secret poison, and all of them were assured that they never tasted any: at the last a poor labouring man came unto them, affirming that he saw the Abbey-cat playing with a Serpent, which the Physitians understanding, presently conceived that the Serpent had emptied some of her poison upon the Cat, which brought the same to the Monks, and they by stroking and handling the Cat, were infected therewith; and whereas there remained one difficulty, namely, how it came to passe, the Cat her self was not poisoned thereby, it was resolved, that for as much as the Serpents poison came from him but in play and sport, and not in malice and wrath, that therefore the venom thereof being lost in play, neither harmed the Cat at all, nor much endangered the Monks: and the very like is observed of Mice that will play with Serpents . . .

The nature of this beast is, to love the place of her breeding, neither will she tarry in any strange place, although carryed far, being never willing to forsake the house, for the love of any man, and most contrary to the nature of a Dog, who will travaile abroad with his master; and although their masters forsake their houses, yet will not these beasts bear them company, and being carryed forth in close baskets or sacks, they will yet return again or lose themselves. A cat is much delighted to play with her image in a glasse, and if at any time she behold it in water, presently she leapeth down into the water which naturally she doth abhor, but if she be not quickly pulled forth and dryed she dyeth thereof, because she is impatient of all wet. Those which will keep their Cats within doors, and from hunting birds abroad, must cut off their ears, for they cannot endure to have drops of rain distill into them, and therefore keep themselves in harbour. Nothing is more contrary to the nature of a Cat, than is wet and water, and for this cause came the proverb that they love not to wet their feet. It is a neat and cleanly creature, oftentimes licking her own body to keep it neat and fair, having naturally a flexible back for this purpose, and washing her face with her forefeet: but some observe, that if she put her feet beyond the crown of her head, that it is a presage of rain, and if the back of a Cat be thin the beast is of no courage or valew. They love fire and warm places, whereby it often falleth out that they often burn their Coats. They desire to lie soft, and in the time of their lust (commonly called cat-wralling) they are wilde and fierce, especially the males, who at that time (except they be gelded) will not keep the house: at which time they have a peculiar direful voice. The manner of their copulation is this, the female lyeth down, and the male standeth, and their females are above measure desirous of procreation, for which cause they provoke the male, and if he yeeld not to their lust, they beat and claw him, but it is only for love of young, and not for lust: the male is most libidinous, and therefore seeing the female will never more engender with him during the time her young ones suck, he killeth and eateth them if he meet with them, (to provoke the female to copulation with him again, for when she is deprived of her young, she seeketh out the male of her own accord) for which the female most warily keepeth them from his sight. During the time of copulation, the female continually cryeth, whereof the Writers give a double cause; one, because she is pinched with the talons or clawes of the male in the time of his lustful rage; and the other, because his seed is so fiery hot, that it almost burneth the females place of conception. When they have littered, or as we commonly say kittened, they rage against Dogs, and will suffer none to come neer their young ones. The best to keep are such as are littered in *March;* they go with young fifty daies, and the females live not above six or seven years, the males live longer, especially if they be gelt or libbed: the reason of their short life is their ravening of meat which corrupteth within them . . .

As this beast hath been familiarly nourished of many, so have they payed dear for their love, being requited with the losse of their health, and sometime of their life for their friendship: and worthily, because they which love any beast in a high measure, have so much the lesse charity unto man.

Therefore it must be considered what harmes and perils come unto men by this beast. It is most certain, that the breath and favour of Cats consume the radical humour and destroy the lungs, and therefore they which keep their Cats with them in their beds have the air corrupted, and fall into severall Hecticks and Consumptions. There was a certain company of Munks much given to nourish and play with Cats, whereby they were so infected, that within a short space none of them were able either to say, read, pray, or sing, in all the Monastery; and therefore also they are dangerous in the time of Pistilence, for they are not only apt to bring home venemous infection, but to poison a man with very looking upon him; wherefore ther is in some men a natural dislike and abhorring of Cats, their natures being so composed, that not only when they see them, but being neer them and unseen, and hid of purpose, they fall into passions, frettings, sweating, pulling off their hats, and trembling fearfully, as I have known many in *Germany;* the reason whereof is, because the constellation which threatneth their bodies which is peculiar to every man, worketh by the presence and offence of these creatures: and therefore they have cryed out to take away the Cats.

EDWARD TOPSELL
[*The History of Four-footed Beasts* (1607)]

Little Miss Muffet

[Tradition has it that Thomas Muffet, who contributed to Topsell's huge book the long supplement on "lesser living creatures," was the father of the famous young lady who sat on a tuffet eating her curds and whey. His obvious affection for spiders makes the tradition seem reasonable enough.]

To praise the Spider as I ought, I shall first set before you the riches of its body . . . then of its fortune, lastly of its mind. If you consider the matter of it, it is light, partaking much of Air and Fire (that are the most active and noblest Elements) but it hath little of earthly dregs and gravity. Consider the figure. It is wholly round and orbicular, or at least oval, that is next unto it. The substance of it is thin, transparent, subtile, and though sometimes by the abundance of plunder and prey, it becomes so crammed that it grows as great as a walnut, and (if Cardan errs not) as great as a sparrow sometimes, yet if you see it hanging in its web, against the light, it shines all through like a chrysolite, and makes reflection of beams most grateful to the eye. It has the same color that Ovid writes that lovers have, that is, pale; and when she flicks aloft with her feet cast every way, she exactly represents a painted star. As if Nature had appointed not only to make it round like the heavens, but with rays like the stars, as if they were alive. The skin of it is so soft, smooth, polished and neat, that she precedes the softest skinned maids, and the daintiest and most beautiful strumpets, and is so clear that you may almost see your face in her as in a glass; she hath fingers that the most gallant virgins desire to have theirs like to them, long, slender, round, of exact feeling, that there is no man, nor any creature that can compare with her: she hath feet not numberless, as the Scolopendrae, nor is she without feet, as some insects are, nor hath only six feet, as those that want wings have, but eight feet, which number is next to the most perfect number, as all men know. These legs also are made in a sesquitertial proportion, which is most admirable and venerable; so that though the latter feet be always shorter than the former, yet they hold still their proportion. Many philosophers who hold that spiders are blind, are blind themselves, for were they blind, how should they make choice of those places that are most convenient for to pitch their nests, and who should lead them to fasten one thread to another, and should know how to mend their webs when they are broken by accident? When as also the tame and familiar spiders will come from a distance to catch a fly that toucheth but the sides of their threads, they are the more bold to pursue them, and will take them as it were from hand to hand, as we have often seen. Truly they are blind at noon-day, and understand nothing, who say, that spiders are blind. In this spider there is no poison nor hurt, for if it bite it is without harm, and it is rather tickling than painful. Also their very carcasses, and their bodies, their eyes, their excrements, are good and useful for many diseases, as we shall make it plain enough when we speak of their use. I know not what it was that made Pennius so frightened when he thought of eating them; for he knew a noble English lady, and Phaerus a physician, that did often eat them without any hurt at all. For the truth is, spiders are free from poison, and are very good for one's health. But because it seems so horrid a creature to some people, that the very sight of it makes them fly from it, I rather attribute that to their melancholy apprehension, tenderness and distemper, than to the ill form of the spider. Nature hath used no less elegancy and bounty in the spider, than she hath done in the butterfly, and fly, and it is no light disease of the mind to disdain so beautiful a work, and to be afraid of a creature that weaves so curiously. Lastly God hath given a wonderful disposition and nature of the skin to so wonderful a body; for it doth not only once a year (as vipers do) but every month if she be well fed she changeth her skin, and recovers a new one that is more curious. Also it is of so excellent a temper, and so frugal in its diet, that in a wholesome place, where she can get any provision, she will live always. I think that to be the chiefest good amongst the goods of fortune, or rather fare, that they carry the matter of their webs in their belly, and they are so well stored with it, that a spider can draw for innumerable threads and weave them, and catch if need be, a hundred flies, and have nets enough to wrap them in. And though they have not meat in a granary as pismires have, nor ready and growing up, as bees have, but they live only upon food they light upon by chance, yet by God's providence the prey comes flying by that sustains them, and oft times they grow fat with plentiful dishes that they take by hostility.

THOMAS MUFFET
[In Topsell's *The History of Four-footed Beasts* (1607)]

The Animals Come to Court

[Only a century and a half separates Topsell from Georges Louis Leclerc, Comte de Buffon, the next great encyclopedic naturalist, who spent a large part of his long life standing before a desk and compiling the forty-four volumes of his Histoire Naturelle. Perhaps no other naturalist ever enjoyed so much prestige or occupied so splendid a position as his, for he represented natural science at the most dazzling court of Europe. Too much a courtier not to feel a certain disdain for less fortunate savants and quite incapable of regarding animals as fellow creatures, he was nevertheless a superb literary artist. Within the limitations imposed by his aloofness no animal portraits have ever surpassed his.]

THE HORSE

The reduction of the horse to a domestic state, is the greatest acquisition, from the animal world, ever made by the art and industry of man. This noble animal partakes of the fatigues of war, and seems to feel the glory of victory. Equally intrepid as his master, he encounters danger and death with ardour and magnanimity. He delights in the noise and tumult of arms, and annoys the enemy with resolution and alacrity. But it is not in perils and conflicts alone that the horse willingly co-operates with his master; he likewise participates of human pleasures. He exults in the chase and the tournament; his eyes sparkle with emulation in the course. But, though bold and intrepid, he suffers not himself to be carried off by a furious ardour; he represses his movements, and knows how to govern and check the natural vivacity and fire of his temper. He not only yields to the hand, but seems to consult the inclination of the rider. Uniformly obedient to the impressions he receives, he flies or stops, and regulates his motion entirely by the will of his master. He in some measure renounces his very existence to the pleasure of man. He delivers up his whole powers; he reserves nothing, and often dies rather than disobey the mandates of his governor.

These are features in the character of the horse whose natural qualities have been matured by art, and tamed with care to the service of man. His education commences with the loss of liberty, and is completed by restraint. The slavery of the horse is so ancient and so universal, that he is rarely seen in a natural state. When employed in labor, he is always covered with the harness; and, even during the time destined for repose, he is never entirely delivered from bonds. If sometimes permitted to roam in the pastures, he always bears the marks of servitude, and often the external impressions of labor and pain. His mouth is deformed by the perpetual friction of the bit; his sides are galled with wounds, or furrowed with cicatrices; and his hoofs are pierced with nails. The natural gestures of his body are constrained by the habitual pressure of fetters, from which it would be in vain to deliver him; for he would not be more at liberty. Those horses, the servitude of which is most mild, which are kept solely for the purposes of luxury and magnificence, and whose golden chains only gratify the vanity of their masters, are more dishonored by the elegance of their trappings, and by the plaits of their hair, than by the iron shoes on their feet.

Art is always excelled by nature; and, in animated beings, liberty of movement constitutes the perfection of their existence. Examine those horses which have multiplied so prodigiously in Spanish America, and live in perfect freedom. Their motions are neither constrained nor measured. Proud of their independence, they fly from the presence of man, and disdain all his care. They search for, and procure the food that is most salutary and agreeable. They wander and frisk about in immense meadows, and collect the fresh productions of a perpetual spring. Without any fixed habitation, or other shelter than a serene sky, they breathe a purer air than in those musty vaults in which we confine them, when subjected to our dominion. Hence wild horses are stronger, lighter, and more nervous than most of those which are in a domestic state. The former possess force and dignity, which are the gifts of nature; the latter have only address and gracefulness, which are all that art can bestow.

These wild horses are by no means ferocious in their temper; they are only wild and fiery. Though of strength superior to most animals, they never make an attack. But, when they are assaulted, they either disdain the enemy, frisk out of his way, or strike him dead with their heels. They associate in troops from no other motive than the pleasure of being together; for they have no fear; but acquire a mutual attachment to each other. As grass and vegetables constitute their food, of which they have enough to satisfy their appetite, and, as they are not carnivorous, they neither make war with other animals, nor among themselves. They dispute not about their common nourishment, and never have occasion to snatch prey from each other, the general source of quarrels and combats among the rapacious tribes. Hence they live in perpetual peace; because their appetites are simple and moderate, and they have no objects to excite envy.

All these features are apparent in young horses, bred together in troops. Their manners are gentle, and their tempers social; their force and ardor are generally rendered conspicuous by marks of emulation. They anxiously press to be foremost in the course, to brave danger in traversing a river, or in leaping a ditch or precipice; and, it has been remarked, that those which are most adventurous and expert in these natural exercises, are the most generous, mild, and tractable, when reduced to a domestic state.

THE DOG

Neither majesty and elegance of form, strength of body, freedom of movement, nor other external qualities, constitute the principal dignity of animated beings. In man, we prefer genius to figure, courage to strength, and sentiment to beauty; and, therefore, we are induced to think, that the chief excellence of an animal consists also of internal qualities. By these he differs from an automaton, rises above the vegetable tribes, and approaches the human species. It is sentiment which ennobles, governs and gives activity to all his organs and propensities. Hence the perfection of an animal depends on sentiment alone; and, in proportion to its extent, his faculties, resources, and relations with the rest of the universe, are augmented. When his sentiment is delicate, and improved by education, he is then fit to associate with man, to concur with his designs, to aid, to defend, and to caress him. By a frequent performance of these services, he conciliates the favor of his master, and, from a tyrant, converts him into a friend and protector.

The dog, independent of the beauty of his figure, his strength, vivacity, and nimbleness, possesses every internal excellence which can attract the regard of man. A passionate, and even a ferocious and sanguinary temper, renders the wild dog formidable to all animals. But, in the domestic dog, these hostile dispositions vanish, and are succeeded by the softer sentiments of attachment, and the desire of pleasing. He runs with cheerfulness and alacrity to his master's foot, where he lays down his courage, his strength, and his talents. He attends for orders, which he is always felicitous to execute. He consults, he interrogates, he supplicates his master. A single glance of the eye is sufficient; for he knows the external signs of our intentions and wishes. Without being endowed, like man, with the faculty of thinking, his feelings are extremely delicate, and he has no fear, but that of displeasing. He is all zeal, ardour, and obedience. More apt to recall benefits than outrages, he is not discouraged by blows or bad treatment, but calmly suffers, and soon forgets them; or he remembers them only to increase his attachment. Instead of flying, or discovering marks of resentment, he exposes himself to torture, and licks the hand from which he received the blow. To the cruelty of his master, he only opposes complaint, patience, and submission.

THE FLY-BIRD (HUMMING-BIRD)

Of all animated beings, the Fly-bird is the most elegant in its form, and the most brilliant in its colours. The precious stones and metals polished by our art cannot be compared to this jewel of nature. Her miniature productions are ever the most wonderful; she has placed it in the order of birds, at the bottom of the scale of magnitude; but all the talents which are only shared among the others, nimbleness, rapidity, sprightliness, grace, and rich decoration, she has bestowed profusely upon this little favorite. The emerald, the ruby, the topaz, sparkle in its plumage, which is never soiled by the dust of the ground. It inhabits the air; it flutters from flower to flower; it breathes their freshness; it feeds on their nectar, and resides in climates where they blow in perpetual succession.

It is in the hottest part of the new world that all the species of Fly-birds are found. They are numerous, and seem confined between the two tropics; for those which penetrate in summer within the temperate zones make but a short stay. They follow the course of the sun; with him they advance or retire; they fly on the wings of the zephyr, to wanton in eternal spring.

The Indians, struck with the dazzle and glow of the colors of these brilliant birds, have named them the *beams* or *locks of the sun*. The Spaniards call them *tomineos,* on account of their diminutive size, *tomine* signifying a weight of twelve grains. "I saw," says Nieremberg, "one of these birds weighed with its nest, and the whole together did not amount to two tomines." The smaller species do not exceed the bulk of the great gad-fly, or the thickness of the drone. Their bill is a fine needle, and their tongue a delicate thread; their little black eyes resemble two brilliant points; the feathers of their wings are so thin as to look transparent; hardly can the feet be perceived, so short they are and so slender: and these are little used, for they rest only during the night. Their flight is buzzing, continued, and rapid; Marcgrave compares the noise of their wings to the *whirr* of a spinning-wheel; so rapid is the quiver of their pinions, that when the bird halts in the air, it seems at once deprived of motion and of life. Thus it rests a few seconds beside a flower, and again shoots to another like a gleam. It visits them all, thrusting its little tongue into their bosom, and caressing them with its wings; it never settles, but it never quite abandons them. Its playful inconstancy multiplies its innocent pleasures; for the dalliance of this little lover of flowers never spoils their beauty. It only sips their honey, and its tongue seems calculated for that purpose; it consists of two hollow fibres, forming a small canal, parted at the end into two filaments: it resembles the proboscis of insects, and performs the same office. The bird protrudes it from its bill, probably by a mechanism of the *os hyoides,* similar to what obtains in the tongue of woodpeckers. It thrusts it to the bottom of the flowers, and sucks their juices. Such is its mode of subsisting according to all the authors who have written on the subject. One person alone denies the fact; he is Badier, who, finding in the oesophagus some portions of insects, concludes that the bird lives on these, and not the nectar of flowers. But we cannot reject a number of respectable authorities for a single hasty assertion; though the Fly-bird swallows some insects, does it thence follow that it subsists upon them? Nay, must it not necessarily happen, that, sucking the honey from the flowers, or gathering their pollen, it will sometimes swallow the little insects which are entangled? Besides, the rapid waste of its spirits, the consequence of its extreme vivacity and its rapid incessant motion, must continually be recruited by rich nutritious aliments: and Sloane, on whose observations I lay the greatest stress, positively avers that he found the stomach of the Fly-bird entirely filled with the pollen, and sweet juice of flowers.

Nothing can equal the vivacity of these little creatures, but their courage, or rather audacity: they furiously pursue birds twenty times larger than themselves, fix in the plumage, and as they are hurried along strike keenly with the bill, till they vent their feeble rage: sometimes even they fight obstinately with each other. They are all impatience; if upon alighting in a flower they find it faded, they will pluck the petals with a precipitation that marks their displeasure. Their voice is only a feeble cry, *screp, screp,* which is frequent and reiterated. They are heard in the woods at the dawn of the morning, and as soon as the sun begins to gild the summits of the trees, they take wing and disperse in the fields.

They are solitary; and indeed, fluttering irregularly in the breeze, they could hardly associate. But the power of love surmounts the elements, and, with its golden chains, it binds all animated beings. The Fly-birds are seen to pair in the breeding season: their nest corresponds to the delicacy of their bodies; it is formed with the soft cotton or silky down gathered from flowers, and has the consistency and feel of a thick smooth skin. The female performs the work, and the male collects the materials. She applies herself with ardour; selects, one by one, the fibres proper to form the texture of this kindly cradle for her progeny; she smooths the margin with her breast, the inside with her tail; she covers the outside with bits of the bark of the gum-tree, which are stuck to shelter from the weather, and give solidity to the fabric: the whole is attached to two leaves, or a single sprig of the orange or citron, or sometimes to a straw hanging from the roof of a hut. The nest is not larger than the half of an apricot, and it is also shaped like a half cup. It contains two eggs, which are entirely white, and not exceeding the bulk of small peas. The cock and hen sit by turn twelve days; on the thirteenth the young are excluded, which are then not larger than flies. "I could not perceive," says Father Dutertre, "how the mother fed them, except that she presented the tongue covered entirely with honey extracted from the flowers."

We may easily conceive that it is impossible to raise these little flutterers. Those who have tried to feed them with syrups could not keep them alive more than a few weeks: these aliments, though of easy digestion, are very different from the delicate nectar collected from the fresh blossoms. Perhaps honey would have succeeded better.

The method of obtaining them is to shoot with sand, or by means of the *trunk-gun;* they will allow one to approach within five or six paces of them. They may be caught by placing a twig smeared over with a clammy gum in a flowering shrub. It is easy to lay hold of the little creature while it hums at a blossom. It dies soon after it is caught, and serves to decorate the Indian girls, who wear two of these charming birds as pendants from their ears. The Peruvians had the art of forming their feathers into pictures, whose beauty is perpetually extolled in the older narratives. Marcgrave, who saw some of these pieces of workmanship, admires their brilliancy and delicacy.

With the lustre and gloss of flowers, these pretty birds have been supposed to have also the perfume; and many authors have asserted that they have the fragrance of musk. The mistake originated probably from the name applied by Oviedo, of *passer mosquitus,* which would easily be changed into *passer moscatus.* But this is not the only marvellous circumstance with which their history has been clouded: it has been said that they are half birds, half flies, and produced from a fly; and a provincial of the Jesuits gravely affirms in Clusius, that he was witness to this transformation. It has been alleged, that, during the winter season, they remain torpid, suspended by the bill from the bark of a tree, and awakened into life when the flowers begin to blow. These fictions have been rejected by intelligent naturalists; and Catesby assures us, that he saw them through the whole year at St. Domingo and Mexico, where nature never entirely loses her bloom. Sloane says the same of Jamaica, only that they are more numerous after the rainy season; and, prior to both, Marcgrave mentioned their being frequent the whole year in the woods of Brazil.

We are acquainted with twenty-four species in the genus of the Fly-bird; and it is probable some have been overlooked. We shall distinguish them by their different denominations, drawn from the most obvious character.

THE SLOTH

In proportion as Nature is vivacious, active, and exalted in the monkey kind, she is slow, restrained, and fettered in the sloths. From a defect in their conformation, the misery of these animals is not more conspicuous than their slowness. They have no cutting teeth; the eyes are obscured with hair; the chops are heavy and thick; the hair is flat, and resembles withered herbs; the thighs are ill jointed to the haunches; the legs are too short, ill turned, and terminated still worse: their feet have no soles, and no toes which move separately, but only two or three claws disproportionally long, and bended downward, which move together, and are more hurtful to the walking, than advantageous in assisting them to climb. Slowness, habitual pain, and stupidity, are the results of this strange and bungled conformation. The sloths have no weapons either offensive or defensive. They are furnished with no means of safety; for they can neither fly nor dig the earth. Confined to a small space, or to the tree under which they are brought forth, they are prisoners in the midst of space, and cannot move the length of one fathom in an hour. They drag themselves up a tree with much labor and pain. Their cry and interrupted accents they dare only utter during the night. All these circumstances announce the misery of the sloths, and recall to our minds those defective monsters, those imperfect sketches of Nature, which, being hardly endowed with the faculty of existence, could not subsist for any length of time, and have accordingly been struck out of the list of beings. If the regions inhabited by the sloths were not desert, but had been long occupied by men and the larger animals, these species would never have descended to our times: they would have been annihilated, as in some future period will be the case. We formerly remarked, that every thing that possibly could be, really did exist; of which the sloths are a striking example. They constitute the last term of existence in the order of animals with flesh and blood. One other defect added to the number would have totally prevented their existence. To regard those bungled sketches as beings equally perfect with others, to call in the aid of final causes to account for such disproportioned productions, and to make Nature as brilliant in these as in her most beautiful animals, is to view her through a narrow tube, and to substitute our own fancies for her intentions.

Why should not some animals be created for misery, since, in the human species, the greatest number of individuals are devoted to pain from the moment of their existence? Evil, it is true, proceeds more from ourselves than from Nature. For a single person who is unhappy, because he was born feeble or deformed, there are millions rendered miserable by the oppression of their superiors. The animals, in general, are more happy, because the species have nothing to fear from individuals: to them there is but one source of evil; to man there are two. Moral evil, of which he himself is the fountain, has accumulated into an immense ocean, which covers and afflicts the whole surface of the earth. Physical evil, on the contrary, is restrained within very narrow bounds: it seldom appears alone; for it is always accompanied with an equal, if not a superior good. Can happiness be denied to animals, when they enjoy freedom, have the faculty of procuring subsistence with ease, and possess more health, and organs capable of affording greater pleasure than those of the human species? Now, the generality of animals are most liberally endowed with all these sources of enjoyment. The degraded species of sloths are perhaps the only creatures to whom Nature has been unkind, and who exhibit to us the picture of innate misery.

Let us take a closer view of the condition of these creatures. By the want of teeth, they can neither seize prey, nor feed upon flesh or herbage. Reduced to the necessity of living upon leaves and wild fruits, they consume much time in trailing their bodies to the foot of a tree, and still more in climbing to the branches; and during this slow and melancholy exercise, which sometimes lasts several days, they are obliged to suffer the most pressing hunger. When arrived upon a tree, they never descend. They cling to the branches, and devour successively the leaves of every twig. They pass several weeks in this situation, without receiving any drink. When they have rendered the tree entirely naked, they still remain; because they cannot descend. In time, when the pressure of hunger becomes superior to the dread of danger or death, being unable to descend, they allow themselves to tumble down like an inanimated mass; for their stiff and inactive limbs have not time to extend themselves in order to break the fall.

When on the ground, they are at the mercy of all their enemies. As their flesh is not absolutely bad, both men and rapacious animals go in quest of these animals. It appears that they do not multiply fast, or, at least, if they produce frequently, it must be in small numbers at a time; for they have only two paps. Every circumstance, therefore, concurs to destroy them; and it is extremely difficult for the species to support itself. But, though slow, awkward, and almost incapable of motion, they are obstinate, strong, and tenacious of life. They can live very long without victuals of any kind. They are covered with thick, dry hair; and, being incapable of exercise, they lose little by perspiration; and, though their food be meager, they fatten by repose. Though they have no horns nor hoofs, nor cutting teeth in the under jaw, yet they belong to the ruminating tribes, and have several stomachs. Hence the quality of their food may be compensated by the quantity they take at a time. What is still more singular, instead of very long intestines, like other ruminating animals, their guts are very short and small, like those of the carnivorous kind. This contrast exhibits the ambiguity of Nature. The sloths are unquestionably ruminating animals: they have four stomachs; and yet they want every other character, both internal and external, which generally belongs to animals of this class. There is still another singularity in the conformation of the sloths: instead of three distinct apertures for the discharge of urine and excrements, and for the purposes of generation, these animals have but one, which terminates in a common canal, as in birds.

Moreover, if the misery resulting from a defect of sentiment be not the worst of all, the pain endured by the sloths, though very apparent, seems not to be real; for their sensations appear to be blunt. Their calamitous air, their dull aspect, and their reception of blows without emotion, announce their extreme insensibility. This bluntness of sensation is farther demonstrated, by their not dying instantly when their hearts and bowels are entirely cut out. Pifo, who made this cruel experiment, tells us, that the heart, after being separated from the body, beat in a lively manner for half an hour; and that the animal continued to contract its legs slowly, as commonly happens during sleep. From these facts, this quadruped seems to approach not only the turtle, but the other reptiles which have no distinct centre of sensation. All these beings may be said to be miserable, but not unhappy: Nature, even in her most neglected productions, always appears more in the character of a parent than of a stepmother.

COMTE DE BUFFON
[*Natural History* (1749-1767)]

The Ivory-billed Woodpecker

[*Alexander Wilson is said to have taken up ornithology (of which he knew nothing) in an effort to forget the failure of three successive love affairs. Undoubtedly he would be the first great American student of birds had he not* happened to be an exact contemporary of John James Audubon. A few individuals of the species he here describes may just possibly still live, but the chances are that the last of them died a few years ago.]

In looking over the accounts given of the ivory-billed woodpecker by the naturalists of Europe, I find it asserted, that it inhabits from New Jersey to Mexico. I believe, however, that few of them are ever seen to the north of Virginia, and very few of them even in that state. The first place I observed this bird at, when on my way to the south, was about twelve miles north of Wilmington in North Carolina. There I found the bird from which the drawing of the figure in the plate was taken. This bird was only wounded slightly in the wing, and, on being caught, uttered a loudly reiterated, and most piteous note, exactly resembling the violent crying of a young child; which terrified my horse so, as nearly to have cost me my life. It was distressing to hear it. I carried it with me in the chair, under cover, to Wilmington. In passing through the streets, its affecting cries surprised every one within hearing, particularly the females, who hurried to the doors and windows with looks of alarm and anxiety. I drove on, and, on arriving at the piazza of the hotel, where I intended to put up, the landlord came forward, and a number of other persons who happened to be there, all equally alarmed at what they heard; this was greatly increased by my asking, whether he could furnish me with accommodations for myself and my baby. The man looked blank and foolish, while the others stared with still greater astonishment. After diverting myself for a minute or two at their expense, I drew my Woodpecker from under the cover, and a general laugh took place. I took him up stairs and locked him up in my room, while I went to see my horse taken care of. In less than an hour I returned, and, on opening the door, he set up the same distressing shout, which now appeared to proceed from grief that he had been discovered in his attempts at escape. He had mounted along the side of the window, nearly as high as the ceiling, a little below which he had begun to break through. The bed was covered with large pieces of plaster; the lath was exposed for at least fifteen inches square, and a hole, large enough to admit the fist, opened to the weather-boards; so that, in less than another hour he would certainly have succeeded in making his way through. I now tied a string round his leg, and, fastening it to the table, again left him. I wished to preserve his life, and had gone off in search of suitable food for him. As I reascended the stairs, I heard him again hard at work, and on entering had the mortification to perceive that he had almost entirely ruined the mahogany table to which he was fastened, and on which he had wreaked his whole vengeance. While engaged in taking the drawing, he cut me severely in several places, and, on the whole, displayed such a noble and unconquerable spirit, that I was frequently tempted to restore him to his native woods. He lived with me nearly three days, but refused all sustenance, and I witnessed his death with regret.

ALEXANDER WILSON
[*American Ornithology* (1808-1814)]

A Tenderfoot Meets Some Natives

['The competence and the cleverness of the coyote is abundantly recognized in the mythology of the American Indian, who knew him well; but the white man has generally regarded this first cousin of man's best friend with undeserved contempt. Mark Twain, who loved and defended all animals, met first the jack rabbit and then the coyote during the course of his first journey westward. His respect for the latter peeps from between the lines of a hilarious portrait.]

By and by we passed through Marysville, and over the Big Blue and Little Sandy; thence about a mile, and entered Nebraska. About a mile further on, we came to the Big Sandy—one hundred and eighty miles from St. Joseph.

As the sun was going down, we saw the first specimen of an animal known familiarly over two thousand miles of mountain and desert—from Kansas clear to the Pacific Ocean—as the "jackass rabbit." He is well named. He is just like any other rabbit, except that he is from one-third to twice as large, has longer legs in proportion to his size, and has the most preposterous ears that ever were mounted on any creature *but* a jackass. When he is sitting quiet, thinking about his sins, or is absent-minded or unapprehensive of danger, his majestic ears project above him conspicuously; but the breaking of a twig will scare him nearly to death, and then he tilts his ears back gently and starts for home. All you can see, then, for the next minute, is his long gray form stretched out straight and "streaking it" through the low sage-brush, head erect, eyes right, and ears just canted a little to the rear, but showing you where the animal is, all the time, the same as if he carried a jib. Now and then he makes a marvelous spring with his long legs, high over the stunted sage-brush, and scores a leap that would make a horse envious. Presently, he comes down to a long, graceful "lope," and shortly he mysteriously disappears. He has crouched behind a sage-bush, and will sit there and listen and tremble until you get within six feet of him, when he will get under way again. But one must shoot at this creature once, if he wishes to see him throw his heart into his heels, and do the best he knows how. He is frightened clear through, now, and he lays his long ears down on his back, straightens himself out like a yardstick every spring he makes, and scatters miles behind him with an easy indifference that is enchanting.

Another night of alternate tranquillity and turmoil. But morning came, by and by. It was another glad awakening to fresh breezes, vast expanses of level greensward, bright sunlight, an impressive solitude utterly without visible human beings or human habitations, and an atmosphere of such amazing magnifying properties that trees that seemed close at hand were more than three miles away. We resumed undress uniform, climbed atop of the flying coach, dangled our legs over the side, shouted occasionally at our frantic mules, merely to see them lay their ears back and scamper faster, tied our hats on to keep our hair from blowing away, and leveled an outlook over the world-wide carpet about us for things new and stange to gaze at. Even at this day it thrills me through and through to think of the life, the gladness and the wild sense of freedom that used to make the blood dance in my veins on those fine overland mornings!

Along about an hour after breakfast we saw the first prairie-dog villages, the first antelope, and the first wolf. If I remember rightly, this latter was the regular *coyote* (pronounced ky-*o*-te) of the farther deserts. And if it *was*, he was not a pretty creature, or respectable either, for I got well acquainted with his race afterward, and can speak with confidence. The coyote is a long, slim, sick and sorry-looking skeleton, with a gray wolf-skin stretched over it, a tolerably bushy tail that forever sags down with a despairing expression of forsakenness and misery, a furtive and evil eye, and a long, sharp face, with slightly lifted lip and exposed teeth. He has a general slinking expression all over. The coyote is a living, breathing allegory of Want. He is *always* hungry. He is always poor, out of luck and friendless. The meanest creatures despise him, and even the fleas would desert him for a velocipede. He is so spiritless and cowardly that even while his exposed teeth are pretending a threat, the rest of his face is apologizing for it. And he is *so* homely!—so scrawny, and ribby, and coarse-haired, and pitiful. When he sees you he lifts his lip and lets a flash of his teeth out, and then turns a little out of the course he was pursuing, depresses his head a bit, and strikes a long, soft-footed trot through the sage-brush, glancing over his shoulder at you, from time to time, till he is about out of easy pistol range, and then he stops and takes a deliberate survey of you; he will trot fifty yards and stop again—another fifty and stop again; and finally the gray of his gliding body blends with the gray of the sage-brush, and he disappears. All this is when you make no demonstration against him; but if you do, he develops a livelier interest in his journey, and instantly electrifies his heels and puts such a deal of real estate between himself and your weapon, that by the time you have raised the hammer you see that you need a minie rifle, and by the time you have got him in line you need a rifled cannon, and by the time you have "drawn a bead" on him you see well enough that nothing but an unusually long-winded streak of lightning could reach him where he is now. But if you start a swift-footed dog after him, you will enjoy it ever so much—especially if it is a dog that has a good opinion of himself, and has been brought up to think he knows something about speed. The coyote will go swinging gently off on that deceitful trot of his, and every little while he will smile a fraudful smile over his shoulder that will fill that dog entirely full of encouragement and worldly ambition, and make him lay his head still lower to the ground, and stretch his neck further to the front, and pant more fiercely, and stick his tail out straighter behind, and move his furious legs with a yet wilder frenzy, and leave a broader and broader, and higher and denser cloud of desert sand smoking behind, and marking his long wake across the level plain! And all this time the dog is only a short twenty feet behind the coyote, and to save the soul of him he cannot understand why it is that he cannot get perceptibly closer; and he begins to get aggravated, and it makes him madder and madder to see how gently the coyote glides along and never pants or sweats or ceases to smile; and he grows still more and more incensed to see how shamefully he has been taken in by an entire stranger, and what an ignoble swindle that long, calm, soft-footed trot is; and next he notices that he is getting fagged, and that the coyote actually has to slacken speed a little to keep from running away from him—and *then* that town-dog is mad in earnest, and he begins to strain and weep and swear, and paw the sand higher than ever, and reach for the coyote with concentrated and desperate energy. This "spurt" finds him six feet behind the gliding enemy, and two miles from his friends. And then, in the instant that a wild new hope is lighting up his face, the coyote turns and smiles blandly upon him once more, and with a something about it which seems to say: "Well, I shall have to tear myself away from you, bub—business is business, and it will not do for me to be fooling along this way all day"—and forthwith there is a rushing sound, and the sudden splitting of a long crack through the atmosphere, and behold that dog is solitary and alone in the midst of a vast solitude!

It makes his head swim. He stops, and looks all around; climbs the nearest sand-mound, and gazes into the distance; shakes his head reflectively, and then, without a word, he turns and jogs along back to his train, and takes up a humble position under the hindmost wagon, and feels unspeakably mean, and looks ashamed, and hangs his tail at half-mast for a week. And for as much as a year after that, whenever there is a great hue and cry after a coyote, that dog will merely glance in that direction without emotion, and apparently observe to himself, "I believe I do not wish any of the pie."

The coyote lives chiefly in the most desolate and forbidding deserts, along with the lizard, the jackass-rabbit and the raven, and gets an uncertain and precarious living, and earns it. He seems to subsist almost wholly on the carcasses of oxen, mules, and horses that have dropped out of emigrant trains and died, and upon windfalls of carrion, and occasional legacies of offal bequeathed to him by white men who have been opulent enough to have something better to butcher than condemned army bacon. He will eat anything in the world that his first cousins, the desert-frequenting tribes of Indians, will, and they will eat anything they can bite. It is a curious fact that these latter are the only creatures known to history who will eat nitroglycerin and ask for more if they survive.

The coyote of the deserts beyond the Rocky Mountains has a peculiarly hard time of it, owing to the fact that his relations, the Indians, are just as apt to be the first to detect a seductive scent on the desert breeze, and follow the fragrance to the late ox it emanated from, as he is himself; and when this occurs he has to content himself with sitting off at a little distance watching those people strip off and dig out everything edible, and walk off with it. Then he and the waiting ravens explore the skeleton and polish the bones. It is considered that the coyote, and the obscene bird, and the Indian of the desert, testify their blood-kinship with each other in that they live together in the waste places of the earth on terms of perfect confidence and friendship, while hating all other creatures and yearning to assist at their funerals. He does not mind going a hundred miles to breakfast, and a hundred and fifty to dinner, because he is sure to have three or four days between meals, and he can just as well be traveling and looking at the scenery as lying around doing nothing and adding to the burdens of his parents.

We soon learned to recognize the sharp, vicious bark of the coyote as it came across the murky plain at night to disturb our dreams among the mail-sacks; and remembering his forlorn aspect and his hard fortune, made shift to wish him the blessed novelty of a long day's good luck and a limitless larder the morrow.

SAMUEL L. CLEMENS
[*Roughing It* (1872)]

An American Perfume

[*What song the sirens sang is no doubt, as Sir Thomas Browne said, "beyond conjecture." What European first smelled a skunk might seem a question no less unresolvable. Actually it isn't, because a passage in the diary of Christopher Columbus describes an odor wafted from a Caribbean island which can hardly have been anything else. John James Audubon was among those who came to realize that the bad odor which surrounds the reputation of this otherwise charming creature is unjust in any except the literal sense.*]

☙

There is no quadruped on the continent of North America the approach of which is more generally detested than that of the Skunk. Although from the great and strong we have to apprehend danger, the feeble and apparently insignificant may have it in their power to annoy us almost beyond endurance. Even the bravest of our boasting race is, by this little animal, compelled suddenly to break off his train of thought, *hold his nose*, and run—as if a lion were at his heels!

Among the first specimens of natural history we attempted to procure was the Skunk, in our early school-boy days. We observed in the path before us a pretty little animal, playful as a kitten, moving quietly along. We pause and gaze; what is it? It is not a puppy or a cat. More gentle than either, it seems desirous to keep company with us, and, like a pet poodle, appears most happy when only a few paces in advance, as if to show the path. What a pretty creature to carry home in our arms! Let us catch it. We run towards it, and it makes no effort to escape, raises its tail as if to invite us to take hold of its brush. We seize it with the energy of a miser clutching a box of diamonds. A short struggle ensues, when—faugh! we are suffocated. We drop our prize and take to our heels, too stubborn to cry, but too much alarmed to take another look at the cause of our misfortune, and undeceived as to the real character of this seemingly mild and playful little fellow.

We were once requested by a venerable clergymen who had for years been a martyr to violent paroxysms of asthma to procure for him the glands of a Skunk, to be kept tightly corked in a smelling bottle, and to be inhaled when the symptoms appeared. For some time he found relief from his distressing complaint, but he uncorked the bottle on one occasion while in the pulpit. His congregation finding the smell too powerful for their olfactories made a hasty retreat, leaving him nearly alone in the church.

JOHN JAMES AUDUBON
[*American Ornithological Biography* (1831-1839)]

Portrait of a Friend

[If Buffon condescended to his subjects, Thoreau lovingly pictured them as fellow creatures. He could, as Mr. Clifton Fadiman once remarked, get more out of twenty minutes with a chickadee than most men from a night with

Cleopatra. *The last sentence of the following is one key to the peculiar magic of his descriptions.*]

✒

Suddenly, looking down the river, I saw a fox some sixty rods off, making across to the hills on my left. As the snow lay five inches deep, he made but slow progress, but it was no impediment to me. So, yielding to the instinct of the chase, I tossed my head aloft and bounded away, snuffing the air like a foxhound, and spurning the world and the Humane Society at each bound. It seemed the woods rang with the hunter's horn, and Diana and all the satyrs joined in the chase and cheered me on. Olympian and Elean youths were waving palms on the hills. In the meanwhile I gained rapidly on the fox; but he showed a remarkable presence of mind, for, instead of keeping up the face of the hill, which was steep and unwooded in that part, he kept along the slope in the direction of the forest, though he lost ground by it. Notwithstanding his fright, he took no step which was not beautiful. The course on his part was a series of most graceful curves. It was a sort of leopard canter, I should say, as if he were nowise impeded by the snow, but was husbanding his strength all the while. When he doubled I wheeled and cut him off, bounding with fresh vigor, and Antaeus-like, recovering my strength each time I touched the snow. Having got near enough for a fair view, just as he was slipping into the wood, I gracefully yielded him the palm. He ran as though there were not a bone in his back, occasionally dropping his muzzle to the snow for a rod or two, and then tossing his head aloft when satisfied of his course. When he came to a declivity he put his forefeet together and slid down it like a cat. He trod so softly that you could not have heard it from any nearness, and yet with such expression that it would not have been quite inaudible at any distance. So, hoping this experience would prove a useful lesson to him, I returned to the village by the highway of the river.

HENRY DAVID THOREAU
[*Journal*, Jan. 30, 1841]

No Pride of Ancestry
and No Hope of Posterity

[Clarence King, pioneer geologist of the western mountains, was regarded by Henry Adams and many other friends as a nearly universal genius, destined to one of the greatest of careers. That career somehow missed fire and he is now best remembered for one delightful book to which he probably attached only very minor significance.]

There are certain women, I am informed, who place men under their spell without leaving them the melancholy satisfaction of understanding how the thing was done. They may have absolutely repulsive features, and a pretty permanent absence of mind; without that charm of cheerful grace before which we are said to succumb. Yet they manage to assume command for certain. It is thus with mules. I have heard them called awkward and personally plain, nor is it denied that their disposition, though rich in individuality, lacks some measure of qualities which should endear them to humanity. Despite all this, and even more, they have a way of tenderly getting the better of us, and, in the long run, absolutely enthroning themselves in our affections. Mystery as it is, I confess to its potent sway, long ago owning it beyond solution.

Live on the intimate terms of brother-explorer with your mule, be thoughtful for his welfare, and you by-and-by take an emotional start toward him which will surprise you. You look into that reserved face, the embodiment of self-contained drollery, and begin to detect soft thought and tender feeling; and sometimes, as you cinch your saddle a little severely, the calm, reproachful visage will swing round and melt you with a single look. Nothing is left but to rub the velvet nose and loosen the girth. When the mere brightness and gayety of mountain life carries one away with their hilarious current, there is something in the meek and humble air of a lot of pack animals altogether chastening in its prompt effect.

My " '69" was one of these insidious beings who within a week of our first meeting asserted supremacy over my life, and formed a silent partnership with my conscience. She was a chubby, black mule, so sleek and rotund as distantly to suggest a pig on stilts. Upon the eye which still remained, a cataract had begun to spread its dimming film. Her make-up was also defective in a weak pair of hind legs, which gave way suddenly in going up steep places. She was clumsy, and in rugged pathways would squander much time in the selection of her foothold. At these moments, when she deliberated, as I fancied, needlessly long, I have very gently suggested with Spanish spur that it might be as well to start; the serious face then turned upon me, its mild eye looking into mine one long, earnest gaze, as much as to say, "I love and would spare you; remember Balaam!" I yielded.

These animals are always of the opposition party; they reverse your wishes, and from one year's end to another defy your best judgment. Yet I love them, and only in extreme moments "go for" them with a fence-rail or theodolite-tripod. Nothing can be pleasanter than to ride them through forest roads, chatting in a bright company, and catching glimpses of far quiet scenery framed by the long, furry ears.

CLARENCE KING
[*Mountaineering in the Sierra Nevada* (1871)]

A Companion in Solitude

[*John Muir—second only to Thoreau among the greatest interpreters of nature —is also Thoreau's perfect complement. Striding alone among the high peaks of the Sierras rather than traveling extensively in Concord, he actually penetrated into that wilderness of which the idea alone was sufficient for Thoreau. Partly, perhaps, for that reason he is commonly more rhapsodist than philoso-*

pher. But in portraits like his very famous description of a bird of the high mountain streams, his spirit seems very close to that of his New England predecessor. Had Thoreau known the ouzel he would have written about it in much the same way.]

The water-falls of the Sierra Nevada are frequented by only one bird, the ouzel or water-thrush (*Cinclus Mexicanus*, Sw.). He is a singularly joyous and lovable little fellow, about the size of a robin, clad in a plain water-proof suit of a blackish, bluish gray, with a tinge of chocolate on the head and shoulders. In form he is about as smoothly plump and compact as a pot-hole pebble; the flowing contour of his body being interrupted only by his strong feet and bill, and the crisp wing-tips, and up-slanted wrenish tail.

Among all the countless water-falls I have met in the course of eight years' explorations in the Sierra, whether in the icy Alps, or warm foot-hills, or in the profound Yosemite cañons of the middle region, not one was found without its ouzel. No cañon is too cold for him, none too lonely, provided it be rich in white falling water. Find a fall, or cascade, or rushing rapid, anywhere upon a clear crystalline stream, and there you will surely find its complementary ouzel, flitting about in the spray, diving in foaming eddies, whirling like a leaf among beaten foam-bells; ever vigorous and enthusiastic, yet self-contained, and neither seeking nor shunning your company.

If disturbed while dipping about in the margin shallows, he either sets off with a rapid whir to some other feeding-ground up or down the stream, or alights on some half-submerged rock or snag out in the foaming current, and immediately begins to nod and curtsy like a wren, turning his head from side to side and performing many other odd dainty manners as if he had been trained at some bird dancing-school.

He is the mountain streams' own darling,—the humming-bird of blooming waters, loving rocky ripple-slopes and sheets of foam, as a bee loves flowers,—as a lark loves sunshine and meadows. Among all the mountain birds, none has cheered me so much in my lonely wanderings,—none so unfailing. For winter and summer he sings, independent alike of sunshine and love; requiring no other inspiration than the stream on which he dwells. While water sings, so must he; in heat or cold, calm or storm, ever attuning his voice in sure accord; low in the drought of summer and drought of winter, but never silent.

De Aquatilibus.

Icon hæc est Ranæ piscatricis, qualem Venetijs depictam olim ab amico accepi. conijcio autem ad piscem aridum factam esse. Rondeletij enim pictura quin legitima sit, non dubito.

B.

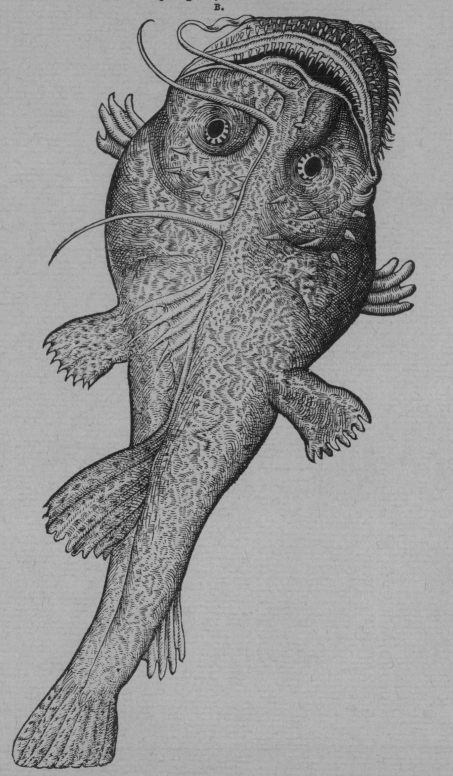

De Serpente Marino

During the golden days of Indian summer the mountain streams are feeble,—a succession of silent pools, linked together with strips of silvery lace-work; then the song of the ouzel is at its lowest ebb. But as soon as the winter clouds have bloomed, and the mountain treasuries are once more replenished with snow, the voices of the streams and ouzels begin to increase in strength and richness until the flood season of early summer. Then the glad torrents chant their noblest anthems, and then too is the flood-time of our songster's melody. But as to the influence of the weather, dark days and sun days are the same to him. The voices of most song-birds, however joyous, suffer a long winter eclipse; but the ouzel sings on around all the seasons, and through every kind of storm. Indeed no storm can be more violent than those of the water-falls in the midst of which he delights to dwell. At least, from whatever cause, while the weather is darkest and most boisterous, snowing, blowing, cloudy or clear, all the same he sings, and never a note of sadness. No need of spring sunshine to thaw *his* song, for it never freezes. Never shall you hear anything wintry from *his* warm breast; no pinched cheeping, no wavering notes between sadness and joy; his mellow, fluty voice is ever tuned to downright gladness, as free from every trace of dejection as cock-crowing.

It is pitiful to see wee frost-pinched sparrows, on cold mornings, shaking the snow from their feathers, and hopping about as if anxious to be cheery, then hastening back to their hidings out of the wind, puffing out their breast feathers, and subsiding among the leaves, cold and breakfastless, while the snow continues to fall, and no sign of clearing. But the ouzel never calls forth a single touch of pity; not because he is strong to endure, but rather because he seems to live a charmed life beyond the reach of every influence that makes endurance necessary.

One wild winter morning, when Yosemite Valley was swept from west to east by a cordial snow-storm, I sallied forth to see what I might learn and enjoy. A sort of gray, gloaming-like darkness was kept up by the storm, and the loudest booming of the falls was at times buried beneath its sublime roar. The snow was already over five feet deep on the meadows, making very extended walks impossible without the aid of snowshoes. I found no great difficulty, however, in making my way to a certain riffle on the river where one of my ouzels lived. He was at home as usual, gleaning his breakfast among the pebbles of a shallow portion of the margin, and apparently altogether unconscious of anything extraordinary in the weather. Presently he flew out to a stone against which the icy current was beating, and turning his back to the wind, sang delightfully as a lark in springtime.

After spending an hour or two with my favorite, I went plodding through the drifts, to learn as definitely as possible how the other birds were spending their time. The Yosemite birds are easily found during the winter, because all excepting the ouzel are restricted to the sunny north side of the valley, the south side being constantly eclipsed by the great frosty shadow of the wall. And because the Indian Cañon groves from their peculiar exposure are the warmest, all the birds congregate there, more especially in severe weather.

I found most of the robins cowering on the lee side of the larger branches where the snow could not fall upon them, while two or three of the most enterprising were making desperate efforts to reach the mistletoe berries by clinging nervously to the under side of the snow-crowned masses, back downward, like woodpeckers. Every now and then they would dislodge some of the loose fringes of the snow-crown which would come sifting down upon their heads and send them screaming back to camp, where they would subside among their companions with a shiver, muttering in low, querulous chatters like hungry children.

Some of the sparrows were busy at the foot of the larger trees gleaning seeds and benumbed insects, joined now and then by a robin weary of his unsuccessful attempts upon the snow-covered berries. The brave woodpeckers were clinging to the snowless sides of the larger boles and overarching branches of the camp trees, making short flights from side to side of the grove, pecking and chattering aimlessly as if unable to keep still, yet evidently putting in the time in a very dull way, like storm-bound travelers at a country tavern. The hardy nuthatches were threading the open furrows of the bark in their usual industrious manner, and uttering their quaint notes, evidently much less discomposed than their neighbors. The Steller's jays were of course making more noisy stir than all the other birds combined; ever coming and going with loud bluster, screaming as if each had a lump of melting sludge in his throat, and taking very good care to improve the favorable opportunity afforded by the storm to steal from the acorn stores of the woodpeckers. I also noticed one solitary gray eagle braving the storm on the top of a tall pine stump just outside the main grove. He was standing bolt upright with his back to the wind, and with a tuft of snow piled on his square shoulders, the very type of passive endurance. Thus every snowbound bird seemed more or less uncomfortable if not in positive distress. The storm was reflected in every gesture, and not one cheerful note, not to say song, came from a single bill; their cowering, joyless endurance offering a most striking contrast to the spontaneous, irrepressible gladness of the ouzel, who could no more help exhaling sweet song, than a rose sweet fragrance. He *must* sing if the heavens fall. I remember noticing the distress of a pair of robins during the violent earthquake of the year 1872, when the pines of the valley, with strange movements, flapped and waved their branches, and beetling rock-brows came thundering to the meadows in fiery avalanches. It did not occur to me in the midst of the excitement of other observations to look for the ouzels, but I doubt not they were singing straight on through it all, regarding its terrible thunders as fearlessly as they do the booming of the water-falls.

What may be regarded as the separate songs of the ouzel are exceedingly difficult of description, because they are so variable and at the same time so confluent. I have been acquainted with my favorite for eight years, and though during most of this time I have heard him sing nearly every day, I still detect notes and strains that are quite new to me. Nearly all of his music is very sweet and tender, lapsing from his round breast like water over the smooth lip of a pool, then breaking farther on into a rich sparkling foam of melodious notes, which glow with subdued enthusiasm, yet without expressing much of the strong, gushing ecstasy of the bobolink or sky-lark.

The more striking strains are perfect arabesques of melody, composed of a few full, round, mellow notes, embroidered with a great variety of delicate trills which fade in long slender cadences like the silken fringes of summer clouds melting in the azure. But as a whole, his music is that of the stream itself, infinitely organized, spiritualized. The deep booming notes of the falls are in it, the trills of rapids, the swirling and gurgling of pot-holes, low hushes of levels, the rapturous bounce and dance of rocky cascades, and the sweet tinkle of separate drops oozing from the ends of mosses and falling into tranquil pools.

The ouzel never sings in chorus with other birds, nor with his kind, but only with the streams. And like flowers that bloom beneath the surface of the ground, some of our favorite's best song-blossoms never rise above the surface of the heavier music of the water. I have oftentimes observed him singing in the midst of beaten spray, his music completely buried beneath the water's roar; yet I knew he was surely singing by the movements of his bill.

His food consists of all kinds of water insects, which in summer are chiefly procured along shallow margins. Here he wades about ducking his head under water, and deftly turning over pebbles and fallen leaves with his bill, seldom choosing to go into deep water where he has to use his wings in diving.

He seems to be especially fond of the larvæ of mosquitoes, found in great quantities attached to the bottom of smooth rock channels where the current is swift and shallow. When feeding in such places he wades upstream, and oftentimes while his head is under water the swift current is deflected upward along the glossy curves of his neck and shoulders, in the form of a clear, crystalline shell, which fairly incloses him like a bell-glass, the shell being constantly broken and reformed as he lifts and dips his head; while ever and anon he sidles out to where the too powerful current carries him off his feet, and sweeps him rapidly downstream; then he dexterously rises on the wing and goes gleaning again in shallower places.

But during the winter, when the stream-banks are all deeply embossed in snow, and the streams themselves are chilled nearly to the freezing point, so that the snow falling into them in stormy weather is not wholly dissolved, but forms a thin blue sludge, thus rendering the current opaque—then he seeks the deeper portions of the main rivers, where he may dive to clear portions of the channel beneath the sludge. Or he repairs to some open lake or millpond, at the bottom of which he feeds in perfect safety. . . .

But it is in withstanding the force of rushing torrents that their strength of wing in this respect is most strikingly manifested. The following may be regarded as a fair illustration of their easy, unconscious powers of sub-aquatic flight. One winter morning, when the Merced River was blue and green with unmelted snow, I observed one of my ouzels perched on a snag out in the midst of a swift rushing rapid. He sang cheerily, as if everything was just to his mind, and while I stood on the bank admiring him, he suddenly plunged into the sludgy current, leaving his song broken abruptly off. After feeding a minute or two at the bottom, and when one would suppose he must inevitably be swept far downstream, he emerged just where he went down, alighted on the same snag, showered the water beads from his feathers, and at once continued his unfinished song, splicing it together as if it had suffered no interruption.

The ouzel alone of all birds dares to enter a white torrent. And though strictly terrestrial in structure, no other is so inseparably related to water, not even the duck, or bold ocean albatross, or stormy petrel. Ducks go ashore when they have done feeding in undisturbed places, and frequently make long overland flights from lake to lake or from field to field. The same is true of most other aquatic birds. But our ouzel, born on the very brink of a stream, seldom leaves it for a single moment. For, notwithstanding he is often on the wing, he never flies overland, but whirs with rapid, quail-like beat above the stream, tracing all its winding modulations with great minuteness. Even when the stream is quite small, say from five to ten feet wide, he will not try to shorten his flight by crossing a bend, however abrupt it may be; and even when disturbed by meeting someone on the bank, he prefers to fly over one's head, to dodging out over the ground. When therefore his flight along a crooked stream is viewed endwise, it appears most strikingly wavered—an interpretation of every curve inscribed with lightning-like rapidity on the air.

The vertical curves and angles of the most precipitous Alpine torrents he traces with the same rigid fidelity. Swooping down the inclines of cascades, dropping sheer over dizzy falls amid the spray, and ascending with the same fearlessness and ease, seldom seeking to lessen the steepness of the acclivity by beginning to ascend before reaching the base of the fall. No matter how high it may be, he holds straight on as if about to dash headlong into the throng of booming rockets, then darts abruptly upward, and, after alighting at the top of the precipice to rest a moment, proceeds to feed and sing. His flight is solid and impetuous without any intermission of wing-beats,—one homogeneous buzz like that of a laden bee on its way home. And while thus buzzing freely from fall to fall, he is frequently heard giving utterance to a long out-drawn train of unmodulated notes, in no way connected with his song, but corresponding closely with his flight, both in sustained vigor and homogeneity of substance.

Were the flights of every individual ouzel in the Sierra traced on a chart, they would indicate the direction of the flow of the entire system of ancient glaciers, from about the period of the breaking up of the ice-sheet until near the close of the glacial winter; because the streams which the ouzels so rigidly follow, are, with the unimportant exceptions of a few side tributaries, all flowing in channels eroded for them out of the solid flank of the range by the vanished glaciers,—the streams tracing the glaciers, the ouzels tracing the streams. Nor do we find so complete compliance to glacial conditions in the life of any other mountain bird, or animal of any kind. Bears frequently accept the path-ways laid down by glaciers as the easiest to travel; but then, they often leave them and cross over from cañon to cañon. So also, most birds found in rocky cañons at all usually fly across at right angles to the courses of the vanished glaciers, because the main forests of these regions to which they come and go are growing upon the lateral moraines which always stretch along the tops of the cañon walls.

The ouzel's nest is one of the most extraordinary pieces of bird architecture I ever beheld; so odd and novel in design, and so perfectly fresh and beautiful, and in every way so fully worthy of the genius of the little builder. It is about a foot in diameter, round and bossy in outline, with a neatly arched opening near the bottom, somewhat like an old-fashioned brick oven, or Hottentot's hut. It is built almost exclusively of green and yellow mosses, chiefly the beautiful fronded hypnum that covers the rocks and old drift-logs in the vicinity of water-falls. These are deftly interwoven, and felted together into a charming little hut; and so situated that many of the outer mosses continue to flourish as if they had not been plucked. A few fine silky-stemmed grasses are occasionally found interwoven with the mosses, but with the exception of a thin layer lining the floor, their presence seems accidental, as they are of a species found growing with the mosses and are probably plucked with them. The site chosen for this curious mansion is usually some little rock-shelf within reach of the spray of a water-fall, so that its walls are kept green and growing, at least during the time of high water.

No harsh lines are presented by any portion of the nest as seen *in situ,* but when removed from its shelf, the back and bottom, and sometimes a portion of the top, is found quite sharply angular because it is made to conform to the surface of the rock, upon which and against which it is built; the little architect always taking advantage of slight crevices and protuberances that may chance to offer, to render his structure stable by means of a kind of gripping and dove-tailing.

In choosing a building spot, concealment does not seem to be taken into consideration at all; yet notwithstanding the nest is so large, and so guilelessly exposed to view, it is far from being easily detected, chiefly because it swells forward like any other bulging moss-cushion growing naturally in such situations. This is more especially the case where the nest is kept fresh by being well sprinkled. Sometimes these romantic little huts have their beauty enhanced by tasteful decorations of rock-ferns and grasses, that spring up around the walls or in front of the doorsill, all dripping with crystal beads.

Furthermore, at certain hours of the day when the sunshine is poured down at the required angle, the whole mass of the spray enveloping the fairy establishment is brilliantly irised; and it is through so glorious a rainbow atmosphere as this that some of our blessed ouzels obtain their first peep at the world.

Ouzels seem so completely part and parcel of the streams they inhabit, they scarce suggest any other origin than the streams themselves, and one might almost be pardoned in fancying they come direct from the living waters like flowers from the ground,—a kind of winged water-lily. At least, from whatever cause, it never occurred to me to look for their nests until more than a year after I had made the acquaintance of the birds themselves, although I found one the very day on which I began the search. In making my way from Yosemite to the glaciers of the adjacent Alps, I camped in a particularly wild and romantic portion of the Nevada cañon where in previous excursions I had never once failed to enjoy the delightful company of my favorites, who were attracted here, no doubt, by the extraordinary abundance of white water. The river, for miles above and below, consists of a succession of small falls from ten to sixty feet in height, connected by flat, plume-like cascades that go flashing from fall to fall, free and channelless, over waving folds of glacier-polished granite.

JOHN MUIR
["The Water Ouzel," *Scribner's Magazine*, February, 1878]

Tomcat Past His Prime

[*Colette's reputation as a somewhat spicy novelist has overshadowed another to which she is equally entitled. She is one of the most original "nature writers" in any language.*]

✍

I once had a name—a terse and furry name—a name suitable to a costly Persian cat. I shed it somewhere . . . on the roofs, in the gurgling gutters, on the peeling moss of old walls—I have become just The Tomcat.

What would I do with any other name? This one satisfies my pride. Those for whom, in days gone by, I was "Sidi," the Lord Cat, never call me any more; they know that I come to no one's bidding.

When they talk of me they say "The Tomcat." I come when I please and the masters of this house are not my masters.

I am so beautiful that I hardly ever smile. My Persian coat shimmers with silver lights, with the grey-mauve tints of wisterias faded by the sun, with the stormy purple of new slate. A wide, low skull, broad lion-like jowls, and what heavy eyebrows overhanging what magnificent, moody eyes! One—only one—frivolous detail in all this majestic beauty: my nose, my dainty, tip-tilted nose, moist and bloomed with blue like a little plum.

I hardly ever smile, even when I am at play. I vouchsafe to break with a royal paw some trinket that may need chastisement. And when I lift that paw against my son—irreverent Infanto!—I appear to fling him back into chaos!

Did you expect me to simper and coquet on your carpets, like "The Shah," my little Sultana, whom I have deserted?

I am The Tomcat and I lead the uneasy life of those whom Love created to serve under heavy bondage. I am solitary, condemned forever to conquer. I am cruel by necessity. I fight, as I feed, with a business-like appetite, like an athlete in training, who fights and conquers without haste or anger.

In the early morning I return to you. I appear with the dawn, my blue coat merging with its blue shadows. I descend from the top of those stripped trees standing in the mist, where, before I stirred, I might have been mistaken for a large nest. Or I slip down the incline of the roof until I land on the wooden balcony and perch on the sill of your half-open window like a winter nosegay. I bring in all the December night with its scent of cool graveyards! Soon, when I have fallen asleep, my warmth will give out a scent of bitter boxwood, of dry blood, of wild musk.

For under my silky fleece I am bleeding. There is a smarting wound on my throat and I don't even lick the broken skin of my paw. I only want to sleep, sleep, sleep, closing my lids tight over my beautiful eyes—my eyes like those of a night-bird—to sleep anywhere, fallen down like a tramp; to sleep inert, clotted with mud, bristling with straws and burrs—like a satiated Faun. . . .

I sleep on and on. . . . Sometimes an electric shock upheaves me. I growl low, like distant thunder, and sink back again. . . . Even at the twilight hour, when I wake for good, I appear absent, still swayed by my recent dreams, my eyes fixed on the window, my ear cocked at the door.

After a hasty and perfunctory toilet, stiff in every joint, I cross the threshold, at the same hour every evening, and depart—less like a guest bidden to a feast than like an outlaw driven by dire necessity. I depart, swaying like a ponderous caterpillar, between shining puddles, my ears flattened against the wind. I go unmindful of the snow. I stop for a second—not that I hesitate, but to listen to the secret stirrings of my kingdom, to consult the darkness, to fling to my invisible enemies the solemn, measured, mournful challenge of the insolent, wandering Tomcat. Then, as if frenzied by the sound of my own voice, I leap forward. For the space of a second you can see me, hardly discernible, there on the top of the wall, fluffed out, blurred, floating like a wisp of cloud. Then I am seen no more.

It is the wild season of roaming and prowling, the season that lures us from all domestic joys, that multiplies diabolically in the garden all our feline tribe. It is not that I prefer the white and slender cat to the one splashed with orange and brown, like a tulip, or to the one black and sleek like a wet eel. Alas! I want them all around me, knowing that if I do not keep them they will turn from my allegiance to that of some detested rival.

These nights are long. . . . I keep my vigil, alert, punctual, a little morose. My little forsaken wife, grey-blue, silky, sleeps in the house. She is too similar to me to arouse my interest. Does she hear, deep-pillowed in her scented basket, the songs that rise toward me? Does she hear, as the fight draws to a climax, a wounded rival bellowing my real name—the name that men do not know?

The night draws out. . . . I feel sad, and more lonely than a god. A guileless longing for light, warmth, peace crosses my stern vigil. . . . How slowly the dawn whitens—the dawn that cheers the birds and bewilders the excited cats! For many years I have reigned, loving and killing. . . . For many years I have been beautiful. . . . I dream, tucked up like a fur ball on the frosted wall. . . . I am afraid of getting old!

COLETTE

[*Cats, Dogs and I*. Translated by Princess Alexandre Gagafine (1924)]

Sea Otters and Civilization

[*Ernest Thompson Seton was far more than that writer of books for boys which commonly come to mind when his name is mentioned. Even professional zoologists (who should know better) sometimes hesitate to acknowledge that his multi-volumed Lives of Game Animals is an authoritative compendium in which great masses of detailed information are enlivened by masterful portraits in the great tradition. The sea otter barely escaped extinction during the years following the discovery of the great northern herds reported by Vitus Bering in 1741. All modern observers have described it as one of the most sportive and charming of animals.*]

Of all the creatures living in the cold North seas, the Sea-otter is alone in that he usually swims on his back. Sailing, paddling, shooting or diving he goes, with his back to the deep, and his shining breast to the sky. But his neck is doublebent, so his big soft eyes sweep the blue world above and around. Propelled almost wholly by his big finlike hind feet, he moves with easy sinuous sweeps through the swell with its huge broad fronds of kelp—with back first, he ever goes forward, until the moment comes to dive—supple as an eel he turns—back up like Seal or Beaver, and down he goes—down, down— long strings of silver bubbles mark the course, and by a strange atmospheric change, the colour of the black merman now is yellow-brown as a seaman's slicker, or golden as a bunch of kelp. Down 30 to 100 feet or more he goes, and gropes around in the gloom, until he finds some big fat squid or sea-urchin. He does not hurry, for he can stay under 4 or 5 minutes. Then up he comes with the prey in his jaws, back to the top, to the borderland, that eternal line between the two kingdoms of air and water, on which he lives.

Here again on his back he lies, as, using his broad chest for dinner table, he tears open the sea beastie, feeds on its meat, and flings its shell aside, if it have any. Then he repeats the dive, and the feasting, until his sleek round belly is well filled. Now, among the heaving, friendly kelp he lazes on his back, plays ball perhaps with a lump of the leathery weed, tossing it from paw to paw, taking keen delight in his cleverness at keeping it aloft, as a juggler does his balls; and sniffing in disappointment if he should foozle the ball and miss the catch.

Other Sea-otters are about him, for Amikuk, like most fishermen, is of a neighbourly spirit and loves good company. His mate may be there with her water baby in her big motherly lap. She tumbles it off into the deep for a swimming lesson; and round and under she swims to exercise "the kid," and make it learn. This is a very ancient game, this water-tag; the earliest monad that ever wriggled tail in the hot first seas, no doubt invented it. It is deep in everything that swims, or moves, and loves good company; so father Otter pitches in, and plays it, too. For half an hour they may keep it up. Father is still strong and frolicsome; so is mother; but the water baby is tired. Its big round eyes are blinking in weariness, and it is ready for sleep. Trust mother to look out for the little one. She curls up and takes it, not pick-a-back, but in the snug bed that she makes by curling belly up, as she floats among the weed. Her four feet are the bedposts, and in some degree the coverlet, too, for she holds it to her breast, crooning softly to it, till its whimpering ceases and it sleeps. Its fur may be wet and cold, but its skin is dry and warm; and drifting like a log of drift among that helpful wrack, they float, and love the lives they live.

But father is full of energy. He is one of thirty or forty that herd along this bed of kelp, that marks a deep-down feeding ridge, where their shiny seafood swarms. And away they go, in a race that recalls the tremendous speed and energy of the Porpoise in the sea. Undulating like water-serpents, or breaking from the side of a billow, to leap in a long curve, splash into the high wet bank of the next; one after another they go, racing round, in air or far below, diving, jumping, plunging, somersaulting, back up, belly up, or sides up— it matters not, so they speed, for the joy of rapid flight, for the wonderful pleasure of using their pent-up energy in mastery of the elements about them.

Strange as it may seem, these merry games have mostly place in rough and heavy weather, almost a storm. Swanson says that, on calmer days, they are never seen playing; that is, the bands of older ones are not. They need the stimulus of a contest with the waves before they do their wonderful best. In quiet times, they are more likely to sleep.

Usually, when one is seen, it is sleeping; otherwise they are too alert to be easily discovered. And even at this time, none but the keenest, best-trained eyes can find them, for the body is sunk below the surface; only the head and flippers show. They have no look of a furry animal form, but pass for a black drift log with snags.

As they float their merman way, they are frequently seen with hind flippers raised and spread, as if catching the breeze to sail or drift before it.

On sunny days, so rare in their wild, stormy ocean home, their big brown eyes might suffer from the unwonted glare; but as they float and dream, they sometimes shade their eyes with one idle paw; just as one of us might do, if we could swim that way, and faced the light.

They do not have those big, fawn-like eyes for nothing. Their vision is all it should be, for such perfect organs. Their ears, too, are keen; but of all their senses, smell is their best, the safest sentinel that guards their life.

Best equipped is he, in this respect, of all the wild things in the wild and windy North. But also hardest pressed. For that matchless robe, worth its weight in gold, has the force of a blood-price on his head. Many a brave and valiant man has been hunted down for less reward than the fetch of this wondrous pelt.

As one reads the full account by Steller, one gets the impression of humanization almost too much, and might question the accuracy of some details. But they have been endorsed by Elliott, Scammon, Stejneger, Snow, and many others since.

And as one reads of its mild and human face, its fish-like hinder parts, its human arms, in which the mother, two-breasted, carries her whimpering babe, and croons it to its slumber, or plays with it, as she sports in the rolling surf, can one not readily believe that in this we have, perhaps, the original of the mermaids and the mermen of the ancient tales?

ERNEST THOMPSON SETON
[*Lives of Game Animals* (1925-1928)]

A Modern Primitive

[In his Plain Words (1954) Sir Ernest Gowers vouches for the following response by a ten-year-old who was invited to do an essay on a bird and a beast. "The writer," Gowers remarks, "had something to say and said it as clearly as he could, and so has unconsciously achieved a style." A complete bestiary by the same hand would be a precious addition to literature.]

The bird that I am going to write about is the owl. The owl cannot see at all by day and at night is as blind as a bat.

I do not know much about the owl, so I will go on to the beast which I am going to choose. It is the cow. The cow is a mammal. It has six sides—right, left, an upper and below. At the back it has a tail on which hangs a brush. With this it sends the flies away so that they do not fall into the milk. The head is for the purpose of growing horns and so that the mouth can be somewhere. The horns are to butt with, and the mouth is to moo with. Under the cow hangs the milk. It is arranged for milking. When people milk, the milk comes and there is never an end to the supply. How the cow does it I have not yet realised, but it makes more and more. The cow has a fine sense of smell; one can smell it far away. This is the reason for the fresh air in the country.

The man cow is called an ox. It is not a mammal. The cow does not eat much, but what it eats it eats twice, so that it gets enough. When it is hungry it moos, and when it says nothing it is because its inside is all full up with grass.

ANONYMOUS

SECTION TWO

HUNTERS AND SPORTSMEN

Now for as much as these sports are many and diverse I think it not amiss to begin and give that recreation precedence and place which in mine opinion . . . doth many degrees go before and precede all others, as being most royal for the stateliness thereof, most artificial for the wisdom and the cunning thereof. And this I hold to be the hunting of wild beasts in general.

GERVASE MARKHAM
Country Contentments

In the last age every gentleman-like man kept a sparrow-hawk, and a priest kept a bobby [a small hawk].

JOHN AUBREY
Papers

It is very strange and very melancholy that the paucity of human pleasures should persuade us ever to call hunting one of them.

SAMUEL JOHNSON
Hester Lynch Piozzi, *Anecdotes of the Late Dr. Samuel Johnson*

We cannot live without destroying animals, but shall we torture them for our sport—sport in their destruction.

HORACE WALPOLE
Letters, edited by W. S. Lewis

If a man takes on himself the heavy responsibility of killing he should not do it for pastime.

BERNARD SHAW
Killing for Sport

Mr. A —— the well-known big game hunter has been missing for ten days. It is feared that something he disagreed with ate him.

ANONYMOUS

The Heroes Go Hunting

["The invention of this art is from the gods, for hunting and dogs were the care of Apollo and Diana who rewarded and honored Chiron with a knowledge of them." Thus Xenophon, who goes on to give detailed and prosy instruction in some of the techniques. But it was the epic poets such as Homer and Virgil who best described the pride, pomp, and circumstance of the classical hunt.]

When now the early rosy-fingered dawn appeared, they started on the hunt; the dogs went forth, the men themselves—the sons of Autolycus—and with them went royal Odysseus too. They climbed the steep and wood-clad mountain of Parnassus and soon they reached its windy ridges. Just then the sun began to touch the fields as he ascended from the calm and brimming stream of Ocean. And now to a glen the prickers came. Before them, following the tracks, the hounds ran on, the sons of Autolycus hastening after. With the same went royal Odysseus, close on the hounds, wielding his outstretched spear. In a dense thicket here a huge boar lay. It was a spot no force of wind with its chill breath could pierce, no sunbeams smite, nor rain pass through, so dense it was, and a thick fall of leaves was in it. Here round the boar there came the tramp of men and dogs, as the prickers pushed along. Facing them from his lair, with bristling back, fire flashing in his eyes, the boar stood close at bay. Odysseus first sprang forward, raising the long spear in his sinewy hand, eager to give the blow; but the boar was quick and struck him on the knee, and by a side-thrust of his tusk tore the flesh deep, but reached no bone. And now Odysseus, by a downward blow, struck the right shoulder of the boar; clean through it the bright spear-point passed. Down in the dust he fell with a moan, and his life flew away.

H O M E R
[*The Odyssey*]

⚞

Meanwhile Aurora has risen, and left the ocean. Rising with the day-star, the chivalry of Carthage streams through the gates, their woven toils, and nets, and hunting-spears tipped with broad iron, and Massylian horsemen hurry along, and a force of keen-scented hounds. There are the Punic princes, waiting for the queen, who still lingers in her chamber; there stands her palfrey, conspicuous in purple and gold, fiercely champing the foaming bit. At length she comes forth, with a mighty train attending, a Tyrian scarf round her, itself surrounded by an embroidered border; her quiver of gold, her hair knotted up with gold, her purple robe fastened with a golden clasp. The Phrygian train, too, are in motion, and Iulus, all exultation. Æneas himself, comely beyond all the rest, adds his presence to theirs, and joins the procession; like Apollo, when he leaves his Lycian winter-seat and the stream of Xanthus, and visits Delos, his mother's isle, and renews the dance; while with mingled voices round the altar shout Cretans and Dryopians, and tattooed Agathyrsians. The god in majesty walks on the heights of Cynthus, training his luxuriant hair with the soft pressure of a wreath of leaves, and twining it with gold; his arrows rattle on his shoulders. Not with less ease than he moved Æneas; such the beauty that sparkles in that peerless countenance. When they reach the high mountains and the pathless coverts, see! the wild goats, dropping from the tops of the crags, have run down the slopes; in another quarter the deer are scouring the open plains, massing their herds as they fly in a whirlwind of dust, and leaving the mountains. But young Ascanius is in the heart of the glens, exulting in his fiery courser. Now he passes one, now another of his comrades at full speed, and prays that in the midst of such spiritless game he may be blest with the sight of a foaming boar, or that a tawny lion may come down the hill. Meantime the sky begins to be convulsed with a mighty turmoil; a storm-cloud follows of mingled rain and hail. The Tyrian train, all in confusion, and the chivalry of Troy, and the hope of Dardania, Venus' grandson, have sought shelter in their terror up and down the country, some here, some there. The streams run in torrents down the hills. Dido and the Trojan chief find themselves in the same cave. Earth, the mother of all, and Juno give the sign.

Lightnings blaze, and heaven flashes in sympathy with the bridal; and from mountain-tops the nymphs give the nuptial shout. That day was the birthday of death, the birthday of woes. Henceforth she has no thought of the common eye or the common tongue; it is not a stolen passion that Dido has now in her mind—no, she calls it marriage; that name is the screen of her sin.

Instantly Fame takes her journey through Libya's great cities— Fame, a monster surpassed in speed by none; her nimbleness lends her life, and she gains strength as she goes. At first fear keeps her low; soon she rears herself skyward, and treads on the ground, while her head is hidden among the clouds. Earth, her parent, provoked to anger against the gods, brought her forth, they say, the youngest of the family of Cœus and Enceladus—swift of foot and untiring of wing, a portent terrible and vast—who, for every feather on her body has an ever-wakeful eye beneath, marvellous to tell, for every eye a loud tongue and mouth, and a pricked-up ear. At night she flies midway between heaven and earth, hissing through the darkness, nor ever yields her eyes to the sweets of sleep. In the daylight she sits sentinel on a high house-top, or on a lofty turret, and makes great cities afraid; as apt to cling to falsehood and wrong as to proclaim the truth. So then she was filling the public ear with a thousand tales—things done and things never done alike the burden of her song—how that Æneas, a prince of Trojan blood, had arrived at Carthage, a hero whom lovely Dido deigned to make her husband, and now in luxurious ease they were wearing away the length of winter together, forgetful of the crowns they wore or hoped to wear, and enthralled by unworthy passion. Such are the tales the fiendlike goddess spreads from tongue to tongue.

VIRGIL
[*The Æneid*]

Sportsman's Vocabulary

[The sportsman as distinguished from the mere hunter (even on the heroic and the royal scale) was largely an invention of the Renaissance and much involved with what had not yet been called "the maintenance of status." Hence the evolution of an "in-group" or "U" vocabulary of which only a faint idea is conveyed by such modern survivals as the salmon fisher's scorn of those who speak of "catching" rather than "taking" this edible fish, or the fox hunter's contempt for anyone who wouldn't die a thousand deaths rather than go costumed in anything other than a "pink" coat.]

There be only four beasts of venery: the Hart, the Hare, the Wild Roe, and the Woolf; and there are none others by the ancient laws of Sir Tristram you may call Beasts of Venery. There be five beasts which we call Beasts of Chase: the Buck, the Doe, the Fox, the Martin, and the Roe: all other of what kind soever, term them Rascal.

Certain Proper terms belonging to all Chase:

A Herd of all manner of Deer.

A Bevy of Roes.

A Sounder of Swine.

A Rout of Wolves.

A Trip or Herd of Goats.

You shall say, an Hart harboureth; a Buck lodgeth; a Roe bedeth. A Hare seateth or fourmed; a Conny sitteth; a Fox kenelleth. A litter of Cubs; a nest of Rabbits. You shall say the Deer is broken; the Fox is cased; the Hare is cased.

We say Dislodge the Buck; Start the Hare; Unkennel the Fox; Rowze the Hart; Bolt the Conny.

Now in the hunting of the Hart, being a princely and Royal

chase, it giveth an exceeding grace unto a huntsman, to use the terms fit and proper unto the same which I have here set down as received from antiquity: First when we see where the Hart hath gone we use to say here he breaketh; and when the Hart entereth a river or pool which we call the Soile, we say he descendeth and when we find where he hath lept into a river we say he proffereth because we are uncertain whether he goeth out at some other way again; and if he turn again that same way, he reproffereth and when we find where he hath come out of the other side of the river we call it the Soile and being come out of the water which fills his footstep we call it defouling.

DAME JULIANA BERNERS
[*The Gentleman's Academy* (1595)]

The Harmonious Hound

[*Dame Berners, who lived in the 14th century, was a less talented writer than her humble fellow countryman, the Elizabethan hack Gervase Markham. His* Country Contentments *was obviously aimed (like some modern books on fox hunting) at those less exalted by birth than Dame Berner's audience, but eager to take advantage of such "social mobility" as might be available.*]

If you would have your kennel for sweetness of cry, then you must compound it of some large dogs, that have deep solemn mouths, and are swift in spending, which must as it were bear the bass in the consort, then a double number of roaring, and loud ringing mouths, which must bear the counter-tenor, then some hollow plain sweet mouths, which must bear the mean or middle part: and so with these three parts of music you shall make your cry perfect: and herein you shall observe that these hounds thus mixed, do run just and even together, and not hang off loose one from another, which is the wildest sight that may be; and you shall understand, that this composition is best to be made of the swiftest and largest deep mouthed dog, the slowest middle sized dog, and the shortest legged slender dog, amongst these you cast in a couple or two of small singing beagles, which as small trebles may warble amongst them: the cry will be a great deal the more sweeter.

If you would have your kennel for loudness of mouth you shall not choose the hollow deep mouth, but the loud clanging mouth, which spendeth freely, and sharply, and as it were redoubleth in the utterance: and if you mix with them the mouth that roareth, and the mouth that whineth, the cry will be both the louder and smarter; and these hounds are for the most part of the middle size, neither extreme tall, nor extreme deep flewed, such as for the most part your Shropshire and pure Worcestershire dogs are, and the more equally you compound these mouths, having as many roarers, as spenders, and as many whiners, as of either, of the other, the louder, and pleasanter your cry will be, especially if it be in sounding tall woods, or under the echo of rocks.

If you would have your kennel for depth of mouth, then you shall compound it of the largest dogs, which have the greatest mouths, and deepest flews, such as your West Country, Cheshire, and Lancashire dogs are, and to five or six couple of bass mouths, you shall not add above two couples of counter-tenors, as many means, and not above one couple of roarers, which being heard but now and then, as at the opening or hitting of a scent, will give much sweetness to the solemness and graveness of the cry, and the music thereof will be much more delightful to the ears of every beholder.

If you would have your kennel for the training of your horse only, laboring thereby to bring him to the full perfection of speed, truth, and toughness, then you shall compound your kennel of the lightest, nimblest and swiftest dogs, such as for the most part all your Northern hounds are, which running swiftly away with the chase will draw your horse up to that extraordinary speed, that he will forget all ease or loitering, and acquaint himself daily with the violence of such exercise, being so familiar therewith, that in the end it will be less troublesome to him than a slow gallop, and hence it was and is that the North parts are so famous for the truth and swiftness of their horses above all other counties in this kingdom.

GERVASE MARKHAM
[*Country Contentments* (1615)]

Fisherman's Defense

[*Fishermen, they say, are more likely than hunters to be thoughtful men.
Perhaps that is why no hunter's book has ever been, like Walton's Compleat
Angler, generally accepted as a literary classic.*]

A Conference betwixt an *Angler,* a *Faulkner,* and a *Hunter,* each commending his Recreation.

PISCATOR   VENATOR   AUCEPS

Pisc. You are well overtaken, Gentlemen, a good morning to you
both; I have stretched my legs up T*ottenham-hill* to overtake you,
hoping your business may occasion you towards W*are* this fine fresh
M*ay* morning.

 vena. Sir, I for my part shall almost answer your hopes, for my
purpose is to drink my morning draught at the T*hatcht* H*ouse* in
H*odsden,* and I think not to rest till I come thither, where I have appointed a friend or two to meet me: but for this Gentleman that you
see with me, I know not how far he intends his journey; he came so
lately into my company, that I have scarce had time to ask him the
question.

 auc. Sir, I shall by your favour bear you company as far as
T*heobalds,* and there leave you, for then I turn up to a friends house
who mews a Hawk for me, which I now long to see.

 vena. Sir, we are all so happy as to have a fine, fresh, cool morning, and I hope we shall each be the happier in the others company.
And Gentlemen, that I may not lose yours, I shall either abate or

amend my pace to enjoy it; knowing that (as the Italians say) *Good company in a journey makes the way to seem the shorter.*

AUC. It may do so Sir, with the help of good discourse, which methinks we may promise from you that both look and speak so cheerfully: and for my part I promise you, as an invitation to it, that I will be as free and open hearted, as discretion will allow me to be with strangers.

VENA. And Sir, I promise the like.

PISC. I am right glad to hear your answers, and in confidence you speak the truth, I shall put on a boldnesse to ask you Sir, Whether businesse or pleasure caused you to be so early up, and walk so fast, for this other Gentleman hath declared he is going to see a Hawk, that a friend mews for him.

VENA. Sir mine is a mixture of both, a little businesse and more pleasure, for I intend this day to do all my businesse, and then bestow another day or two in hunting the *Otter,* which a friend that I go to meet, tells me, is much pleasanter than any other chase whatsoever; howsoever I mean to try it; for to-morrow morning we shall meet a pack of Otter dogs of *noble* Mr. S*adlers* upon A*mwell* H*ill,* who will be there so early, that they intend to prevent the Sun-rising.

PISC. Sir, my fortune has answered my desires, and my purpose is to bestow a day or two in helping to destroy some of those villanous vermin, for I hate them perfectly, because they love fish so well, or rather, because they destroy so much; indeed so much, that in my judgment all men that keep *Otter-dogs* ought to have pensions from the King to incourage them to destroy the very breed of those base *Otters,* they do so much mischief.

VENA. But what say you to the Foxes of the Nation, would not you as willingly have them destroyed? for doubtless they do as much mischief as O*tters* do.

PISC. Oh Sir if they do, it is not so much to me and my fraternity as those base Vermine the O*tters* do.

AUC. Why Sir, I pray, of what Fraternity are you, that you are so angry with the poor O*tters?*

PISC. I am (Sir) a brother of the A*ngle,* and therefore an enemy to the O*tter:* for you are to note, that we Anglers all love one another, and therefore do I hate the O*tter* both for my own and for their sakes who are of my brotherhood.

VENA. And I am a lover of Hounds, I have followed many a pack of dogs many a mile, and heard many merry men make sport and scoff at Anglers.

AUC. And I profess myself a Faulkner, and have heard many grave serious men pity them, 'tis such a heavy, contemptible, dull recreation.

PISC. You know Gentlemen, 'tis an easie thing to scoff at any Art or Recreation; a little *wit* mixt with ill nature, confidence, and *malice*, will do it; but though they often venture boldly, yet they are often caught even in their own trap, according to that of *Lucian*, the father of the family of Scoffers.

> *Lucian* well skill'd in scoffing, this hath writ,
> Friend, that's your folly which you think your wit:
> This you vent oft, void both of wit and fear,
> Meaning another, when your self you jeere.

If to this you add what *Solomon* sayes of Scoffers, That *they are abomination to mankind*. Let him that thinks fit be a Scoffer still, but I account them enemies to me, and to all that love *vertue* and *Angling*.

And for you that have heard many grave serious men pity Anglers; let me tell you Sir, there be many men that are by others taken to be serious grave men, which we contemn and pity. Men that are taken to be grave, because Nature hath made them of a sowre complexion, money-getting-men, men that spend all their time first in getting, and next in anxious care to keep it; men that are condemned to be rich, and then always busie or discontented: for these poor-rich-men, we Anglers pity them perfectly, and stand in no need to borrow their thoughts to think our selves happy. No, no, Sir, we enjoy a contentednesse above the reach of such dispositions, and as the learned and ingenuous M*ountagne* sayes like himself freely, "When my Cat and I entertain each other with mutual apish tricks (as playing with a garter) who knowes but that I make my Cat more sport than she makes me? shall I conclude her to be simple, that has her time to begin or refuse sportiveness as freely as I my self have? Nay, who knowes but that it is a defect of my not understanding her language (for doubtless Cats talk and reason with one another) that we agree no better: and who knows but that she pitties me for being no wiser, and laughs and censures my follie for making sport for her when we play together."

Thus freely speaks M*ountagne* concerning Cats, and I hope I may take as great a liberty to blame any man, and laugh at him too, let him be never so serious, that hath not heard what Anglers can say in the justification of their Art and Recreation, which I may again tell you is so full of pleasure, that we need not borrow their thoughts to think our selves happy.

    VENA. Sir, you have almost amazed me, for though I am no scoffer, yet I have (I pray let me speak it without offence) alwayes looked upon Anglers as more patient and more simple men, then I fear I shall find you to be.

    PISC. Sir, I hope you will not judge my earnestness to be impatience: and for my *simplicity*, if by that you mean a harmlessness, or that simplicity which was usually found in the primitive Christians, who were (as most Anglers are) quiet men, and followers of peace; men that were so simply-wise, as not to sell their Consciences to buy riches, and with them vexation and a fear to die. If you mean such simple men as lived in those times when there were fewer Lawyers; when men might have had a Lordship safely conveyed to them in a piece of Parchment no bigger than your hand (though several sheets will not do it safely in this wiser age) I say, Sir, if you take us Anglers to be such simple men as I have spoken of, then my self and those of my Profession will be glad to be so understood: But if by simplicity you meant to express a general defect in those that profess and practise the excellent art of Angling, I hope in time to disabuse you, and make the contrary appear so evidently, that if you will but have patience to hear me, I shall remove all the Anticipations that discourse, or time, or prejudice have possess'd you with against that laudable and ancient art; for I know it is worthy the *knowledge* and *practice* of a wise man.

    VENA. Pray Sir speak of them what you think fit; for we have yet five miles to the *Thatcht*-House, during which walk I dare promise you my patience and diligent attention shall not be wanting. And if you shall make that to appear which you have undertaken, first, that it is an Art, and an Art worth the learning, I shall beg that I may attend you a day or two a fishing, and that I may become your Scholar, and be instructed in the Art it self which you so much magnifie.

    PISC. O Sir, doubt not but that *Angling* is an Art, and an Art worth your learning: the Question is rather whether you be capable of learning it? for *Angling* is somewhat like *Poetry*, men are to be born so: I mean, with inclinations to it, though both may be heightned by practice and experience: but he that hopes to be a good *Angler* must not onely bring an inquiring, searching, observing wit, but he must bring a large measure of hope and patience, and a love and propensity to the Art it self; but having once got and practis'd it, then doubt not but *Angling* will prove to be so pleasant, that it will prove like Vertue, a reward to it self.

VENA. Sir, I am now become so full of expectation that I long much to have you proceed, and in the order that you propose.

PISC. Then first, for the *antiquity* of *Angling,* of which I shall not say much, but onely this; Some say it is as ancient as *Deucalions* Flood: others, that *Belus,* who was the first Inventor of Godly and vertuous Recreations, was the first Inventor of *Angling:* and some others say (for former times have had their disquisitions about the Antiquity of it) that *Seth,* one of the sons of *Adam,* taught it to his Sons, and that by them it was derived to posterity: others say, that he left it ingraven on those pillars which he erected, and trusted to preserve the knowledge of the *Mathematicks, Musick,* and the rest of that precious knowledge, and those useful Arts which by Gods appointment or allowance and his noble industry were thereby preserved from perishing in *Noahs* flood.

These, Sir, have been the opinions of several men, that have possibly endeavoured to make *Angling* more ancient than is needful, or may well be warranted; but for my part, I shall content my self in telling you that Angling is much more ancient than the Incarnation of our Saviour; for in the Prophet *Amos* mention is made of *fish-hooks;* and in the Book of *Job* (which was long before the days of *Amos,* for that book is said to be writ by *Moses*) mention is made also of Fish-hooks, which must imply Anglers in those times.

But my worthy friend, as I would rather prove my self a *Gentleman* by being *learned,* and *humble, valiant,* and *inoffensive, vertuous,* and *communicable,* than by any fond ostentation of riches, or wanting these vertues my self, boast that these were in my Ancestors (and yet I grant that where a noble and ancient descent and such merits meet in any man, it is a double dignification of that person:) So if this Antiquity of *Angling* (which for my part I have not forced) shall like an ancient family, be either an honour or an ornament to this vertuous Art which I profess to love and practice, I shall be the gladder that I made an accidental mention of the antiquity of it; of which I shall say no more but proceed to that just commendation which I think it deserves.

And for that I shall tell you, that in ancient times a debate hath risen (and it remains yet unresolved) Whether the happiness of man in this world doth consist more in *Contemplation* or *action.*

Concerning which some have endeavoured to maintain their opinion of the first, by saying, *That the nearer we Mortals come to*

God by way of imitation, the more happy we are. And they say, T*hat God enjoys himself onely by a contemplation of his own infinitenesse,* E*ternity,* P*ower and* G*oodness,* and the like. And upon this ground many Cloysteral men of great learning and devotion prefer C*ontemplation* before A*ction.* And many of the Fathers seem to approve this opinion, as may appear in their Commentaries upon the words of our Saviour to M*artha,* L*uke* 10.41, 42.

And on the contrary, there want not men of equal authority and credit, that prefer *action* to be the more excellent, as namely, *experiments in* P*hysick, and the application of it, both for the ease and prolongation of mans life;* by which each man is enabled to act and do good to others; either to serve his Countrey, or do good to particular persons; and they say also, T*hat action is* D*octrinal, and teaches both art and vertue, and is a maintainer of humane society;* and for these and other like reasons to be preferred before *contemplation.*

Concerning which two opinions I shall forbear to add a third, by declaring my own, and rest my self contented in telling you (my very worthy friend) that both these meet together, and do most properly belong to the most *honest, ingenuous, quiet,* and *harmlesse* art of A*ngling.*

And first, I shall tell you what some have observed, (and I have found it to be a real truth) that the very sitting by the Rivers side is not onely the quietest and fittest place for *contemplation,* but will invite an Angler to it: and this seems to be maintained by the learned P*et. du* M*oline,* who (in his Discourse of the Fulfilling of Prophecies) observes, that when God intended to reveal any future events or high notions to his Prophets, he then carried them either to the D*eserts* or the S*ea-shore,* that having so separated them from amidst the press of *people,* and *businesse,* and the cares of the world, he might settle their minds in a quiet repose, and there make them fit for Revelation.

IZAAK WALTON
[*The Compleat Angler* (1653)]

Country Squire

[*The First Earl of Shaftsbury was that statesman immortalized by Dryden as "In friendship false, implacable in hate/Resolved to ruin or to rule the state." He deserves to be remembered also as one of the first great writers of modern English prose—as witness the following, which he left unpublished among his private papers. Here, to the life, is that English squire to whom hunting had become a way of life. Henry Fielding drew him again a century later in Squire Western.*]

Mr. Hastings, by his quality, being the son, brother, and uncle to the Earls of Huntington, and his way of living, had the first place among us. He was peradventure an original in our age, or rather a copy of our nobility in ancient days in hunting and not warlike times; he was low, strong, and very active, of reddish flaxen hair, his cloths always green cloth, and never all worth when new five pounds. His house was perfectly of the old fashion, in the midst of a large park well stocked with deer, and near the house rabbits to serve his kitchen, many fish-ponds, and great store of wood and timber; a bowling-green in it, long but narrow, full of high ridges, it being never levelled since it was ploughed; they used round sand bowls, and it had a banqueting-house like a stand, a large one built in a tree. He kept all manner of sport-hounds that ran buck, fox, hare, otter, and badger, and hawks long and short winged; he had all sorts of nets for fishing: he had a walk in the New Forest and the manor of Christ Church. This last supplied him with red deer, sea and river fish; and indeed all his neighbours' grounds and royalties were free to him, who bestowed all his time in such sports, but what he borrowed to caress his neighbours' wives and daughters, there being not a woman in all his walks of the degree of a yeoman's wife or under, and under the age of forty, but it was extremely her fault if he were not intimately acquainted with her. This made him very popular, always speaking kindly to the husband, brother, or father, who was to boot very welcome to his house whenever he came. There he found beef pudding and small beer in great plenty, a house not so neatly kept as to shame him or his dirty shoes, the great hall strewed with marrow bones, full of hawks' perches, hounds, spaniels, and terriers, the upper sides of the hall hung with the fox-skins of this and the last year's skinning, here and there a polecat intermixed, guns and keepers' and huntsmen's poles in abundance. The parlour was a large long room, as properly furnished; on a great hearth paved with brick lay some terriers and the choicest hounds and spaniels; seldom but two of the great chairs had litters of young cats in them, which were not to be disturbed, he having always three or four attending him at dinner, and a little white round stick of fourteen inches long lying by his trencher, that he might defend such meat as he had no mind to part with to them. The windows, which were very large, served for places to lay his arrows, crossbows, stonebows, and other such like accoutrements; the corners of the room full of the best chose hunting and hawking poles; an oyster-table at the lower end, which was of constant use twice a day all the year round, for he never failed to eat oysters before dinner and supper through all seasons: the neighbouring town of Poole supplied him with them. The upper part of this room had two small tables and a desk, on the one side of which was a church Bible, on the other the Book of Martyrs; on the tables were hawks' hoods, bells, and such like, two or three old green hats with their crowns thrust in so as to hold ten or a dozen eggs, which were of a pheasant kind of poultry he took much care of and fed himself; tables, dice, cards, and boxes were not wanting. In the hole of the desk were store of tobacco-pipes that had been used. On one side of this end of the room was the door of a closet, wherein stood the strong beer and the wine, which never came thence but in single glasses, that being the rule of the house exactly observed, for he never exceeded in drink or permitted it.

He was well natured but soon angry, calling his servants bastard and cuckoldy knaves, in one of which he often spoke the truth from his own knowledge, and sometimes in both, though of the same man. He lived to be a hundred, but always wrote and read without spectacles, and got to horse without help. Until past fourscore he rode to the death of a stag as well as any.

ANTHONY COOPER,
FIRST EARL OF SHAFTSBURY
[Autobiographical fragment (late seventeenth century)]

Sir Roger Spares a Rabbit

[What hunters call "sentimentality" hardly appears in English literature before the beginning of the eighteenth century. There is no evidence that even Shakespeare was shocked by the cruelty to animals which formed so important a part of various Elizabethan entertainments. But within a century of his death the minority which has ever since raised an occasional voice came into being. Addison's Sir Roger de Coverley was a squire considerably less robust than the type Shaftsbury described above.]

Sir Roger is so keen at this sport, that he has been out almost every day since I came down; and upon the chaplain's offering to lend me his easy pad, I was prevailed on yesterday morning to make one of the company. I was extremely pleased, as we rode along, to observe the general benevolence of all the neighborhood towards my friend. The farmers' sons thought themselves happy if they could open a gate for the good old knight as he passed by; which he generally requited with a nod or a smile, and a kind inquiry after their fathers and uncles.

After we had ridden about a mile from home, we came upon a large heath, and the sportsmen began to beat. They had done so for some time, when, as I was at a little distance from the rest of the company, I saw a hare pop out from a small furze-brake almost under my horse's feet. I marked the way she took, which I endeavored to make the company sensible of by extending my arm; but to no purpose, till Sir Roger, who knows that none of my extraordinary motions are in-

significant, rode up to me and asked me *if puss was gone that way?*
Upon my answering *yes*, he immediately called in the dogs, and put
them upon the scent. As they were going off, I heard one of the coun-
try-fellows muttering to his companion, *that 'twas a wonder they had
not lost all their sport, for want of the silent gentleman's crying,*
"Stole away."

    This, with my aversion to leaping hedges, made me withdraw
to a rising ground, from whence I could have the pleasure of the
whole chase, without the fatigue of keeping in with the hounds. The
hare immediately threw them above a mile behind her; but I was
pleased to find, that instead of running straight forwards, or in hunter's language, *flying the country*, as I was afraid she might have done,
she wheeled about, and described a sort of circle round the hill where
I had taken my station, in such manner as gave me a very distinct
view of the sport. I could see her first pass by, and the dogs some time
afterwards unravelling the whole track she had made, and following
her through all her doubles. I was at the same time delighted in observing that deference which the rest of the pack paid to each particular hound, according to the character he had acquired amongst them:
if they were at a fault, and an old hound of reputation opened but
once, he was immediately followed by the whole cry; while a raw dog
or one who was a noted liar, might have yelped his heart out, without
being taken notice of.

    The hare now, after having squatted two or three times, and
been put up again as often, came still nearer to the place where she
was first started. The dogs pursued her, and these were followed by
the jolly knight, who rode upon a white gelding, encompassed by his
tenants and servants, and cheering his hounds with all the gaiety of
five and twenty. One of the sportsmen rode up to me, and told me,
that he was sure the chase was almost at an end, because the old dogs,
which had hitherto lain behind, now headed the pack. The fellow
was in the right. Our hare took a large field just under us, followed by
the full cry in view. I must confess the brightness of the weather, the
cheerfulness of everything around me, the *chiding* of the hounds,
which was returned upon us in a double echo from two neighboring
hills, with the hollowing of the sportsmen, and the sounding of the
horn, lifted my spirits into a most lively pleasure, which I freely
indulged because I was sure it was innocent. If I was under any
concern, it was on the account of the poor hare, that was now quite
spent and almost within the reach of her enemies; when the huntsman
getting forward threw down his pole before the dogs. They were now

within eight yards of that game which they had been pursuing for almost as many hours; yet on the signal before-mentioned they all made a sudden stand, and though they continued opening as much as before, durst not once attempt to pass beyond the pole. At the same time Sir Roger rode forward, and alighting, took up the hare in his arms which he soon delivered up to one of his servants, with an order, if she could be kept alive, to let her go in his great orchard; where it seems he has several of these prisoners of war, who live together in a very comfortable captivity. I was highly pleased to see the discipline of the pack, and the good nature of the knight, who could not find in his heart to murder a creature that had given him so much diversion.

JOSEPH ADDISON
[*The Spectator* (1711-1712)]

The Fox Hunt

[*The England of the fox hunter was, of course, also the England of poets and philosophers. That the former sometimes interfered with the latter is recorded with some indignation by Bishop George Berkeley, for whom the California university town was named.*]

We amused ourselves next Day every one to his Fancy till Nine of the Clock, when Word was brought that the Tea-table was set in the Library, which is a Gallery on a Ground-floor, with an arched Door at one End opening into a Walk of Limes; where, as soon as we had drunk Tea, we were tempted by fine Weather to take a Walk which led us to a small Mount of easy Ascent, on the Top whereof we found a Seat under a spreading Tree. Here we had a Prospect on one hand of a narrow Bay or Creek of the Sea, enclosed on either Side by a Coast beautified with Rocks and Woods, and green Banks and Farmhouses. At the End of the Bay was a small Town, placed upon the Slope of a Hill, which, from the Advantage of its Situation, made a

The Boas

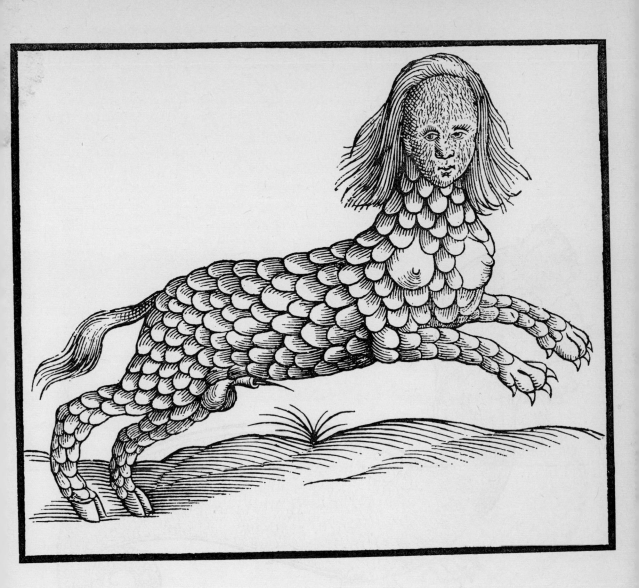

considerable Figure. Several Fishing-boats and Lighters, gliding up and down on a Surface as smooth and bright as Glass, enlivened the Prospect. On the other Side, we looked down on green Pastures, Flocks, and Herds basking beneath in Sunshine, while we, in our superior Situation, enjoyed the Freshness of Air and Shade.

Here we felt that sort of joyful Instinct which a rural Scene and fine Weather inspire; and proposed no small Pleasure in resuming and continuing our Conference without Interruption till Dinner. But we had hardly seated ourselves and looked about us when we saw a Fox run by the Foot of our Mount into an adjacent Thicket. A few Minutes after, we heard a confused Noise of the opening of Hounds, the winding of Horns, and the roaring of Country Squires. While our Attention was suspended by this Event, a Servant came running, out of Breath, and told *Crito* that his Neighbour *Ctesippus,* a Squire of Note, was fallen from his Horse, attempting to leap over a Hedge, and brought into the Hall, where he lay for dead. Upon which we all rose, and walked hastily to the House, where we found *Ctesippus* just come to himself, in the midst of half-a-dozen Sun-burnt Squires, in Frocks, and short Wigs, and Jockey-Boots. Being asked how he did, he answered it was only a broken Rib. With some Difficulty *Crito* persuaded him to lie on a Bed till the Chirurgeon came. These Fox hunters, having been up early at their Sport, were eager for Dinner, which was accordingly hastened. They passed the Afternoon in a loud rustic Mirth, gave Proof of their Religion and Loyalty by the Healths they drank, talked of Hounds, and Horses, and Elections, and Country Affairs, till the Chirurgeon, who had been employed about *Ctesippus,* desired he might be put into *Crito's* Coach, and sent home, having refused to stay all Night.

Our Guests being gone, we reposed ourselves after the Fatigue of this tumultuous Visit, and next Morning assembled again at the Seat on the Mount.

Now, *Lysicles,* being a nice man and a *bel esprit,* had an infinite contempt for the rough Manners and Conversation of Fox-hunters, and could not reflect with Patience that he had lost, as he called it, so many Hours in their Company. I flattered myself, said he, that there had been none of this Species remaining among us: Strange that Men should be diverted with such uncouth Noise and Hurry, or find Pleasure in the Society of Dogs and Horses! How much more elegant are the Diversions of the Town!

There seems, replied *Euphranor,* to be some Resemblance between Fox-hunters and Free-thinkers; the former exerting their an-

imal Faculties in pursuit of Game, as you Gentlemen employ your
Intellectuals in the pursuit of Truth. The kind of Amusement is the
same, although the Object be different.

GEORGE BERKELEY
[*Alciphron* (1732)]

Connecticut Wolf Hunt

[*It is hard to remember that wolves were once common over a large part of
the United States. Before Israel Putnam became a commander of the Revolu-
tionary forces he took part in a famous wolf hunt.*]

The first years, on a new farm, are not, however, exempt from dis-
asters and disappointments, which can only be remedied by stubborn
and patient industry. Our farmer, sufficiently occupied in building a
house and barn, felling woods, making fences, sowing grain, planting
orchards and taking care of his stock, had to encounter, in turn, the
calamities occasioned by drought in summer, blast in harvest, loss of
cattle in winter, and the desolation of his sheep-fold by wolves. In one
night he had seventy fine sheep and goats killed, besides many lambs
and kids wounded. This havoc was committed by a she-wolf, which,
with her annual whelps, had for several years infested the vicinity.
The young were commonly destroyed by the vigilance of the hunters,
but the old one was too sagacious to come within reach of gunshot:
upon being closely pursued she would generally fly to the western
woods, and return the next winter with another litter of whelps.

This wolf, at length, became such an intolerable nuisance that
Mr. Putnam entered into a combination with five of his neighbors to
hunt alternately until they could destroy her. Two, by rotation, were
to be constantly in pursuit. It was known that, having lost the toes from
one foot, by a steel trap, she made one track shorter than the other.
By this vestige, the pursuers recognized, in a light snow, the route of

this pernicious animal. Having followed her to Connecticut River, and found she had turned back in a direct course towards Pomfret, they immediately returned, and by ten o'clock the next morning, the bloodhounds had driven her into a den, about three miles distant from the house of Mr. Putnam. The people soon collected with dogs, guns, straw, fire, and sulphur, to attack the common enemy. With this apparatus several unsuccessful efforts were made to force her from the den. The hounds came back badly wounded and refused to return. The smoke of blazing straw had no effect. Nor did the fumes of burnt brimstone, with which the cavern was filled, compel her to quit the retirement. Wearied with such fruitless attempts (which had brought the time to ten o'clock at night) Mr. Putnam tried once more to make his dog enter, but in vain. He proposed to his Negro man to go down into the cavern and shoot the wolf: the Negro declined the hazardous service. Then it was, that their master, angry at the disappointment, and declaring that he was ashamed to have a coward in his family, re-solved himself to destroy the ferocious beast, lest she should escape through some unknown fissure in the rock. His neighbors strongly re-monstrated against the perilous enterprise: but he, knowing that wild animals were intimidated by fire, and having provided several strips of birch bark, the only combustible material which he could obtain, that would afford light in this deep and darksome cave, prepared for his descent. Having, accordingly, divested himself of his coat and waistcoat, and having a long rope fastened round his legs, by which he might be pulled back, at a concerted signal, he entered head foremost, with the blazing torch in his hand.

The aperture of the den, on the east side of a very high ledge of rocks, is about two feet square; from thence it descends obliquely fifteen feet, then running horizontally about ten more, it ascends gradually sixteen feet towards its termination. The sides of this sub-terraneous cavity are composed of smooth and solid rocks, which seem to have been divided from each other by some former earthquake. The top and bottom are also of stone, and the entrance, in winter, be-ing covered with ice, is exceedingly slippery. It is in no place high enough for a man to raise himself upright: nor in any part more than three feet in width.

Having groped his passage to the horizontal part of the den, the most terrifying darkness appeared in front of the dim circle of light afforded by his torch. It was silent as the house of death. None but monsters of the desert had ever before explored this solitary man-sion of horror. He, cautiously proceeding onward, came to the ascent, which he slowly mounted on his hands and knees, until he discovered the glaring eyeballs of the wolf, who was sitting at the extremity of the cavern. Startled at the sight of fire, she gnashed her teeth and gave a sullen growl. As soon as he had made the necessary discovery, he kicked the rope as a signal for pulling him out. The people at the mouth of the den, who had listened with painful anxiety, hearing the growling of the wolf and supposing their friend to be in the most imminent danger, drew him forth with such celerity that his shirt was stripped over his head and his skin severely lacerated. After he had adjusted his clothes and loaded his gun with nine buckshot, holding a torch in one hand and the musket in the other, he descended the second time. When he drew nearer than before, the wolf, assuming a still more fierce and terrible appearance, howling, rolling her eyes, snapping her teeth, and dropping her head between her legs, was evidently in the attitude and on the point of springing at him. At the critical instant, he levelled and fired at her head. Stunned with the shock, and suffocated with the smoke, he immediately found himself drawn out of the cave. But having refreshed himself, and permitted the smoke to dissipate, he went down the third time. Once more he came within sight of the wolf, who appearing very passive, he applied the torch to her nose; and perceiving her dead, he took hold of her ears, and then kicking the rope (still tied round his legs) the people above, with no small exultation, dragged them both out together.

DAVID HUMPHREYS
[*Life of Major General Israel Putnam* (1780)]

The Eskimo and the Seal

[*Within historic times Europe never supported a population of wild animals large enough to permit its commercial exploitation on a massive scale. In the New World, on the contrary, man had never until the coming of the whites been numerous enough seriously to disturb the balance which permitted the original fauna to flourish rather more successfully than man himself. Once the* efficient European had arrived, he began almost immediately the process which was soon to bring what Thoreau called "the nobler animals" close to the point of extinction. One of the earliest accounts of the seal-based culture of the Eskimo as it existed before commercial exploitation disturbed a balance which might otherwise have lasted indefinitely was written by a distinguished eighteenth-century naturalist.]

⚙

These animals may be called the flocks of the Greenlanders, and many other of the Arctic people. I cannot describe the uses of them to the former more expressively than in the very words of Mr. Crantz, a gentleman very long resident in their chilly country.

"Seals are more needful to them than sheep are to us, though they furnish us with food and raiment; or than the cocoa tree is to the Indians, although that presents them not only with meat to eat, and covering for their bodies, but also houses to dwell in, and boats to sail in, so that in case of necessity they could live solely from it. The seal's flesh (together with the reindeer, which is already grown pretty scarce) supplies the natives with their most palatable and substantial food. Their fat furnishes them with oil for lamplight, chamber and kitchen fire; and whoever sees their habitations, presently finds, that if they even had a superfluity of wood, it would not do, they can use nothing but train in them. They also mollify their dry food, mostly fish, in the train; and finally, they barter it for all kinds of necessaries with the factor. They can sew better with fibres of the seals' sinews than with thread or silk. Of the skins of the entrails they make their windows, curtains for their tents, shirts, and part of the bladders they use at their harpoons; and they make train bottles of the maw. Formerly, for want of iron, they made all manner of instruments and working-tools of their bones. Neither is the blood wasted, but boiled with other ingredients, and eaten as soup. Of the skin of the seal they stand in the greatest need; for, supposing the skins of reindeer and birds would furnish them with competent clothing for their bodies, and coverings for their beds; and their flesh, together with fish, with sufficient food; and provided they could dress their meat with wood, and also new model their housekeeping, so as to have light, and keep themselves warm with it too; yet without the seals' skins they would not be in a capacity of acquiring these same reindeer, fowls, fishes, and wood; because they must cover over with sealskin both their large and small boats, in which they travel and seek their provisions. They must also cut their thongs or straps out of them, make the bladders for their harpoons, and cover their tents with them; without which they could not subsist in summer.

"Therefore no man can pass for a right Greenlander who cannot catch seals. This is the ultimate end they aspire at, in all their device and labor from their childhood up. It is the only art (and in truth a difficult and dangerous one it is) to which they are trained from their infancy; by which they maintain themselves, make themselves agreeable to others, and become beneficial members of the community.

"The Greenlanders have three ways of catching seals: either singly, with the bladder; or in company, by the *clapper-hunt;* or in the winter on the ice: whereto may be added the shooting them with a gun.

"The principal and most common way is the taking them with the bladder. When the Greenlander sets out equipped according to the 7th Section, and spies a seal, he tries to surprise it unawares, with the wind and sun in his back, that he may not be heard or seen by it. He tries to conceal himself behind a wave, and makes hastily, but softly, up to it, till he comes within four, five, or six fathom of it; meanwhile he takes the utmost care that the harpoon, line, and bladder lie in proper order. Then he takes hold of the oar with his left hand, and the harpoon with his right by the hand-board, and so away he throws it at the seal, in such a manner that the whole dart flies from the hand-board and leaves that in his hand. If the harpoon hits the mark, and buries itself deeper than the barbs, it will directly disengage itself from the bone-joint, and that from the shaft; and also unwind the string from its lodge on the kayak. The moment the seal is pierced, the Greenlander must throw the bladder, tied to the end of the string, into the water, on the same side as the seal runs and dives; for that he does instantly, like a dart. Then the Greenlander goes and takes up the shaft swimming on the water, and lays it in its place. The seal often drags the bladder with it under water, though 'tis a considerable impediment, on account of its great bigness; but it so wearies itself out with it, that it must come up again in about a quarter of an hour to take breath. The Greenlander hastens to the spot where he sees the bladder rise up, and smites the seal, as soon as it appears, with the great lance described in the 6th Section. This lance always comes out of its body again; but he throws it at the creature afresh every time it comes up, till 'tis quite spent. Then he runs the little lance into it, and kills it outright, but stops up the wound directly to preserve the blood; and lastly, he blows it up, like a bladder, betwixt skin and flesh, to put it into a better capacity of swimming after him; for which purpose he fastens it to the left side of his kayak, or boat.

"In this exercise the Greenlander is exposed to the most and greatest danger of his life; which is probably the reason that they call this hunt, or fishery, *kamavock,* i.e., the extinction, *viz.* of life. For if the line should entangle itself, as it easily may, in its sudden and violent motion; or if it should catch hold of the kayak, or should wind itself round the oar, or the hand, or even the neck, as it sometimes does in windy weather; or if the seal should turn suddenly to the other side of the boat; it cannot be otherwise than the kayak must be overturned by the string, and drawn down under water. On such desperate occasions the poor Greenlander stands in need of all the arts described in the former Section, to disentangle himself from the string, and to raise himself up from under the water several times successively; for he will continually be overturning till he has quite disengaged himself from the line. Nay, when he imagines himself to be out of all danger, and comes too near the dying seal, it may still bite him in the face or hand; and a female seal that has young, instead of flying the field, will sometimes fly at the Greenlander in the most vehement rage, and do him a mischief, or bite a hole in his kayak that he must sink.

"In this way, singly, they can kill none but the careless stupid seal, called *attarfoak.* Several in company must pursue the *kaffigiak* by the *clapper-hunt.* In the same manner they also surround and kill the *attarfoit* in great numbers at certain seasons of the year; for in autumn they retire into the creeks or inlets in stormy weather, as in the *Nepifet* found in Ball's River, between the mainland and the island *Kangek,* which is full two leagues long, but very narrow. There the Greenlanders cut off their retreat, and frighten them under water by shouting, clapping, and throwing stones; but, as they must come up again continually to draw breath, then they persecute them again till they are tired, and at last are obliged to stay so long above water, that they surround them, and kill them with the fourth kind of dart, described in the 6th Section. During this hunt we have a fine opportunity to see the agility of the Greenlanders, or, if I may call it so, their hussar-like maneuvers. When the seal rises out of the water, they all fly upon it, as if they had wings, with a desperate noise; the poor creature is forced to dive again directly, and the moment he does, they disperse again as fast as they came, and every one gives heed to his post, to see where it will start up again; which is an uncertain thing, and is commonly three quarters of a mile from the former spot. If a seal has a good broad water, three or four leagues each way, it can keep the sportsmen in play for a couple of hours, before 'tis so spent that they can surround and kill it. If the seal, in its fright, betakes itself to the land for a retreat, 'tis welcomed with sticks and stones by the women and children, and presently pierced by the men in the rear. This is a very lively and a very profitable diversion for the Greenlanders, for many times one man will have eight or ten seals for his share.

"The third method of killing seals upon the ice, is mostly practiced in *Disco,* where the bays are frozen over in the winter. There are several ways of proceeding. The seals themselves make sometimes holes in the ice, where they come and draw breath; near such a hole a Greenlander seats himself on a stool, putting his feet on a lower one to keep them from the cold. Now when the seal comes and puts its nose to the hole, he pierces it instantly with his harpoon; then breaks the hole larger, and draws it out and kills it quite. Or a Greenlander lays himself upon his belly, on a kind of a sledge, near other holes, where the seals come out upon the ice to bask themselves in the sun. Near this great hole they make a little one, and another Greenlander puts a harpoon into it with a very long shaft or pole. He that lies upon the ice looks into the great hole, till he sees a seal coming under the harpoon; then he gives the other the signal, who runs the seal through with all his might.

"If the Greenlander sees a seal lying near its hole upon the ice, he slides along upon his belly towards it, wags his head, and grunts like a seal; and the poor seal, thinking 'tis one of its innocent companions, lets him come near enough to pierce it with his long dart.

"When the current wears a great hole in the ice in the spring, the Greenlanders plant themselves all around it, till the seals come in droves to the brim to fetch breath, and then they kill them with their harpoons. Many also are killed on the ice while they lie sleeping and snoring in the sun."

Nature has been so niggardly in providing variety of provision for the Greenlanders, that they are necessitated to have recourse to such which is offered to them with a liberal hand. The *Kamtschatkan* nations, which enjoy several animals, as well as a great and abundant choice of fish, are so enamored with the taste of the fat of seals, that they can make no feast without making it one of the dishes. Of that both *Russians* and *Kamtschatkans* make their candles. The latter eat the flesh boiled, or else dried in the sun. If they have a great quantity, they preserve it in the following manner:

They dig a pit of a requisite depth, and pave it with stones; then fill it with wood, and set it on fire so as to heat the pit to the warmth of a stove. They then collect all the cinders into a heap. They strew the bottom with the green wood of alder, on which they place separately the flesh and the fat, and put between every layer branches of the same tree; when the pit is filled they cover it with sods, so that the vapour cannot escape. After some hours they take out both fat and flesh, and keep it for winter's provisions, and they may be preserved a whole year without spoiling.

The *Kamtschatkans* have a most singular ceremony. After they take the flesh from the heads of the seals, they bring a vessel in form of a canoe, and fling into it all the skulls, crowned with certain herbs, and place them on the ground. A certain person enters the habitation with a sack filled with *Tonchitche,* sweet herbs, and a little of the bark of willow. Two of the natives then roll a great stone towards the door, and cover it with pebbles; two others take the sweet herbs and dispose them, tied in little packets. The great stone is to signify the seashore, the pebbles the waves, and the packets seals. They then bring three dishes of a hash, called *Tolkoucha;* of this they make little balls, in the middle of which they stick the packets of herbs: of the willow bark they make a little canoe, and fill it with *Tolkoucha,* and cover it with the sack. After some time, the two *Kamtschatkans* who had put the mimic seals into the *Tolkoucha,* take the balls, and a vessel re-sembling a canoe, and draw it along the land, as if it was on the sea, to convince the real seals how agreeable it would be to them to come among the *Kamtschatkans,* who have a sea in their very *jurts,* or dwell-ings. And this they imagine will induce the seals to suffer themselves to be taken in great numbers. Various other ceremonies, equally ri-diculous, are practiced; in one of which they *invoke the winds, which drive the seals on their shores, to be propitious.*

Besides the uses which are made of the flesh and fat of seals, the skins of the largest are cut into soles for shoes. The women make their summer boots of the undressed skins, and wear them with the hair outmost. In a country which abounds so greatly in furs, very little more use is made of the skins of seals in the article of dress than what has been mentioned. But the *Koriaks,* the *Oloutores,* and *Tchut-schi,* form with the skins canoes and vessels of different sizes, some large enough to carry thirty people.

THOMAS PENNANT
[*Arctic Zoology* (1785-1787)]

Poaching as a Way of Life

[*The sporting squire created the game laws and the game laws generated the poacher—hated because he shot the animals which should have been left for his betters, and despised because he killed for food rather than for fun. Sometimes he was merely a peasant with mouths to feed; sometimes a rebel, proud of his success in outwitting the law. To Parson Gilbert White of Selborne he was an interesting part of the fauna in that parish he had made it his business to describe.*]

Though large herds of deer do much harm to the neighbourhood, yet the injury to the morals of the people is of more moment than the loss of their crops. The temptation is irresistible; for most men are sportsmen by constitution: and there is such an inherent spirit for hunting in human nature, as scarce any inhibitions can restrain. Hence, towards the beginning of this century, all this country was wild about deer-stealing. Unless he was a *hunter,* as they affected to call themselves, no young person was allowed to be possessed of manhood or gallantry. The *Waltham blacks* at length committed such enormities, that government was forced to interfere with that severe and sanguinary act called the *black act,* which now comprehends more felonies than any law that ever was framed before; and, therefore, a late bishop of *Winchester,* when urged to re-stock *Waltham-chase,* refused, from a motive worthy of a prelate, replying, that "it had done mischief enough already."

Our old race of deer-stealers are hardly extinct yet. It was but a little while ago that, over their ale, they used to recount the exploits of their youth; such as watching the pregnant hind to her lair, and when the calf was dropped, paring its feet with a penknife to the quick, to prevent its escape, till it was large and fat enough to be killed; the shooting at one of their neighbours with a bullet, in a turnip-field, by moonshine, mistaking him for a deer; and the losing a dog in the following extraordinary manner:—Some fellows, suspecting that a calf new-fallen was deposited in a certain spot of thick fern, went with a lurcher to surprise it; when the parent hind rushed out of the brake, and taking a vast spring, with all her feet close together, pitched upon the neck of the dog, and broke it short in two.

GILBERT WHITE
[*Natural History and Antiquities of Selborne* (1789)]

The Man in the Coonskin Hat

[*The discovery of America revealed a continent stocked with "game" beyond the dreams of any European sportsman. The frontiersman often took down his rifle much as a European housewife took down her market basket: merely to fetch his dinner. But though he was little inclined to bother with any of the rituals of "sport," the chase was often a pleasure as well as a necessity. David Crockett shrewdly exploited his legend and was responsible for a self-consciously naïve autobiography which probably should have borne on its title page the now too-familiar legend: "As told to . . ."*]

☙

That night there fell a heavy rain, and it turned to a sleet. In the morning all hands turned out hunting. My young man, and a brother-in-law who had lately settled close by me, went down the river to hunt for turkeys; but I was for larger game. I told them, I had dreamed the night before of having a hard fight with a big black nigger, and I knowed it was a sign that I was to have a battle with a bear; for in a bear country, I never know'd such a dream to fail. So I started to go up above the harricane, determined to have a bear. I had two pretty good dogs, and an old hound, all of which I took along. I had gone about six miles up the river, and it was then about four miles across to the main Obion; so I determined to strike across to that, as I had found nothing yet to kill. I got on to the river, and turned down it; but the sleet was still getting worse and worse. The bushes were all bent down, and locked together with ice, so that it was almost impossible to get along. In a little time my dogs started a large gang of old turkey goblers, and I killed two of them, of the biggest sort. I shouldered them up, and moved on, until I got through the harricane, when I was so tired I laid my goblers down to rest, as they were confounded heavy, and I was mighty tired. While I was resting, my old hound went to a log, and smelt it awhile, and then raised his eyes toward the sky, and cried out. Away he went, and my other dogs with him, and I shouldered up my turkeys again, and followed on as hard as I could drive. They were soon out of sight, and in a very little time I heard them begin to bark. When I got to them, they were barking up a tree, but there was no game there. I concluded it had been a turkey, and that it had flew away.

When they saw me coming, away they went again; and, after a little time, began to bark as before. When I got near them, I found they were barking up the wrong tree again, as there was no game there. They served me in this way three or four times, until I was so infernal mad, that I determined, if I could get near enough, to shoot the old hound at least. With this intention I pushed on the harder, till I came to the edge of an open parara, and looking on before my dogs, I saw in and about the biggest bear that ever was seen in America. He looked, at the distance he was from me, like a large black bull. My dogs were afraid to attack him, and that was the reason they had stop'd so often, that I might overtake them. They were now almost up with him, and I took my goblers from my back and hung them up in a sapling, and broke like a quarter horse after my bear, for the sight of him had put new springs in me. I soon got near to them, but they were just getting into a roaring thicket, and so I couldn't run through it, but had to pick my way along, and had close work even at that.

In a little time I saw the bear climbing up a large black oak-tree, and I crawled on till I got within about eighty yards of him. He was setting with his breast to me; and so I put fresh priming in my gun, and fired at him. At this he raised one of his paws and snorted loudly. I loaded again as quick as I could, and fired as near the same place in his breast as possible. At the crack of my gun he came tumbling down; and the moment he touched the ground, I heard one of my best dogs cry out. I took my tomahawk in one hand, and my big butcher-knife in the other, and run up within four or five paces of him, at which he let my dog go, and fixed his eyes on me. I got back in all sorts of a hurry, for I know'd if he got hold of me, he would hug me altogether too close for comfort. I went to my gun and hastily loaded her again, and shot him the third time, which killed him good.

I now began to think about getting him home, but I didn't know how far it was. So I left him and started; and in order to find him again, I would blaze a sapling every little distance, which would show me the way back. I continued this till I got within about a mile of home, for there I know'd very well where I was, and that I could easily find the way back to my blazes. When I got home, I took my brother-in-law and my young man, and four horses, and went back. We got there just before dark, and struck up a fire, and commenced butchering my bear. It was some time in the night before we finished it; and I can assert, on my honour, that I believed he would have weighed six hundred pounds. It was the second largest I ever saw. I killed one, a few years after, that weighed six hundred and seventeen pounds. I now felt fully compensated for my sufferings in going after my powder; and well satisfied that a dog might sometimes be doing a good business, even when he seemed to be *barking up the wrong tree.* We got our meat home, and I had the pleasure to know that we now had plenty, and that of the best; and I continued through the winter to supply my family abundantly with bear-meat and venison from the woods.

DAVID CROCKETT
[*Autobiography* (1834)]

Cockneys Afield

[When Dickens captivated the English-speaking world with Pickwick Papers, the cockney who invaded the hunting field was already a well-established figure of fun. But he was glorified as never before in the persons of Mr. Winkle and Mr. Tupman.]

🐎

The birds, who, happily for their own peace of mind and personal comfort, were in blissful ignorance of the preparations which had been making to astonish them on the first of September, hailed it, no doubt, as one of the pleasantest mornings they had seen that season. Many a young partridge who strutted complacently among the stubble, with all the finicking coxcombry of youth, and many an older one who watched his levity out of his little round eye, with the contemptuous air of a bird of wisdom and experience, alike unconscious of their approaching doom, basked in the fresh morning air with lively and blithesome feelings, and a few hours afterwards were laid low upon the earth. But we grow affecting: let us proceed.

In plain, commonplace matter of fact, then, it was a fine morning—so fine that you would scarcely have believed that the few months of an English summer had yet flown by. Hedges, fields, and trees, hill and moorland, presented to the eye their ever-varying shades of deep, rich green; scarce a leaf had fallen, scarce a sprinkle of yellow, mingled with the hues of summer, warned you that autumn had begun. The sky was cloudless; the sun shone out bright and warm; the songs of birds and hum of myriads of summer insects filled the air; and the cottage gardens, crowded with flowers of every rich and beautiful tint, sparkled, in the heavy dew, like beds of glittering jewels. Everything bore the stamp of summer, and none of its beautiful colours had yet faded from the dye.

Such was the morning, when an open carriage, in which were three Pickwickians (Mr. Snodgrass having preferred to remain at home), Mr. Wardle, and Mr. Tupman, with Sam Weller on the box beside the driver, pulled up by a gate at the road-side, before which stood a tall, raw-boned gamekeeper, and a half-booted, leather-leggined boy; each bearing a bag of capacious dimensions, and accompanied by a brace of pointers.

"I say," whispered Mr. Winkle to Wardle, as the man let down the steps, "they don't suppose we're going to kill game enough to fill those bags, do they?"

"Fill them!" exclaimed old Wardle. "Bless you, yes! You shall fill one, and I the other; and when we've done with them, the pockets of our shooting-jackets will hold as much more."

Mr. Winkle dismounted without saying anything in reply to this observation; but he thought within himself that, if the party remained in the open air until he had filled one of the bags, they stood a considerable chance of catching colds in their heads.

"Hi, Juno, lass—hi, old girl; down, Daph, down," said Wardle, caressing the dogs. "Sir Geoffrey still in Scotland, of course, Martin?"

The tall gamekeeper replied in the affirmative, and looked with some surprise from Mr. Winkle, who was holding his gun as if he wished his coat-pocket to save him the trouble of pulling the trigger, to Mr. Tupman, who was holding his as if he were afraid of it— as there is no earthly reason to doubt he really was.

"My friends are not much in the way of this sort of thing yet, Martin," said Wardle, noticing the look. "Live and learn, you know. They'll be good shots one of these days. I beg my friend Winkle's pardon, though; he has had some practice."

Mr. Winkle smiled feebly over his blue neckerchief in acknowledgment of the compliment, and got himself so mysteriously entangled with his gun, in his modest confusion, that if the piece had been loaded he must inevitably have shot himself dead upon the spot.

"You mustn't handle your piece in that 'ere way, when you come to have the charge in it, sir," said the tall gamekeeper gruffly, "or I'm damned if you won't make cold meat of some of us."

Mr. Winkle, thus admonished, abruptly altered its position, and in so doing contrived to bring the barrel into pretty smart contact with Mr. Weller's head.

"Hallo!" said Sam, picking up his hat, which had been knocked off, and rubbing his temple. "Hallo, sir! if you comes it this vay, you'll fill one o' them bags, and something to spare, at one fire."

Here the leather-leggined boy laughed very heartily, and then tried to look as if it was somebody else, whereat Mr. Winkle frowned majestically.

"Where did you tell the boy to meet us with the snack, Martin?" inquired Wardle.

"Side of One-tree Hill, at twelve o'clock, sir."

"That's not Sir Geoffrey's land, is it?"

"No, sir; but it's close by it. It's Captain Boldwig's land; but there'll be nobody to interrupt us, and there's a fine bit of turf there."

"Very well," said old Wardle. "Now, the sooner we're off the better. Will you join us at twelve, then, Pickwick?"

Mr. Pickwick was particularly desirous to view the sport, the more especially as he was rather anxious in respect of Mr. Winkle's life and limbs. On so inviting a morning, too, it was very tantalising to turn back, and leave his friends to enjoy themselves. It was, therefore, with a very rueful air that he replied,—

"Why, I suppose I must."

"Ain't the gentleman a shot, sir?" inquired the long gamekeeper.

"No," replied Wardle; "and he's lame besides."

"I should very much like to go," said Mr. Pickwick, "very much."

There was a short pause of commiseration.

"There's a barrow t'other side the hedge," said the boy. "If the gentleman's servant would wheel along the paths, he could keep nigh us, and we could lift it over the stiles and that."

"The wery thing," said Mr. Weller, who was a party interested, inasmuch as he ardently longed to see the sport. "The wery thing. Well said, Smallcheck; I'll have it out in a minute."

But here a difficulty arose. The long gamekeeper resolutely protested against the introduction into a shooting party of a gentleman in a barrow, as a gross violation of all established rules and precedents.

It was a great objection, but not an insurmountable one. The gamekeeper having been coaxed and fed, and having, moreover, eased his mind by "punching" the head of the inventive youth who had first suggested the use of the machine, Mr. Pickwick was placed in it, and off the party set; Wardle and the long gamekeeper leading the way, and Mr. Pickwick in the barrow, propelled by Sam, bringing up the rear.

"Stop, Sam," said Mr. Pickwick, when they had got half across the first field.

"What's the matter now?" said Wardle.

"I won't suffer this barrow to be moved another step," said Mr. Pickwick resolutely, "unless Winkle carries that gun of his in a different manner."

"How *am* I to carry it?" said the wretched Winkle.

"Carry it with the muzzle to the ground," replied Mr. Pickwick.

"It's so unsportsman-like," reasoned Winkle.

"I don't care whether it's unsportsman-like or not," replied Mr. Pickwick; "I am not going to be shot in a wheelbarrow, for the sake of appearances, to please anybody."

"I know the gentleman'll put that 'ere charge into somebody afore he's done," growled the long man.

"Well, well—I don't mind," said poor Mr. Winkle, turning his gunstock uppermost;—"there."

"Anythin' for a quiet life," said Mr. Weller; and on they went again.

"Stop!" said Mr. Pickwick, after they had gone a few yards further.

"What now?" said Wardle.

"That gun of Tupman's is not safe: I know it isn't," said Mr. Pickwick.

"Eh? What! not safe?" said Mr. Tupman, in a tone of great alarm.

"Not as you are carrying it," said Mr. Pickwick. "I am very sorry to make any further objection, but I cannot consent to go on, unless you carry it, as Winkle does his."

"I think you had better, sir," said the long gamekeeper, "or you're quite as likely to lodge the charge in yourself as in anything else."

Mr. Tupman, with the most obliging haste, placed his piece in the position required, and the party moved on again; the two amateurs marching with reversed arms, like a couple of privates at a royal funeral.

The dogs suddenly came to a dead stop, and the party, advancing stealthily a single pace, stopped too.

"What's the matter with the dogs' legs?" whispered Mr. Winkle. "How queer they're standing."

"Hush, can't you?" replied Wardle softly. "Don't you see, they're making a point?"

"Making a point!" said Mr. Winkle, staring about him, as if he expected to discover some particular beauty in the landscape, which the sagacious animals were calling special attention to. "Making a point! What are they pointing at?"

"Keep your eyes open," said Wardle, not heeding the question in the excitement of the moment. "Now, then."

There was a sharp whirring noise, that made Mr. Winkle start back as if he had been shot himself. Bang, bang, went a couple of guns;—the smoke swept quickly away over the field, and curled into the air.

"Where are they?" said Mr. Winkle, in a state of the highest excitement, turning round and round in all directions. "Where are they? Tell me when to fire. Where are they—where are they?"

"Where are they?" said Wardle, taking up a brace of birds which the dogs had deposited at his feet. "Where are they? Why, here they are."

"No, no; I mean the others," said the bewildered Winkle.

"Far enough off by this time," replied Wardle, coolly reloading his gun.

"We shall very likely be up with another covey in five minutes," said the long gamekeeper. "If the gentleman begins to fire now, perhaps he'll just get the shot out of the barrel by the time they rise."

"Ha! ha! ha!" roared Mr. Weller.

"Sam," said Mr. Pickwick, compassionating his follower's confusion and embarrassment.

"Sir."

"Don't laugh."

"Certainly not, sir." So, by way of indemnification, Mr. Weller contorted his features from behind the wheelbarrow, for the exclusive amusement of the boy with the leggings, who thereupon burst into a boisterous laugh, and was summarily cuffed by the long gamekeeper, who wanted a pretext for turning round, to hide his own merriment.

"Bravo, old fellow!" said Wardle to Mr. Tupman; "you fired that time, at all events."

"Oh, yes," replied Mr. Tupman, with conscious pride. "I let it off."

"Well done. You'll hit something next time, if you look sharp. Very easy, ain't it?"

"Yes, it's very easy," said Mr. Tupman. "How it hurts one's shoulder, though. It nearly knocked me backwards. I had no idea these small fire-arms kicked so."

"Ah," said the old gentleman, smiling; "you'll get used to it in time. Now, then—all ready—all right with the barrow there?"

"All right, sir," replied Mr. Weller.

"Come along, then."

"Hold hard, sir," said Sam, raising the barrow.

"Ay, ay," replied Mr. Pickwick; and on they went, as briskly as need be.

"Keep that barrow back now," cried Wardle, when it had been hoisted over a stile into another field, and Mr. Pickwick had been deposited in it once more.

"All right, sir," replied Mr. Weller, pausing.

"Now, Winkle," said the old gentleman, "follow me softly, and don't be too late this time."

"Never fear," said Mr. Winkle. "Are they pointing?"

"No, no; not now. Quietly now, quietly." On they crept, and very quietly they would have advanced, if Mr. Winkle, in the performance of some very intricate evolutions with his gun, had not accidentally fired, at the most critical moment, over the boy's head, exactly in the very spot where the tall man's brain would have been, had he been there instead.

"Why, what on earth did you do that for?" said old Wardle, as the birds flew unharmed away.

"I never saw such a gun in my life," replied poor Winkle, looking at the lock, as if that would do any good. "It goes off of its own accord. It *will* do it."

"Will do it!" echoed Wardle, with something of irritation in his manner. "I wish it would kill something of its own accord."

"It'll do that afore long, sir," observed the tall man, in a low, prophetic voice.

"What do you mean by that observation, sir?" inquired Mr. Winkle angrily.

"Never mind, sir, never mind," replied the long gamekeeper; "I've no family myself, sir; and this here boy's mother will get something handsome from Sir Geoffrey, if he's killed on his land. Load again, sir, load again."

"Take away his gun," cried Mr. Pickwick from the barrow, horror-stricken at the long man's dark insinuations. "Take away his gun, do you hear, somebody?"

Nobody, however, volunteered to obey the command; and Mr. Winkle, after darting a rebellious glance at Mr. Pickwick, reloaded his gun, and proceeded onwards with the rest.

We are bound, on the authority of Mr. Pickwick, to state that Mr. Tupman's mode of proceeding evinced far more of prudence and deliberation than that adopted by Mr. Winkle. Still, this by no means detracts from the great authority of the latter gentleman on all matters connected with the field; because, as Mr. Pickwick beautifully observes, it has somehow or other happened, from time immemorial, that many of the best and ablest philosophers, who have been perfect lights of science in matters of theory, have been wholly unable to reduce them to practice.

Mr. Tupman's process, like many of our most sublime discoveries, was extremely simple. With the quickness and penetration of a man of genius, he had at once observed that the two great points to be attained were—first, to discharge his piece without injury to himself, and, secondly, to do so without danger to the by-standers;—obviously, the best thing to do, after surmounting the difficulty of firing at all, was to shut his eyes firmly, and fire into the air.

On one occasion, after performing this feat, Mr. Tupman, on opening his eyes, beheld a plump partridge in the very act of falling wounded to the ground. He was on the point of congratulating Mr. Wardle on his invariable success, when that gentleman advanced towards him, and grasped him warmly by the hand.

"Tupman," said the old gentleman, "you singled out that particular bird?"

"No," said Mr. Tupman, "no."

"You did," said Wardle. "I saw you do it—I observed you pick him out—I noticed you, as you raised your piece to take aim; and I will say this, that the best shot in existence could not have done it more beautifully. You are an older hand at this than I thought you, Tupman; you have been out before."

It was in vain for Mr. Tupman to protest, with a smile of self-denial, that he never had. The very smile was taken as evidence to the contrary; and from that time forth his reputation was established. It is not the only reputation that has been acquired as easily, nor are such fortunate circumstances confined to partridge-shooting.

Meanwhile, Mr. Winkle flashed, and blazed, and smoked away, without producing any material results worthy of being noted down; sometimes expending his charge in mid-air, and at others sending it skimming along so near the surface of the ground as to place the lives of the two dogs on a rather uncertain and precarious tenure. As a display of fancy shooting, it was extremely varied and curious; as an exhibition of firing with any precise object, it was, upon the whole, perhaps a failure. It is an established axiom that "every bullet has its billet." If it apply in an equal degree to shot, those of Mr. Winkle were unfortunate foundlings, deprived of their natural rights, cast loose upon the world, and billeted nowhere.

"Well," said Wardle, walking up to the side of the barrow, and wiping the streams of perspiration from his jolly red face; "smoking day, isn't it?"

"It is, indeed," replied Mr. Pickwick. "The sun is tremendously hot, even to me. I don't know how you must feel it."

"Why," said the old gentleman, "pretty hot. It's past twelve, though. You see that green hill there?"

"Certainly."

"That's the place where we are to lunch; and, by Jove, there's the boy with the basket, punctual as clock-work!"

"So he is," said Mr. Pickwick, brightening up. "Good boy, that. I'll give him a shilling. Now, then, Sam, wheel away."

"Weal pie," said Mr. Weller, soliloquising, as he arranged the eatables on the grass. "Wery good thing is a weal pie, when you know the lady as made it, and is quite sure it ain't kittens; and arter all, though, where's the odds, when they're so like weal that the wery pie-men themselves don't know the difference?"

"Don't they, Sam?" said Mr. Pickwick.

"Not they, sir," replied Mr. Weller, touching his hat. "I lodged in the same house with a pieman once, sir, and a wery nice man he was—reg'lar clever chap, too—make pies out o' anything, he could. 'What a number o' cats you keep, Mr. Brooks,' says I, when I'd got intimate with him. 'Ah,' says he, 'I do—a good many,' says he. 'You must be wery fond o' cats,' says I. 'Other people is,' says he, a winkin' at me; 'they ain't in season till the winter, though,' says he. 'Not in season!' says I. 'No,' says he, 'fruits is in, cats is out.' 'Why, what do you mean?' says I. 'Mean?' says he. 'That I'll never be a party to the combination o' the butchers, to keep up the prices o' meat,' says he. 'Mr. Weller,' says he, a squeezing my hand wery hard, and vispering in my ear—'don't mention this here agin—but it's the seasonin' as does it. They're all made o' them noble animals,' says he a pointin' to a wery nice little tabby kitten, 'and I seasons 'em for beef-steak, weal, or kidney, 'cordin' to the demand. And more than that,' says he, 'I can make a weal a beef-steak, or a beef-steak a kidney, or any one on 'em a mutton, at a minute's notice, just as the market changes, and appetites wary!' "

"He must have been a very ingenious young man, that, Sam," said Mr. Pickwick, with a slight shudder.

"Just was, sir," replied Mr. Weller, continuing his occupation of emptying the basket, "and the pies was beautiful."

CHARLES DICKENS
[*Pickwick Papers* (1837)]

Sport on the Plantation

[If no European before Columbus had ever smelled a skunk, neither had any before the discovery of America suspected the existence of those primitive mammals called marsupials. Only one, the opossum, survived in North America, and in the South he soon became a sort of back-country analogue of the English fox—not so totally inedible but, like the fox, hunted primarily "for fun." John James Audubon—who was himself not averse to the rifle—has left a picturesque account of how the 'possum was hunted. Also some naturalist's observations on the peculiar nature of the beast.]

The domicile of the Opossum in which it is concealed during the day, and where it brings forth its young, which we have often examined, is found in various localities. This animal is a tolerable digger, although far less expert in this quality than the Maryland marmot, its den is usually under the roots of trees or stumps, when the ground is so elevated as to secure it from rains and inundations. The hollow of a large fallen tree, or an opening at the roots of a standing one, also serve as a convenient place for its nest. The material which we have usually found composing this nest along the seaboard of Carolina is the long moss (*Tillandsia usnoides*); although we have sometimes found it composed of a bushel or more of oak and other leaves.

On firing into a squirrel's nest which was situated in the fork of a tree some forty feet from the ground, we brought down an Opossum, which had evidently expelled its legitimate occupant. The Florida rat is known to collect heaps of sticks and leaves, and construct nests sometimes a yard in diameter and two feet high: these are usually placed on the ground, but very frequently on the entangled vines of the grape, smilax, and supple jack (*Ziziphus volubilis*). In these nests an Opossum may occasionally be found, dozing as cozily as if he had a better right than that of mere possession.

Hunting the Opossum is a very favourite amusement among domestics and field labourers on our Southern plantations, of lads broke loose from school in the holidays, and even of gentlemen, who are sometimes more fond of this sport than of the less profitable and more dangerous and fatiguing one of hunting the gray fox by moonlight. Although we have never participated in an Opossum hunt, yet we have observed that it afforded much amusement to the sable group that in the majority of instances make up the hunting party, and we have on two or three occasions been the silent and gratified observers of the preparations that were going on, the anticipations indulged in, and the excitement apparent around us.

On a bright autumnal day, when the abundant rice crop has yielded to the sickle, and the maize has just been gathered in, when one or two slight white frosts have tinged the fields and woods with a yellowish hue, ripened the persimmon, and caused the acorns, chestnuts and chinquepins (*Castanea pumilla*) to rattle down from the trees and strewed them over the ground, we hear arrangements entered into for the hunt. The Opossums have been living on the delicacies of the season, and are now in fine order, and some are found excessively fat; a double enjoyment is anticipated, the fun of catching and the pleasure of eating this excellent substitute for roast pig.

"Come, men," says one, "be lively, let us finish our tasks by four o'clock, and after sundown we will have a 'possum hunt." "Done," says another, "and if an old coon comes in the way of my smart dog, Pincher, I be bound for it, he will shake de life out of him." The labourers work with increased alacrity, their faces are brightened with anticipated enjoyment, and ever and anon the old familiar song of " 'Possum up the gum tree" is hummed, whilst the black driver can scarcely restrain the whole gang from breaking out into a loud chorus.

The paraphernalia belonging to this hunt are neither showy nor expensive. There are no horses caparisoned with elegant trappings —no costly guns imported to order—no pack of hounds answering to the echoing horn; two or three curs, half hound or terriers, each having his appropriate name, and each regarded by his owner as the best dog on the plantation, are whistled up. They obey the call with alacrity, and their looks and intelligent actions give evidence that they too are well aware of the pleasure that awaits them. One of these humble rustic sportsmen shoulders an axe and another a torch, and the whole arrangement for the hunt is completed. The glaring torchlight is soon seen dispersing the shadows of the forest, and like a jack o'lantern, gleaming along the skirts of the distant meadows and copses. Here are no old trails on which the cold-nosed hound tries his nose for half an hour to catch the scent. The tongues of the curs are by no means silent—ever and anon there is a sudden start and an uproarious outbreak: "A rabbit in a hollow, wait, boys, till I twist him out with a hickory." The rabbit is secured and tied with a string around the neck: another start, and the pack runs off for a quarter of a mile, at a rapid rate, then double around the cotton fields and among the ponds in the pine lands—"Call off your worthless dog, Jim, my Pincher has too much sense to bother after a fox." A loud scream and a whistle brings the pack to a halt, and presently they come panting to the call of the black huntsman. After some scolding and threatening, and resting a quarter of an hour to recover their breath and scent, they are once more hied forwards. Soon a trusty old dog, by an occasional shrill yelp, gives evidence that he has struck some trail in the swamp. The pack gradually make out the scent on the edges of the pond, and marshes of the rice fields, grown up with willows and myrtle bushes (*Myrica cerifera*). At length the mingled notes of shrill and discordant tongues give evidence that the game is up. The race, though rapid, is a long one, through the deep swamp, crossing the muddy branch into the pine lands, where the dogs come to a halt, unite in conclave, and set up an incessant barking at the foot of a pine. "A coon, a coon! din't I tell you," says Monday, "that if Pincher come across a coon, he would do he work?" An additional piece of split light-wood is added to the torch, and the coon is seen doubled up in the form of a hornet's nest in the very top of the long-leaved pine (*P. palustris*). The tree is without a branch for forty feet or upwards, and it is at once decided that it must be cut down: the axe is soon at work, and the tree felled. The glorious battle that ensues, the prowess of the dogs, and the capture of the coon, follow as a matter of course.

Another trail is soon struck, and the dogs all open upon it at once: in an instant they rush, pell mell, with a loud burst of mingled tongues, upon some animal along the edge of an old field destitute of trees. It proves to be an Opossum, detected in its nightly prowling expedition. At first it feigns death, and, rolling itself into a ball, lies still on the ground; but the dogs are up to this " 'possum playing," and seize upon it at once. It now feels that they are in earnest, and are not to be deceived. It utters a low growl or two, shows no fight, opens wide its large mouth, and, with few struggles, surrenders itself to its fate. But our hunters are not yet satisfied, either with the sport or the meat: they have large families and a host of friends on the plantation, the game is abundant, and the labour in procuring it not fatiguing, so they once more hie on the dogs. The Opossum, by its slow gait and heavy tread, leaves its foot-prints and scent behind it on the soft mud and damp grass. Another is soon started, and hastens up the first small gum, oak, or persimmon tree, within its reach; it has clambered up to the highest limb, and sits crouching up with eyes closed to avoid the light. "Off jacket, Jim, and shake him down; show that you know more about 'possum than your good-for-nutten fox-dog." As the fellow ascends, the animal continues mounting higher to get beyond his reach; still he continues in pursuit, until the affrighted Opossum has reached the farthest twig on the extreme branches of the tree. The Negro now commences shaking the tall pliant tree top; while with its hind hands rendered convenient and flexible by its opposing thumb, and with its prehensile tail, the Opossum holds on with great tenacity. But it cannot long resist the rapidly accumulating jerks and shocks: suddenly the feet slip from the smooth tiny limb, and it hangs suspended for a few moments only by its tail, in the meantime trying to regain its hold with its hind hands; but another sudden jerk breaks the twig, and down comes the poor animal, doubled up like a ball, into the opened jaws of eager and relentless canine foes; the poor creature drops, and yields to fate without a struggle.

In this manner half a dozen or more Opossums are sometimes captured before midnight. The subsequent boasts about the superior noses, speed and courage of the several dogs that composed this small motley pack—the fat feast that succeeded on the following evening, prolonged beyond the hour of midnight, the boisterous laugh and the merry song, we leave to be detailed by others, although we confess we have not been uninterested spectators of such scenes.

"Let not ambition mock their useful toil,
"Their homely joys and destiny obscure,
"Nor grandeur hear with a disdainful smile,
"The simple pleasures of the humble poor."

The habit of feigning death to deceive an enemy is common to several species of quadrupeds, and we on several occasions witnessed it in our common red fox (*V. Fulvus*). But it is more strikingly exhibited in the Opossum than in any other animal with which we are acquainted. When it is shaken from a tree and falls among grass and shrubbery, or when detected in such situations, it doubles itself into a heap and feigns death so artfully, that we have known some schoolboys carrying home for a quarter of a mile an individual of this species, stating that when they first saw it, it was running on the ground, and they could not tell what had killed it. We would not, however, advise that the hand should on such occasions be suffered to come too familiarly in contact with the mouth, lest the too curious meddler should on a sudden be startled with an unexpected and unwelcome gripe.

This species has scarcely any note of recognition, and is remarkably silent; when molested, it utters a low growl; at other times its voice resembles the hissing of a cat. The Opossum displays no cunning in avoiding traps set to capture it, entering almost any kind of trap, very commonly being taken in a log trap called a dead fall.

From its very prolific nature it can afford to have many enemies. In addition to the incessant war waged against it by men and dogs, we have ascertained that its chief enemy among rapacious birds is the Virginian owl (*Strix Virginiana*), which flying abroad at the same hour in which the Opossum is on foot, pounces on it, and kills it with great ease. We have heard of an instance in which it was seen in the talons of the white-headed eagle (*Halietus leucocephalus*) and of two or three in which the great hen-hawk (*F. Borealis*) was observed feeding upon it. We recollect no instance of its having been killed by the wild cat or the fox. The wolf, it is said, seizes on every Opossum it can find, and we have heard of two instances where half-grown animals of this species were found to have been swallowed by the rattlesnake.

Although the dog hunts it so eagerly, yet we have never been able to ascertain that it ever feeds upon its flesh; indeed, we have witnessed the dog passing by the body of a fresh killed Opossum, and going off half a mile farther to feed on some offensive carcase.

The Opossum is easily domesticated when captured young. We have, in endeavouring to investigate one of the very extraordinary characteristics of this species, preserved a considerable number in confinement, and our experiments were continued through a succession of years. Their nocturnal habits were in a considerable degree relinquished, and they followed the servants about the premises, becoming troublesome by their familiarity and their mischievous habits. They associated familiarly with a dog on the premises, which seemed to regard them as necessary appendages of the motley group that constituted the family of brutes in the yard. They devoured all kinds of food: vegetables, boiled rice, hominy, meat both raw and boiled, and the scraps thrown from the kitchen; giving the preference to those that contained any fatty substance.

On one occasion a brood of young with their mother made their escape, concealed themselves under a stable, and became partially wild; they were in the habit of coming out at night, and eating scraps of food, but we never discovered that they committed any depredations on the poultry or pigeons. They appeared however to have effectually driven off the rats, as during the whole time they were occupants of the stable, we did not observe a single rat on the premises. It was ascertained that they were in the habit of clambering over fences and visiting the neighbouring lots and gardens, and we occasionally found that we had repurchased one of our own vagrant animals. They usually, however, returned towards daylight to their snug retreat, and we believe would have continued in the neighbourhood and multiplied the species had they not in their nightly prowlings been detected and destroyed by the neighbouring dogs.

A most interesting part of the history of this animal, which has led to the adoption of many vulgar errors, remains to be considered, viz., the generation of the Opossum.

Our investigations on this subject were commenced in early life, and resumed as time and opportunity were afforded, at irregular, and sometimes after long intervals, and were not satisfactorily concluded until within a month of the period of our writing this article (June, 1849). The process by which we were enabled to obtain the facts and arrive at our conclusions is detailed in an article published in the Transactions of the Academy of Natural Sciences, April, 1848, p. 40. Subsequent investigations have enabled us to verify some of these facts, to remove some obscurities in which the subject was yet involved, and finally to be prepared to give a correct and detailed history of a peculiarity in the natural history of this quadruped, around which there has hitherto been thrown a cloud of mystery and doubt.

Our early authors—MARCGRAVE, PISON, VALENTINE, BEVERLY, the MARQUIS of CHASTELLUX, PENNANT, and others—contended that "the pouch was the matrix of the young Opossum, and that the mammæ are, with regard to the young, what stalks are to their fruits." DE BLAINVILLE and DR. BARTON speak of two sorts of gestation, one uterine and the other mammary. BLUMENBACH calls the young when they are first seen on the mammæ, abortions; and Dr. BARTON's views (we quote from GRIFFITH) are surprisingly inaccurate: "The Didelphes," he says, "put forth, not fœtuses but gelatinous bodies; they weigh at their first appearance generally about a grain, some a little more, and seven of them together weighed ten grains." In 1819, GEOFFROY St. HILLAIRE propounded to naturalists the following question: "Are the pouched animals born attached to the teats of the mother?" GODMAN, in his American Natural History, published in 1826, gave to the world a very interesting article on the Opossum, full of information in respect to the habits, &c., comprising all the knowledge that existed at that day in regard to this species. He was obliged, however, to admit, vol. 2, p. 7, "the peculiarities of its sexual intercourse, gestation, and parturition, are to this day involved in profound obscurity. Volumes of facts and conjectures have been written on the subject, in which the proportion of conjecture to fact has been as a thousand to one, and the difficulties still remain to be surmounted." And DEKAY, in the work on the Quadrupeds of the State of N. York (Nat. Hist. of N.York, 1842, p. 4), states: "The young are found in the external abdominal sac, firmly attached to the teat in the form of a small gelatinous body, not weighing more than a grain. It was a long time believed that there existed a direct passage from the uterus to the teat, but this has been disproved by dissection. Another opinion is, that the embryo is excluded from the uterus in the usual manner and placed by the mother to the teat; and a third, that the embryo is formed where it is first found. Whether this transfer actually takes place, and if so, the physiological considerations connected with it, still remain involved in great obscurity."

The approaches to truth in these investigations have been very gradual, and the whole unusually slow. COWPER, TYSON, DE BLAINVILLE, HOME and others, by their examinations and descriptions of the organs of the Marsupialiæ, prepared the way for farther developments. A more judicious examination and scientific description by OWEN and others, of the corresponding organs in the kangaroo, the largest of all the species composing these genera, and the discovery of the fœtus in utero, enabled naturalists to conclude, that the similar structure in the Opossum would indicate a corresponding result. No one, however, was entitled to speak with positive certainty until the young were actually detected in the uterus, nor could an explanation of the peculiarity in the growth of the fœtus be made until it was examined in its original bed.

We have been so fortunate in five instances as to have procured specimens in which the young were observed in this position, and therefore feel prepared to speak with certainty. We are not aware that the young of the Virginian Opossum had been previously detected in the uterus.

All our investigations were made in South Carolina, where this is a very abundant species. For some years we attempted to arrive at the object of our researches by preserving these animals in a state of confinement. But they were subject to many accidents: they frequently made their escape from their cages, and some of them became overburdened with fat and proved sterile, so that we did not succeed in a single instance in obtaining young from females in a state of confinement. From this cause the naturalists of Europe, and especially those of France, who were desirous of making investigations in regard to our Opossum, have been so long unsuccessful. Their usual complaint has been, "Your Opossums do not breed in confinement." In this, Dr. BARTON and our young friend Dr. MICHEL were more fortunate, but in both cases the young were produced before they were enabled to detect them in their previous existing position. We varied our experiments by endeavouring to discern the precise period when young were usually produced. We ascertained, by having a number of females procured with young in their pouches, that about the close of the first week in March, a little earlier or later, according to the age of the individual, or warmth, or coldness, of the previous winter, was the time when in this latitude this event usually occurs. Here, however,

another difficulty presented itself, which for several successive seasons, thwarted us in our investigations. In the third week of February 1847, by offering premiums to the servants on several neighbouring plantations we obtained in three nights thirty-five Opossums, but of that number there was not a single female. A week afterwards, however, when the young were contained in the pouch, we received more females than males. From this circumstance we came to the conclusion that during the short period of gestation, the females, like those of some other species of quadrupeds, particularly the American black bear, conceal themselves in their burrows and can seldom be found. We then changed our instructions for capturing them, by recommending that they should be searched for in the day time, in hollow logs and trees and places where they had been previously known to burrow. By this means we were enabled at different times to obtain a small number in the state in which we were desirous of examining them. We feel under great obligations to several gentlemen of Carolina for aiding us in our investigations by procuring specimens, especially our relative Colonel HASKELL, Mr. JOHNSON, and JAMES FISHER, Esq., a close observer and intelligent naturalist. The latter, by his persevering efforts, pursued for some years at Jordan's Mills, on the upper waters of the Edisto, obtained two females in May, 1849, in the particular state in which he knew we were anxious to procure them, and brought them to us without having been previously aware that we had published the facts a year before.

The Opossums we were enabled to examine were dissected on the 11th, 14th and 18th February, 1848, and on the 12th and 22d May, 1849. Some of these had advanced to near the time of parturition. The young of those brought us by Mr. FISHER each weighed 2½ grains. Those of one, sent us by Col. HASKELL, weighed 3 grains; and the young of another which we obtained by a Cæsarian operation, at a moment when all the rest had been excluded, and this individual alone remained, weighed 4 grains.

We remarked, that this however was a little the largest of six that composed the family, five of which were already in the pouch and attached to the teats. The largest one weighed 3¾, and another 3½ grains. The weight, then, of the young Opossum at the moment of birth, is between 3 and 4 grains, varying a little in different specimens as is the case in the young of all animals.

The degree of life and animation in young Opossums at the moment of birth has been greatly underrated. They are neither abortions, as BLUMENBACH represented them, nor as Dr. BARTON has described them—"not fœtuses, but gelatinous bodies, weighing about a grain more or less, seven of them together weighing 10 grains"— but little creatures that are nearly as well developed at birth as the young of the white-footed mouse and several other species of rodentia. They are covered by an integument, nourished by the mammæ, breathe through nostrils, perform the operations of nature, are capable of a progressive movement at the moment of their birth, and are remarkably tenacious of life. The individual which was dissected from the parent in the manner above detailed, moved several inches on the table by crawling and rolling, and survived two hours; the thermometer in the room was at the time standing at 66° Fahrenheit. The period of gestation is from fifteen to sixteen days. We received a female from a servant who informed us, that he had that morning seen it in intercourse with the male. We first saw the young on the morning of the 17th day. Our friend Dr. MIDDLETON MICHEL, a gentleman of high scientific attainments, and who had long been engaged in investigating the characters and habits of this species, in a communication made to us (Trans. of the Acad. Nat. Sciences, April, 1848, p. 46), assured us from his personal observation in which he was careful to note the hour of the day, the exact period is 15 days. As he possessed better opportunities of deciding in regard to the time, the animals being in a state of domestication, we are rather more disposed to yield to his observations than to our own; there is, however, only the difference of a day between us.

The young, when first born, are naked and flesh-coloured; the eyes, together with the ears, are covered by a thin integument through which these organs and the protuberances of the ears are distinctly visible. The mouth is closed, with the exception of a small orifice, sufficiently large to receive the teat, which is so thin and attenuated that it seems no larger than the body of a pin. Length of body, 7-12ths of an inch; of tail, 2-10ths. The nails, which can be seen with the naked eye, are very distinct when viewed with a microscope, and are of a dark brown colour, small and much hooked. The nostrils are open; the lungs filled with air, and when placed in water, the young float on the surface.

The number of young usually found in the pouch appear to be less than those that are born. The highest number we have found in the pouch was thirteen, the smallest six; whereas the preserved uterus brought to us by Mr. FISHER, contained fifteen. In all such cases, where a greater number of young are produced than there are teats, the last of the brood must inevitably perish, as those that are attached appear incapable of relinquishing their hold.

The manner in which the young at birth reach the pouch, and become attached to the teats, has been the subject of much speculation and inquiry. We had an opportunity of examining this process in part, without, however, having been aware at the time that it was going on. We intended to dissect a small female Opossum, which had been a few days in our possession, but ascertained in the morning at seven o'clock on the day our examination was to have been made, that she had three young in her pouch; supposing from her small size, that she would produce no additional number, we concluded to spare her life. She was confined in a box in our study; when we occasionally looked at her, we found her lying on one side, her shoulders elevated, her body drawn up in the shape of a ball; the pouch was occasionally distended with her paws—in this position the parts reached the edge of the pouch; she was busily employed with her nose and mouth licking, as we thought, her pouch, but in which we afterwards ascertained, were her young.

At six o'clock in the afternoon we were induced to examine her again, in consequence of having observed that she had for several hours appeared very restless, when we discovered that she had added four more to her previous number, making her young family now to consist of seven. With no inconsiderable labour and the exercise of much patience, we removed three of the young from the teats, one of which perished under the process, we replaced the two living ones in the pouch; at nine o'clock examined her again and found both the young once more attached. We came to the conclusion, that she shoved them into the pouch, and with her nose or tongue moved them to the vicinity of the teats, where by an instinct of nature, the teat was drawn into the small orifice of the mouth by suction. We observed subsequently, that a young one that had been extracted from its parent a few moments before the time when it would have been born, and which had been rolled up in warm cotton, was instinctively engaged in sucking at the fibres of the cotton, and had succeeded in drawing into its mouth a considerable length of thread. A nearly similar process was observed by our friend Dr. MICHEL. He states: "The female stood on her hind legs, and the body being much bent, the young appeared and were licked into the pouch."

There is a great difficulty in deciding the question, whether the mother aids the young in finding the teats, in consequence of the impossibility of the spectators being able to know what she is actually doing, whilst her nose is in the pouch. We believe the majority of naturalists who had an opportunity of witnessing our experiments came to the conclusion, that the mother, after shoving them into the pouch, left them to their own instinct, and they became attached without her assistance. We tried another experiment that suggested itself to us. Believing that the mother would not readily adopt the young of another, or afford them any assistance, we removed six out of ten that composed her brood, returned two of her own to the pouch, together with three others fully double the size, that had been obtained from another female. She was soon observed doubled up with her nose in the pouch, and continued so for an hour, when she was examined and one of her own small ones was found attached to the teat. Seven hours afterwards she was examined again, and both the small ones were attached, but the three larger ones still remained crawling about the pouch. On the following morning, it was ascertained that the mother had adopted the strangers, as the whole family of different sizes were deriving sustenance from her.

On another occasion, a female Opossum had been sent to us caught by a dog and much wounded, in consequence of which she died a few days afterwards, but first producing seven young which to every appearance had been still born. Yet they were in the pouch, and it appeared to us that the mother's uncontrollable attachment to her young, induced her to place her offspring in the pouch, even after they were dead.

An interesting inquiry remains to be answered: Is the Opossum a placental or non-placental animal? Until we were favoured with a recent opportunity of carefully examining a uterus, containing nine young on one side, and six on the other, kindly brought to us by our friend JAMES FISHER, we were unable fully to answer this question. Our dissections and examinations were witnessed by Professors MOULTRIE, HUME, Drs. HORLBECK MICHEL, PORCHER and others.

The Opossum is, as far as we are able to judge from the specimens examined, a non-placental animal, inasmuch as there could not be detected the slightest adhesion between the exterior membrane of the fœtus and the internal surface of the mother. The membranes consisted of a vitelline sac, filled with ramifications of omphalo-mesenteric vessels, there was a slight appearance of an umbilical cord and umbilical vessels, constituting a true allantois, but no portions of them were attached to the uterus. There was no appearance of a placenta.

The growth of the young Opossum is surprisingly rapid. We weighed the largest young one at a week old and found it had increased from 3¾ grains to 30 grains. Length of head and body exclusive of tail, 1¼ inch; tail, ½ inch. The young at this age were very tenacious of life, as on removing two, they remained alive on the floor without any covering through a cool night, in a room containing no fire, and still exhibited a slight motion at twelve o'clock on the following day. The teats of the mother after the young had been gently drawn off measured an inch in length, having been much distended, and appeared to have been drawn into the stomach of the young. The pouches of the young females were quite apparent; they used their prehensile tails, which could now be frequently seen entwined around the necks of others. At twelve days old the eyes were still closed, a few hairs had made their appearance on the moustache; the orifice of the ears were beginning to be developed, and the nails were quite visible and sharp.

When the young are four weeks old, they begin from time to time to relax their hold on the teats, and may now be seen with their heads occasionally out of the pouch. A week later, and they venture to steal occasionally from their snug retreat in the pouch, and are often seen on the mother's back securing themselves by entwining their tails around hers. In this situation she moves from place to place in search of food, carrying her whole family along with her, to which she is much attached, and in whose defence she exhibits a considerable degree of courage, growling at any intruder, and ready to use her teeth with great severity on man or dog. In travelling, it is amusing to see this large family moving about. Some of the young, nearly the size of rats, have their tails entwined around the legs of the mother, and some around her neck, thus they are dragged along.

JOHN JAMES AUDUBON
[*The Quadrupeds of America* (1846-1854)]

Leviathan

[*It was the fur bearers of northern woods or waters and the great oil-bearing whale which first felt the effects of remorseless, methodical and cold-blooded exploitation. Herman Melville is, of course, the Homer of the whalers' bloody epoch, and he achieved a unique effect by combining accurate realism with an almost Oriental heightening of language and mood.]*

If to Starbuck the apparition of the squid was a thing of portents, to Queequeg it was quite a different object.

"When you see him 'quid," said the savage, honing his harpoon in the bow of his hoisted boat, "then you quick see him 'parm whale."

The next day was exceedingly still and sultry, and with nothing special to engage them, the *Pequod*'s crew could hardly resist the spell of sleep induced by such a vacant sea. For this part of the Indian Ocean through which we then were voyaging is not what whalemen call a lively ground; that is, it affords fewer glimpses of porpoises, dolphins, flying-fish, and other vivacious denizens of more stirring waters, than those off the Rio de la Plata, or the inshore ground off Peru.

It was my turn to stand at the foremast head; and with my shoulders leaning against the slackened royal shrouds, to and fro I idly swayed in what seemed an enchanted air. No resolution could withstand it; in that dreamy mood losing all consciousness, at last my soul went out of my body; though my body still continued to sway as a pendulum will, long after the power which first moved it is withdrawn.

Ere forgetfulness altogether came over me, I had noticed that the seamen at the main and mizzen-mastheads were already drowsy. So that at last all three of us lifelessly swung from the spars, and for every swing that we made there was a nod from below from the slumbering helmsman. The waves, too, nodded their indolent crests; and across the wide trance of the sea, east nodded to west, and the sun over all.

Suddenly bubbles seemed bursting beneath my closed eyes; like vises my hands grasped the shrouds; some invisible, gracious agency preserved me; with a shock I came back to life. And lo! close under our lee, not forty fathoms off, a gigantic Sperm Whale lay rolling in the water like the capsized hull of a frigate, his broad, glossy back of an Ethiopian hue, glistening in the sun's rays like a mirror. But lazily undulating in the trough of the sea, and ever and anon tranquilly spouting his vapoury jet, the whale looked like a portly burgher smoking his pipe of a warm afternoon. But that pipe, poor whale, was thy last. As if struck by some enchanter's wand, the sleepy ship and every sleeper in it all at once started into wakefulness; and more than a score of voices from all parts of the vessel, simultaneously with the three notes from aloft, shouted forth the accustomed cry, as the great fish slowly and regularly spouted the sparkling brine into the air.

"Clear away the boats! Luff!" cried Ahab. And obeying his own order, he dashed the helm down before the helmsman could handle the spokes.

The sudden exclamations of the crew must have alarmed the whale; and ere the boats were down, majestically turning, he swam away to the leeward, but with such a steady tranquillity, and making so few ripples as he swam, that thinking after all he might not as yet be alarmed, Ahab gave orders that not an oar should be used, and no man must speak but in whispers. So seated like Ontario Indians on the gunwales of the boats, we swiftly but silently paddled along; the calm not admitting of the noiseless sails being set. Presently, as we thus glided in chase, the monster perpendicularly flitted his tail forty feet into the air, and then sank out of sight like a tower swallowed up.

"There go flukes!" was the cry, an announcement immediately followed by Stubb's producing his match and igniting his pipe, for now a respite was granted. After the full interval of his sounding had elapsed, the whale rose again, and being now in advance of the smoker's boat, and much nearer to it than to any of the others, Stubb counted upon the honour of the capture. It was obvious now, that the whale had at length become aware of his pursuers. All silence or cautiousness was therefore no longer of use. Paddles were dropped, and oars came loudly into play. And still puffing at his pipe, Stubb cheered on his crew to the assault.

Yes, a mighty change had come over the fish. All alive to his jeopardy, he was going "head out"; that part obliquely projecting from the mad yeast which he brewed.[1]

"Start her, start her, my men! Don't hurry yourselves; take plenty of time—but start her; start her like thunderclaps, that's all," cried Stubb, spluttering out the smoke as he spoke. "Start her, now; give 'em the long and strong stroke, Tashtego. Start her, Tash, my boy —start her, all; but keep cool, keep cool—cucumbers is the word—

---

1 It will be seen in some other place of what a very light substance the entire interior of the sperm whale's enormous head consists. Though apparently the most massive, it is by far the most buoyant part about him. So that with ease he elevates it in the air, and invariably does so when going at his utmost speed. Besides, such is the breadth of the upper part of the front of his head, and such the tapering cut-water formation of the lower part, that by obliquely elevating his head, he thereby may be said to transform himself from a bluff-bowed, sluggish galliot into a sharp-pointed New York pilot boat.

easy, easy—only start her like grim death and grinning devils, and raise the buried dead perpendicular out of their graves, boys—that's all. Start her!"

"Woo-hoo! Wa-hee!" screamed the Gay-Header in reply, raising some old war-whoop to the skies; as every oarsman in the strained boat involuntarily bounced forward with the one tremendous leading stroke which the eager Indian gave.

But his wild screams were answered by others quite as wild. "Kee-hee! Kee-hee!" yelled Daggoo, straining forwards and backwards on his seat, like a pacing tiger in his cage.

"Ka-la Koo-loo!" howled Queequeg, as if smacking his lips over a mouthful of Grenadier's steak. And thus with oars and yells the keels cut the sea. Meanwhile, Stubb retaining his place in the van, still encouraged his men to the onset, all the while puffing the smoke from his mouth. Like desperadoes they tugged and they strained, till the welcome cry was heard—"Stand up, Tashtego!—give it to him!" The harpoon was hurled. "Stern all!" The oarsmen backed water; the same moment something went hot and hissing along every one of their wrists. It was the magical line. An instant before, Stubb had swiftly caught two additional turns with it round the loggerhead, whence, by reason of its increased rapid circlings, a hempen blue smoke now jetted up and mingled with the steady fumes from his pipe. As the line passed round and round the loggerhead; so also, just before reaching that point, it blisteringly passed through and through both of Stubb's hands, from which the hand-cloths, or squares of quilted canvas sometimes worn at these times, had accidentally dropped. It was like holding an enemy's sharp two-edged sword by the blade, and that enemy all the time striving to wrest it out of your clutch.

"Wet the line! wet the line!" cried Stubb to the tub oarsmen (him seated by the tub) who, snatching off his hat, dashed the sea-water into it.[1] More turns were taken, so that the line began holding its place. The boat now flew through the boiling water like a shark all fins. Stubb and Tashtego here changed places—stem for stern—a staggering business truly in that rocking commotion.

From the vibrating line extending the entire length of the upper part of the boat, and from its now being more tight than a harpstring, you would have thought the craft had two keels—one

[1] Partly to show the indispensableness of this act, it may here be stated, that, in the old Dutch fishery, a mop was used to dash the running-line with water; in many other ships, a wooden piggin, or bailer, is set apart for that purpose. Your hat, however, is the most convenient.

cleaving the water, the other the air—as the boat churned on through both opposing elements at once. A continual cascade played at the bows; a ceaseless whirling eddy in her wake; and, at the slightest motion from within, even but of a little finger, the vibrating, cracking craft canted over her spasmodic gunwale into the sea. Thus they rushed: each man with might and main clinging to his seat, to prevent being tossed to the foam; and the tall form of Tashtego at the steering-oar crouching almost double, in order to bring down his centre of gravity. Whole Atlantics and Pacifics seemed passed as they shot on their way, till at length the whale somewhat slackened his flight.

"Haul in—haul in!" cried Stubb to the bowsman! and, facing round towards the whale, all hands began pulling the boat up to him, while yet the boat was being towed on. Soon ranging up by his flank, Stubb, firmly planting his knee in the clumsy cleat, darted dart after dart into the flying fish; at the word of command, the boat alternately sterning out of the way of the whale's horrible wallow, and then ranging up for another fling.

The red tide now poured from all sides of the monster like brooks down a hill. His tormented body rolled not in brine but in blood, which bubbled and seethed for furlongs behind in their wake. The slanting sun playing upon this crimson pond in the sea, sent back its reflection into every face, so that they all glowed to each other like red men. And all the while, jet after jet of white smoke was agonisingly shot from the mouth of the excited headsman; as at every dart, hauling in upon his crooked lance (by the line attached to it), Stubb straightened it again and again by a few rapid blows against the gunwale, then again and again sent it into the whale.

"Pull up—pull up!" he now cried to the bowsman, as the waning whale relaxed in his wrath. "Pull up!—close to!" and the boat ranged along the fish's flank. When reaching far over the bow, Stubb slowly churned his long sharp lance into the fish, and kept it there, carefully churning and churning, as if cautiously seeking to feel after some gold watch that the whale might have swallowed, and which he was fearful of breaking ere he could hook it out. But that gold watch he sought was the innermost life of the fish. And now it is struck; for, starting from this trance into that unspeakable thing called his "flurry," the monster horribly wallowed in his blood, overwrapped himself in impenetrable, mad, boiling spray, so that the imperilled craft instantly dropping astern, had much ado blindly to struggle out from that frenzied twilight into the clear air of the day.

And now abating in his flurry, the whale once more rolled out into view; surging from side to side; spasmodically dilating and contracting his spout-hole, with sharp, cracking, agonised respirations. At last, gush after gush of clotted red gore, as if it had been the purple lees of red wine, shot into the frighted air; and falling back again, ran dripping down his motionless flanks into the sea. His heart had burst!

"He's dead, Mr. Stubb," said Daggoo.

"Yes; both pipes smoked out!" and withdrawing his own from his mouth, Stubb scattered the dead ashes over the water; and, for a moment, stood thoughtfully eyeing the vast corpse he had made.

HERMAN MELVILLE
[*Moby Dick* (1851)]

Crocodile Tears

[*The big-game hunter as distinguished from the home-haunting sportsman is an invention of the nineteenth century. Sometimes he is not clearly distinguishable from the explorer and he may be both, as was one of the most famous, Paul du Chaillu, said to have been the first ever to bring a live gorilla to Europe. The crocodile tears with which the following vivid account ends are not uncharacteristic of others of his calling.*]

I left America for the Western Coast of Africa in the month of October, 1855. My purpose was to spend some years in the exploration of a region of territory lying between lat. 2° north and 2° south, and stretching back from the coast to the mountain-range called the *Sierra del Crystal,* and beyond as far as I should be able to penetrate.

The coast-line of this region is dotted here and there with Negro villages, and at a few points "factories" have been established for the prosecution of general trade. The power and knowledge of the white man extend but a very few miles from the coast, and the interior was still a *terra incognita.* Of its tribes, several of whom were reported to be cannibals, nothing was known, though terrible stories were told of their dark superstitions and untameable ferocity; of its productions only a rough guess could be made from the scant supplies of ivory, ebony, bar-wood, and caoutchouc which were transmitted to the coast by the people inhabiting the river-banks. Of the natural history—which was the subject that interested me most—sufficient was known to assure me that here was a field worthy of every effort of an explorer and naturalist.

This unexplored region was the home of that remarkable ape, the fierce, untameable *gorilla,* which approaches nearest, in physical conformation and in certain habits, to man, and whose unconquerable ferocity has made it the terror of the bravest native hunters—an animal, too, of which hitherto naturalists and the civilized world knew so little, that the name even was not found in most natural histories. Here, too, in these dense woods, were to be found—if the natives told aright—the nest-building *nshiego-mbouvé,* an ape next in the scale to the gorilla; several varieties of other apes; hippopotami and manatees, in the rivers; and birds and beasts of many and various kinds, many entirely unknown to us, in the forests and among the hills.

To ascend the various rivers, hunt in the woods, and acquaint myself alike with the haunts and habits of the gorilla, and with the superstitions, customs, and modes of life of the black tribes, who had not hitherto been visited by white men: these were among the chief objects of my present visit to the African Coast. Another purpose I had in view was to ascertain if in the interior, among the mountainous ranges in which the rivers took their rise, there was not to be found a region of country fertile and populous, and at the same time healthy, where the missionaries, who now suffer and die on the low coast, could work in safety and to advantage, and where might be established profitable trading-stations, which would benefit alike whites and natives.

Several years' residence on the Coast, where my father had formerly a factory, had given me a knowledge of the languages, habits, and peculiarities of the Coast natives, which I hoped to find serviceable in my interior explorations, and had also sufficed to inure my constitution in some degree to the severities of an African hot season, or at least to familiarize me with the best means for preserving health and life against the deadly fevers of *the Coast.*

The Gaboon River, which takes its rise among the Sierra del Crystal mountains, empties its sluggish waters into the Atlantic a few miles north of the equator. Its mouth forms a bay, which is the finest harbour on the West Coast; and here on the right bank the French formed a settlement and built a fort in the year 1842. It was under the protection of this fort that my father for several years, through agents, carried on a trade with the natives, and here I gained my first knowledge of Africa and my first acquaintance with the Gaboon tribes.

On Tuesday, the 20th of April, we set out for one of our great hunts, going up the river a short distance and then striking into the forests. We found many open spots in these woods, where the soil was sandy, and the grass was not very luxuriant, growing not more than two feet high. The sun is very oppressive in these clear spots.

We were troubled, too, on the prairie by two very savage flies, called by the Negroes the *boco* and the *nchouna*. These insects attacked us with a terrible persistency which left us no peace. They were very quiet bloodsuckers, and I never knew of their attacks till I felt the itch which follows the bite when the fly has left it. This is again followed by a little painful swelling.

The next day we were out after gorillas, which we knew were to be found hereabouts by the presence of a pulpy pear-shaped fruit growing close to the ground, the *tondo*, of which this animal is very fond. I also am very fond of the subdued and grateful acid of this fruit, which the Negroes eat as well as the gorilla. It is curious that that which grows in the sandy soil of the prairie is not fit to eat.

We found everywhere gorilla-marks, and so recent that we began to think the animals must be avoiding us. This was the case, I think, though I am not sure. At any rate we beat the bush for two hours before, at last, we found the game. Suddenly an immense gorilla advanced out of the wood straight towards us, and gave vent as he came up to a terrible howl of rage—as much as to say, "I am tired of being pursued, and will face you."

It was a lone male—the kind who are always most ferocious; and this fellow made the woods ring with his roar, which is really an awful sound, resembling very much the rolling and muttering of distant thunder.

He was about twenty yards off when we first saw him. We at once gathered together, and I was about to take aim and bring him down where he stood, when Malaouen stopped me, saying, in a whisper, "Not time yet."

We stood therefore in silence, guns in hand. The gorilla looked at us for a minute or so out of his evil gray eyes, then beat his breast with his gigantic arms, gave another howl of defiance, and advanced upon us.

Again he stopped, now not more than fifteen yards away. Still Malaouen said, "Not yet."

Then again an advance upon us. Now he was not twelve yards off. I could see plainly the ferocious face of the monstrous ape. It was working with rage; his huge teeth were ground against each other so that we could hear the sound; the skin of the forehead was moved rapidly back and forth, and gave a truly devilish expression to the hideous face: once more he gave out a roar which seemed to shake the woods like thunder, and, looking us in the eyes and beating his breast, advanced again. This time he came within eight yards of us before he stopped. My breath was coming short with excitement as I watched the huge beast. Malaouen said only, "Steady!" as he came up.

When he stopped, Malaouen said, "Now." And before he could utter the roar for which he was opening his mouth, three musket-balls were in his body. He fell dead almost without a struggle.

"Don't fire too soon. If you do not kill him he will kill you," said Malaouen to me—a piece of advice which I found afterwards was too literally true.

It was a huge old beast indeed. Its height was 5 feet 6 inches. Its arms had a spread of 7 feet 2 inches. Its huge brawny chest measured 50 inches around. The big toe or thumb of its foot measured 5¾ inches in circumference. Its arm seemed only immense bunches of muscle, and its legs and claw-like feet were so well fitted for *grabbing* and holding, that I could see how easy it was for the Negroes to believe that this animal conceals itself in trees, and pulls up with its foot any living thing—leopard, ox, or man—that passes beneath. There is no doubt the gorilla *can* do this, but that he *does* it I do not believe. They are ferocious, mischievous, but not carnivorous.

The face of this gorilla was intensely black. The vast chest, which proved his great power, was bare, and covered with a parchment-like skin. Its body was covered with gray hair. Though there are sufficient points of diversity between this animal and man, I never kill one without having a sickening realization of the horrid human likeness of the beast. This was particularly the case to-day, when the animal approached us in its fierce way, walking on its hind legs, and facing us as few animals dare face man.

PAUL DU CHAILLU
[*Explorations and Adventures in Equatorial Africa* (1861)]

Slaughter of the Elephant Seal

[*If the whaler contributed one of the most romantic as well as one of the most heroic chapters to American history it is also one of the cruelest. Perhaps the best, the truest, and the most vivid account of what it involved was written by the now almost forgotten Captain Charles M. Scammon, who shifted his base from New England to San Francisco and spent ten years ranging the Pacific. A man of keen intelligence and commanding personality, he was also a scientist who knew the marine mammals as a zoologist knows them. Nevertheless, he was a commercial hunter first of all and evidently regarded efficient slaughter as merely the practice of a demanding profession. Here is his account of the techniques employed against the elephant seal which he helped drive to near extinction because it was, next to the whale itself, the most abundant source of oil.*]

Among the varieties of marine mammals which periodically resort to the land, no one attains such gigantic proportions as the Sea Elephant. This animal, which was sometimes called the Elephant Seal, and known to the old Californians as the *Elefante marino,* had a geographical distribution from Cape Lazaro, latitude 24° 46′ north, longitude 112° 20′ west, to Point Reyes, latitude 38° north, longitude 122° 58′ west on the coast of California; and, strange as it may appear, we have no authentic accounts of this species of amphibious animal being found elsewhere in the northern hemisphere. At the south, however, about Patagonia, Tierra del Fuego, and numerous islands in both the Atlantic and Pacific, and the Crozets, Kerguélen, and Herd's Islands, in the high latitudes of the Indian Ocean, have been points where the Sea Elephants have gathered in almost incredible numbers, and where hundreds of thousands of them have been slain by the seamen, pursuing their prey in those distant regions.

The sexes vary much in size, the male being frequently triple the bulk of the female; the oldest of the former will average fourteen to sixteen feet; the largest we have ever seen measured twenty-two feet from tip to tip. The following measurements (in feet and inches) and notes were taken of two large females and one new-born pup, obtained on the coast of Lower California:

	No. 1		No. 2	
Length from tip to tip	9	0	10	0
Round the body behind fore flippers	5	10	5	9
Length of tail	0	2	0	2½
Breadth of tail at root	0	2	0	2½
Length of posterior flippers	1	7	1	10
Expansion of posterior flippers	1	8	1	8
Length of fore flippers	1	5	1	2
Width of fore flippers	0	6	0	6

. . . The habits of the huge beasts, when on shore, or loitering about the foaming breakers, are in many respects like those of the Leopard Seals. Our observations on the Sea Elephants of California go to show that they have been found in much larger numbers from February to June than during other months of the year; but more or less were at all times found on shore upon their favorite beaches, which were about the islands of Santa Barbara, Cerros, Guadalupe, San Bonitos, Natividad, San Roque, and Asuncion, and some of the most inaccessible points on the main-land between Asuncion and Cerros. When coming up out of the water, they were generally first seen near the line of surf; then crawling up by degrees, frequently reclining as if to sleep; again, moving up or along the shore, appearing not content with their last resting-place. In this manner they would ascend the ravines, or "low-downs," half a mile or more, congregating by hundreds. They are not so active on land as the seals; but, when excited to inordinate exertion, their motions are quick—the whole body quivering with their crawling, semi-vaulting gait, and the animal at such times manifesting great fatigue. Notwithstanding their unwieldiness, we have sometimes found them on broken and elevated gound, fifty or sixty feet above the sea.

The principal seasons of their coming on shore, are, when they are about to shed their coats, when the females bring forth their young (which is one at a time, rarely two), and the mating season. These seasons for "hauling up" are more marked in southern latitudes.

The different periods are known among the hunters as the "pupping cow," "brown cow," "bull and cow," and "March bull" seasons; but on the California coast, either from the influence of climate or some other cause, we have noticed young pups with their mothers at quite the opposite months. . . .

The time of gestation is supposed to be about three-fourths of the year. The most marked season we could discover was that of the adult males, which shed their coats later than the younger ones and the females. Still, among a herd of the largest of those fully matured (at Santa Barbara Island, in June, 1852), we found several cows and their young, the latter apparently but a few days old.

When the Sea Elephants come on shore for the purpose of "shedding," if not disturbed they remain out of water until the old hair falls off. By the time this change comes about, the animal is supposed to lose half its fat; indeed, it sometimes becomes very thin, and is then called a "slim-skin."

In the stomach of the Sea Elephant a few pebbles are found, which has given rise to the saying that "they take in ballast before going down" (returning to the sea). On warm and sunny days we have watched them come up singly on smooth beaches, and burrow in the dry sand, throwing over their backs the loose particles that collect about their fore limbs, and nearly covering themselves from view; but when not disturbed, the animals follow their gregarious propensity, and collect in large herds.

The mode of capturing them is thus: the sailors get between the herd and the water; then, raising all possible noise by shouting, and at the same time flourishing clubs, guns, and lances, the party advance slowly toward the rookery, when the animals will retreat, appearing in a state of great alarm. Occasionally an overgrown male will give battle, or attempt to escape; but a musket-ball through the brain dispatches it; or some one checks its progress by thrusting a lance into the roof of its mouth, which causes it to settle on its haunches, when two men with heavy oaken clubs give the creature repeated blows about the head, until it is stunned or killed. After securing those that are disposed to show resistance, the party rush on the main body. The onslaught creates such a panic among these peculiar creatures, that, losing all control of their actions, they climb, roll, and tumble over each other, when prevented from farther retreat by the projecting cliffs. We recollect in one instance, where sixty-five were captured, that several were found showing no signs of having been either clubbed or lanced, but were smothered by numbers of their kind heaped upon them. The whole flock, when attacked, manifested alarm by their peculiar roar, the sound of which, among the largest males, is nearly as loud as the lowing of an ox, but more prolonged in one strain, accompanied by a rattling noise in the throat. The quantity of blood in this species of the seal tribe is supposed to be double that contained in an ox, in proportion to its size.

After the capture, the flaying begins. First, with a large knife, the skin is ripped along the upper side of the body its whole length, and then cut down as far as practicable, without rolling it over; then the coating of fat that lies between the skin and flesh—which may be from one to seven inches in thickness, according to the size and condition of the animal—is cut into "horse-pieces," about eight inches wide, and twelve to fifteen long, and a puncture is made in each piece sufficiently large to pass a rope through. After flensing the upper portion of the body, it is rolled over, and cut all around, as above described. Then the "horse-pieces" are strung on a raft-rope (a rope three fathoms long, with an eye-splice in one end), and taken to the edge of the surf; a long line is made fast to it, the end of which is thrown to a boat lying just outside of the breakers; they are then hauled through the rollers and towed to the vessel, where the oil is tried out by boiling the blubber, or fat, in large pots set in a brick furnace for the purpose. The oil produced is superior to whale oil for lubricating purposes. Owing to the continual pursuit of the animals, they have become nearly if not quite extinct on the California coast, or the few remaining have fled to some unknown point for security.

Thus far, we have been writing of the Sea Elephant and manner of capturing it on the islands and coasts of the Californias; and, although thousands of the animals, in past years, gathered upon the shores of the islands contiguous to the coast, as well as about the pebbly or sandy beaches of the peninsula, affording full cargoes to the oil-ships, yet their numbers were but few, when compared with the multitudes which once inhabited the remote, desolate islands, or places on the main, within the icy regions of the southern hemisphere; and even at the expense of digression, we have thought it well to give an account of the animal in those regions. Several geographical points have already been mentioned, and among these Kerguélen Land, or Desolation Island, and Herd's Island, are the great resorting-places of these animals at the present day. The last-named place is in latitude 53° 03′ south, and longitude 72° 30′ to 73° 30′ east. Its approximate extent is sixty miles. Its shores are somewhat bold, broken, and dangerous to land upon; no harbor being found that is secure for the smallest vessel. In the smoothest time, when landing, the boat's crew are obliged to jump into the water, to hold and steady the boat, that it may not be staved on the beach, or swept out by the receding under-tow. In fact, a heavy surge always beats upon those frozen, rock-bound shores, varied only by the combing seas, that dart higher yet up the precipitous cliffs, when urged on by the oft-repeated gales that sweep over the southern portions of the Indian Ocean.

Captain Cook, the celebrated explorer, on his voyages of dis-covery in the *Resolution,* when he visited Kerguélen Land, called it the Island of Desolation, on account of its barren and uninhabitable appearance, although it possessed fine harbors, where the hardy mari-ner could rest securely with his ship during the violent winter storms. But not so at Herd's Island. The Sea Elephant oil-ship, breasting the changing winds and waves to procure a cargo, is officered by the most fearless and determined men, who have had experience in whaling, sealing, or Sea Elephant hunting in those rough seas. The majority of the men are shipped at the Cape de Verde Islands, they being of a muscular race, who have proved themselves to be excellent hands for the laborious work. The ship, when first sent out, is provided with a "double crew," and is accompanied by a small vessel, of a hundred tons or less, for a "tender." On arriving at the island, the ship is moored with heavy chains and anchors, and every other preparation is made for riding out any gale that may blow toward the land. The sails are unbent, all the spars above the topmasts are sent down, and, with the spare boats, are landed and housed during the "season," which begins about the middle of November, and ends in the middle of February. Quarters are provided for that portion of the ship's com-pany which is assigned to duty on shore. The habitation is a small hut, properly divided off into apartments—one for the mates, one for the steerage officers, and another for the men. This dwelling is no larger than necessity demands. Its walls are built of the detached pieces of lava, or boulders, nearest at hand; rough boards and tarred canvas, supplied from the ship, form the roof, which must be made water-proof and snow-proof. During the day, light is admitted to each room through a single pane of glass, or a spare deck or side light—perhaps found among the rubbish on board the vessel; and doors are made after the fashion of "good old colony times," with the latch-string ever swinging in the wind. In this dank habitation, planted between an iceberg on one side and a bluff volcanic mountain on the other, these rough men of the sea at once adapt themselves to their several situa-tions, and all the discipline is maintained that they would be subject to if on board ship. The high surf at this island renders it impracticable to haul off the blubber in "rafts," as at Desolation Island and on the coasts of the Californias: hence it is usually "minced" (the "horse-pieces" cut into thin slices) and put into tight casks to prevent any waste of the oil; then, when a smooth day comes, they are rolled down the beach, and pulled through the rollers by the boats; or the tender is anchored near shore, a line is run to the vessel, and the casks hauled alongside, hoisted in, and transferred to the ship, where the oil is tried out and "stowed down" in the usual manner.

As soon as the season is over—or, rather, when the time has come for the ship to leave, either for home, or to find shelter in some harbor at the Island of Desolation—the shore-party is supplied with provisions, all the surplus articles that were landed are re-embarked, the heavy anchors are at last weighed, and amid hail, snow, and sleet, the ship under her half-frozen canvas bounds over the billows, and soon disappears in the offing.

The vessels having departed, the officers and men left on the island resume their daily occupations. Usually the number is divided into two "gangs," stationed at separate places, where clusters of huts have sprung up for the use of those belonging to the different vessels, who have from time to time made it a temporary abiding-place. Try-works are built, and a shanty is erected for a cooper's shop. These two habitable spots are known as "Whisky Bay" and "The Point;" the former being a slight indentation of the shore-line, where the Elephants in countless numbers were found by the first vessel visiting there, which, as report says, had a supply of "old rye" stowed in her run. The captain, in the heat of his successful prosecution of the arduous business of procuring a cargo, gave his men permission to "splice the main brace strong and often," so long as the work went briskly on; and it is humorously told that this noted landing-place was "christened" at the cost of barrels of the beverage, thus securing to it a name as lasting as that of the prominent headland on the borders of the Okhotsk Sea, well known to whalemen as "Whisky Bluff." From day to day the separated parties, living some thirty miles apart, hunt the animals for leagues along the shores, with the varied success incident to season or circumstances; and, although on the same island, the face of the country is so broken—being rent into deep chasms, walled in as it were by giddy, shelving heights, making it impossible to travel, even on foot, far inland toward its extremities, and the shores hedged in by sharp ridges of basalt, stretching out into the sea—the two divisions know nothing of each other until the vessels return, which is frequently after an absence of from eight to twelve months, and during that time a thousand or more barrels of oil may have been collected.

Notwithstanding the hardships and deprivations that are undergone to make a successful voyage, there is no lack of enterprising merchants ready to invest their capital in any adventure when there is a prospect of ultimate gain; and no ocean or sea where there is a possibility of navigating appears too perilous for the adventurous seamen to try their luck upon. The very fact of the voyage being fraught with danger and difficulty tends to stimulate them to action. And in this remote part of the world of which we have spoken, that was unknown to the early explorers, as well as to those who have more recently voyaged toward the Antarctic continent—and for the geographical position of which we are indebted to the enterprise and nautical skill of those of our countrymen who commenced the life of a sailor by "coming through the hawse-holes"—we find that rival parties are left on its bleak shores, who, when opposed the one to the other, watch with greater care every movement that may be made, than the coming and going of the creatures which are the objects of pursuit. Many a war of words has arisen, with the brandishing of club and lance in the strife; but, like the pioneer California miners, when left to rely on their own good sense for self-government, there was little to fear but that all laws made would be simple, just, and strictly adhered to. When parties from different vessels are located on the same beach, the custom is for all to work together when killing the animals, as well as when skinning and cutting the blubber from the bodies into "horse-pieces." These are thrown into one or more piles; after which, the men of each party are ranged in squads, and each one, in turn, draws a piece from the heap, until all is disposed of. These divisions are made whenever the animals are found and killed in any considerable numbers; and, if far from the rendezvous, the blubber is "backed," or rolled in casks to the main depot. "Backing" is the stringing of eight or ten pieces on a pole, which is carried on the shoulders of two men; but if a cask is used, three men are allotted to each one of six or eight barrels' capacity, to roll which the distance of two miles is allowed to be a day's work. While the ship is away, homeward bound, or returning to the island for another cargo, the tender may be at Desolation Island, picking up what scattering Elephants can be found upon shores that once swarmed with millions of those huge beasts; or a short whaling-cruise is made, until the time comes for commencing operations at the island.

Hunting for the scattering animals about the shores of Desolation Island, "between seasons," is the most exposed and solitary pursuit either in the whale or seal fishery. The tender takes a detachment of the crew, and plies along the island coast, landing one or two men on each of the best beaches, with a supply of water and provisions; a tent or shanty is erected, partly of wood, partly of canvas; and the skins of the Elephants furnish the floor, couch, and covering of the temporary habitation. Here the banished hunter or hunters rest at night, after the fatigues of ranging along the shores, killing and flaying the animals met with, and transporting the blubber to a place of deposit, where it is buried, to prevent the gulls from devouring it, until taken aboard. As the season returns at Herd's Island, the vessels are usually "on the ground;" the treacherous surf is again passed and repassed in the light, frail whale-boats, landing the fresh crew from home, who relieve those who have thus literally "seen the elephant." The time passes quickly away, in the toil and excitement of killing and flensing; and again the floating fragment of the world departs for the land of civilization, leaving her last crew from home to pass an Antarctic winter, amid the solitudes of icebergs and the snow-covered peaks of the mountain land. No passing sail is seen to break the monotony of their voluntary exile; even many varieties of sea-birds found at Desolation Island do not deign to visit them. Multitudes of penguins, however, periodically resort to the island, and their eggs, together with the tongues of the Sea Elephants, and one or two kinds of fish, furnish a welcome repast for all hands, by way of change from that substantial fare called "salt-horse" and "hard-tack." Beside the close stoves in their apartments, which are heated with coal from the ship, or the fat of the Elephant pups, and the flickerings of a murky oil-lamp, the long winter evenings are passed in smoking and playing amusing games—"old sledge" and "seven-up" being favorites—and the reckless joking that circulates among adventurers who make light of ill-luck, and turn reverses into ridicule.

The extent and value of the Sea Elephant fishery, from its commencement up to the present date, is not definitely known, as the ships engaged in the enterprise, when whaling and sealing was at its height in the southern ocean, were also in pursuit of the valuable fur-bearing animals, as well as the Cachalot and the balæna; hence their cargoes were often made up of a variety of the oils of commerce. We have reliable accounts, however, of the Sea Elephant being taken for its oil as early as the beginning of the present century. At those islands, or upon the coasts on the main, where vessels could find secure shelter from all winds, the animals have long since been virtually annihilated; and now they are only sought after in the remote places we have mentioned, and these points are only accessible under the great difficulties that beset the mariner when sailing near the polar regions of the globe. Enough data are at hand, nevertheless, to show that hundreds of thousands of the animals, yielding as many barrels of oil, have been taken from Desolation and Herd's Islands, by American ships, which for many years have maintained a monopoly of the business.

CHARLES M. SCAMMON
[*The Marine Mammals of the North-Western Coast of North America* (1874)]

Tiger, Tiger Burning Bright

[Since India is, next to Africa, the home of the largest and handsomest animals, it is naturally almost as popular with those hunters who like their victims to be large and handsome.]

The hunting party meanwhile made good progress down the river, and on arriving at the scene of Briggs's misadventure, they formed line, and proceeded to beat the jungle from south to north. The ground, right in the centre, was too boggy for the elephants, but din enough was raised to startle, one would have thought, every living thing out of its recesses. The occupants of the various *guddees* and *howdahs* threw clods and stones into every clump of bushes and grass that the elephants could not reach, but not a rustle or sign of any living thing rewarded their efforts.

Knowing well how close a tiger will lie, and rightly assuming that the cubs would not likely have gone far from cover, "The General" was not satisfied, even after they had thus beaten the jungle twice lengthways, and once again across from corner to corner.

A number of the natives having become emboldened somewhat by the apparent absence of anything uncanny, now boldly leapt into the jungle, and plunging about in the miry and uncertain foothold, belaboured the bushes and clumps with their long *lathees,* poked their spears into every likely recess, and had gone nearly three-parts through the tangled brake, when a joyful shout from Green announced a discovery. He had gone saunteringly and quite aimlessly round to the northern end of the little valley, and passing close to a rather overhanging ledge of rock which jutted forward from the hillside, he discovered in a sparse fringe of trailing bushes the objects of their quest.

There lay the two little vixens, not bigger than spaniels, their green eyes glaring in the semi-obscurity; and with their backs set against the hollow in the cleft rock, they snarled and spat and showed their teeth in such defiant fashion as to make the attempt to capture them alive anything but an inviting or engaging task.

At Green's shout a number of the beaters near the edge of the jungle hurried up, and presently the Major jolted up on his elephant to enjoy the spectacle of the lucky find.

Now, right in the centre of the morass, in the most inaccessible part of it, there was a dense tangled patch of jungle, consisting of *Thamun* and other bushes all interlaced and tangled together; the still black water showing clear around the gnarled and twisted roots and branches. A sort of natural platform had been formed by the deposition of layers of flood-wrack at different times; and both "The General" and Steel, who were old, experienced *shikarees,* had noted the spot as just the very place a leopard would choose for a stronghold.

They had noticed, too, that while a few egrets and water-hens had been flushed from other parts of the swamp, not a solitary bird had been seen near this most likely of all spots, where they might have been most looked for.

The beaters, too, seemed to manifest a strange and suspicious aversion to going near the place; and the elephants betrayed a very suggestive and significant inquietude when brought as close up to it as the nature of the boggy ground permitted.

At the first beat Steel had said, "By Jove! what a place for leopard!"

"The General" now came up, and quietly said to Steel—

"I say, old man, I could almost swear there's something lying up in that *Baree* there"—pointing to the tangled thicket I have just described.

"Hi! Gopal!" he shouted to a lean, cadaverous, old fellow, who stood apart from the others, on the bank.

Gopal, tucking up his clothes inside his waistbelt, immediately responded to the summons, and plunged into the jungle.

"Gopal," said "The General," in a low tone and in Hindostanee, "we think there's a *janwar* inside here. The others are afraid to go in—are you afraid?"

"Whatever 'the Protector of the Poor' orders, *that* will his slave perform," was the ready answer of Gopal.

"Bravo! then see! get round if possible to that firm landing-stage on the other side, and note the signs."

"*Bahut utchha,*" was all the response. Divesting his wiry frame of every shred of clothing, and handing his clothes up to the *mahout*, keeping only his *puggaree* on which he more tightly wound round his elf-like locks, Gopal, cautiously probing with his iron-bound staff, and feeling the inky, oozy depths in front of him, slipped in up to his shoulders, and half swimming, half floundering, lurched across the worst part of the treacherous ooze, and presently emerged, dripping with mud and water and slime, on to a quaking sort of island, right in the centre of the swamp, whereon no foot of beater had yet trod.

One quick glance around, a step or two forward, a close, peering scrutiny among the sedge and bushes, then with a quick, lithe, backward motion, Gopal seemed to glide like a snake backwards into the water again, and hurrying back announced to "The General," while his eyes fairly blazed with excitement, that there were evidently *not one*, BUT TWO LEOPARDS even now in the thicket. The marks were fresh, and there could be no doubt on the matter.

"Ah, I thought so!"

"Didn't I tell you?" broke simultaneously from the lips of "The General" and Steel. Just at this moment it was that Green's joyful shout announced the discovery of the two tiger cubs, already narrated.

Glad, rather, of the diversion, our two friends made their way out of the jungle, and rejoined Green and the Major, and very shortly the full strength of the party was congregated round the hollow, in the depths of which the two cubs were now plainly visible.

The little beggars were not captured without a tussle. But at length, by cutting down bundles of reeds, and with these blocking up the sides of the crevice, and then pushing these fascines before them, the natives were able almost to smother the two hapless little cubs, and after a deal of scuffling and excitement the two young tigers were fairly caught, enveloped in country-made blankets, and, despite their snarling and fighting and biting, were strapped and tied down, and consigned to safe keeping.

"Now, boys," said "The General," "we had better have a go at the leopards."

"A go at the leopards?" said the Major. "What leopards?"

"What do you mean?" queried Green.

"Mean!" quoth Steel. "He means that there's a pair of leopards in the *Baree* there, that's all!"

The others were still incredulous, till Gopal was recalled and re-examined, and then the ardour of the chase revived, and it was resolved to make a determined effort to dislodge the two spotted robbers from their stronghold.

Well, to make a long story short, they tried for over two hours to force the leopards to break.

Despite large promises of reward, the beaters only perfunctorily performed their functions. Gopal was the only one that would venture across the Stygian bog; and he, armed with a puggaree full of stones, once again forced his way across; and although he succeeded in actually getting a glimpse of one of the leopards, he could not prevail on them to break.

Fact was, the two brutes knew well enough the impregnability of their position.

This fact by-and-by became discernible to "the General."

"Boys! it's no use," he said. "They will never break while so many of us are all around. Small blame to them! let's go to lunch."

So posting various scouts to keep watch, an adjournment was made for tiffin, and a messenger was despatched on horseback for sundry persuaders from the bungalow, in the shape of native bombs and other fireworks, which are very often used in like circumstances, where the beaters are afraid to enter the cover, as in the present case; and as a rule the bombs are used with signal success.

So it was on this occasion.

A dead silence settled down over the little swampy valley, so recently the scene of wild din and commotion.

Possibly the leopards thought the danger all over. They were mistaken if they thought anything of the kind.

It was now getting late in the afternoon, and the shadows were lengthening. "The General" had posted his men judiciously and well. The messenger had returned with a load of fire bombs. The line of beaters, now swelled by various additions from the villages round the jungle, were marshalled in imposing array by "The General" himself; and then, at a given signal, they gave tongue like a pack of hounds, pressed into the covert, and when near enough, the old Director of the Hunt, igniting one—two—three of the bombs, hurled them with all his force right into the heart of the dense covert, where it was known the sulky and treacherous quarry lurked.

The combined din of the yelling beaters rent the air. The very elephants seemed to catch the contagion and trumpeted shrilly with excitement. The sputtering bombs fizzled and crackled, and emitted a dense grey column of smoke, and then breaking into active ignition, there was a hissing roar, as they volleyed forth their pent-up fires; and with a sharp note of rage and defiance the two leopards sprang from their long hugged covert, and while one fell at once to a well-directed shot from Steel, who was advantageously posted, the other doubled like a hare, sprang unharmed through the beaters, and quickly disappeared over the brow of the eminence right behind the line.

The wounded one lay sprawling and floundering, making impotent attempts to get up and do mischief; but it was "spined" (the shot had been a lucky one); and presently it got its *"coup de grace,"* and was padded.

Then away went the whole cavalcade in hot pursuit after the survivor of the long and wearisome beat.

They never caught it up.

So ended a very memorable hunt. Briggs was so bad that he had to be taken into the station, and I became so ill that I had in a few days to follow him; and shortly afterwards I left the Oude jungles, never again I fear to revisit them, and for many months—first at Bombay, then at Bareilly with my brother, then in Calcutta—I fairly fought with death, and by-and-by, after long, long months of pain and weariness, I found renewed health and a fresh lease of life in the glorious atmosphere of sunny Australia, laden with the scent of the fragrant gum trees, and redolent with the perfume of the golden wattle bloom.

THE HON. JAMES INGLIS
[*Tent Life in Tigerland* (1892)]

Shooting Elephants for Fun

[One of the mightiest of hunters, Frederick Courteney Selous, spent more than twenty years hunting big game in Africa. Sometimes, as the following narrative will prove, he was quite touched by the plight of a baby elephant whose mother his gun had not been able to resist.]

It was still early when we took up the spoor, which there was no difficulty about following, as the herd was a very large one, and had trodden broad paths wherever they had crossed the open grassy glades intersecting the belts of forest; whilst, in the forests themselves, so many trees had been broken and stripped of their bark that one could ride straight ahead without looking at the ground at all. The elephants, I think, must have passed where I first saw their spoor in the early morning, not long before daylight, and had been moving very slowly, feeding quietly along, utterly unconscious of danger, otherwise we should not have overtaken them as soon as we did. Cantering briskly along the spoor, we ere long crossed the Lundaza river, and upon emerging from a broad belt of forest, about a couple of miles beyond it, suddenly saw the elephants in front of us. The herd was one of the largest it has ever been my fate to look upon, and as, when the animals first came into view, they were crossing a broad open grassy valley, between two patches of forest, I had an unusually good opportunity of observing them. They were moving in masses across the valley, walking at that slow majestic step natural to the wild elephant when entirely unsuspicious of the presence of man.

As I reined in my horse on the border of the forest, and gazed over the valley across which stretched this great herd of mighty beasts, a thrill of excitement shot through my frame and braced my fever-

weakened nerves; for never can elephants be beheld by the South African hunter without feelings of intense excitement. When elephant-
hunting, one seldom comes up with the animals without having followed them for several hours, and as a rule it is a pursuit which en-
tails great hardships: fatigue, thirst, and exposure to the intense heat
of the tropical sun. On the present occasion, however, I had come up
with the elephants without having endured privation or hardship of
any kind. It was a pure stroke of luck, and in many ways never had I
had such a chance of doing a good day's work with these animals before. There was an immense herd of them before me—numbering
probably nearer two hundred than one hundred—and for some miles
all round the forests were fairly open. I had also a good little rifle and
seventy cartridges. My bodily weakness, the result of fever, was certainly much against me, but what militated more against my success
that day than anything else was the obstinacy of my horse, whose disposition I was soon to find out. Even to-day, as I think of this episode
in my hunting career, I cannot but lament and rail at fate, when I
think of what I did, and what I might have done that day had I but
had my good horse Nelson between my knees. However, regret is
vain; the past is irrevocable, and I will now proceed to relate what
happened to me.

As I looked eagerly over this great mass of elephants, the foremost amongst which were close upon the forest that skirted the farther
side of the open valley, I could see but one bull, whose mighty form
showed well above the backs of the cows that surrounded him. A fine
pair of tusks showed out well beyond his trunk, but I could see that,
though of fair length, they were not very thick. He was amongst the
rearmost elephants, walking slowly forwards through the grass, which
was some three or four feet high over the whole valley, and more resembled a field of wheat than an English meadow. Riding quickly
down into the open with Laer following me, I was soon even with him,
and about a hundred yards to his left. He then, in common with a lot
of the rearmost elephants, seemed to become suspicious of danger, for,
though none of them looked towards me, they all commenced to walk
a great deal faster than they had been doing. I now dismounted, and
taking a steady shot for his lungs, aiming rather high up behind his
shoulder, fired. I felt sure I had given him a good shot, but had no
time to mark its effect, for at the very instant of the report a tuskless
cow that was some distance beyond the bull I had just fired at,
wheeled round with a loud scream, whirling her trunk at the same
time high in the air, and then dropping it before her chest, came rush-

ing towards me, accompanying the charge with shrill and oft-repeated screams. At first, I suppose she only heard the shot, and perhaps saw the smoke of the powder; but, it being perfectly open, she must very soon have caught sight of me, as she came on in the most determined manner. I was obliged to gallop away, and so take my eyes off the bull, but thought that I would be able to shake my pursuer off by galloping hard for a hundred yards or so, and could then circle round and get up to him again before he gained the shelter of the forest on the farther side of the valley.

I now plied my stallion hard with the spurs, but soon found that it was one of his sulky days, as I could not get him to gallop; in fact, he was going considerably slower than the enraged elephant behind him, who kept up a constant succession of shrill screams, and who, seeing that she was gaining on the horse, pertinaciously kept up the chase, which she would have long ago abandoned had she been losing ground. Nearer and nearer she came, till at last I saw that it was getting serious, and that if I did not manage to get into the bush and dodge her there, she would infallibly catch me. Laer had wisely galloped straight back into the forest when she first screamed. I now made for a patch of rather thick machabel bush that projected into the valley, and, as I entered it, I do not think she was thirty yards behind me; and when she first charged, she was at least one hundred and fifty yards away, probably considerably more. Of course such an experience could only happen in a perfectly open piece of country devoid of trees. Once in the bush, I turned suddenly to the left, and, being no longer able to see me, and the wind being luckily in my favour, she lost me immediately.

As soon as I found that I had shaken off my pursuer I gave my sulky horse a good spurring, and then galloped across the valley into the forest beyond, which now seemed alive with elephants. I could not see my bull anywhere, however, and as I was looking for him, I saw a small lot of elephants coming at a quick pace obliquely from behind me, amongst which was a big bull, though his tusks were very poor for his size. These elephants, I feel sure, were not in the open when I first sighted the main herd, but must have been still behind in the forest to my left. Thinking that if I had hit the other bull through both lungs with my first shot he must be dead, and that if not I had lost him irretrievably, I now turned my attention to the next best animal I could see. Just as I got up to him he turned and entered rather a thickish piece of machabel bush, with two cows just in front of him. He was not going very fast, so jumping off, I took a careful aim for the ridge of bone which shows out so distinctly in an elephant from above the root of the tail to the top of the back. My bullet, a solid toughened 540-grain missile, propelled by only 75 grains of powder, struck him exactly in the centre of the bone, and stopped him instantly. His hind quarters seemed partially paralysed, as on mounting again and riding in front of him he was unable to come towards me, though he tried hard, poor brute, raising his great ears and screaming fearfully. Though so near the elephant, and in spite of the terrific trumpeting, my stallion paid no more attention to the furious though disabled beast than if he had been a rock. I quickly got on one side of him and gave him a shot through both lungs, to which he succumbed very rapidly; then, remounting, I was soon galloping on the tracks of a portion of the retreating elephants, and presently got up to about thirty, and could see another lot of about the same number to my right.

By this time I think that the whole of this great herd of elephants had broken up into a number of smaller ones, each diverging on its own line from the point where I had first disturbed them. One of these herds turned right back, recrossing the Lundaza, and passing through the valley on the edge of which my waggons were outspanned, in plain view of all my people. Just as I was getting up to the elephants again, Laer came up to me. As elephants, when running away, and when there are a number of them together, go at a very different pace from a single elephant when charging, I had no difficulty in getting alongside them, and gave one, apparently a cow with nice tusks, but which afterwards proved to be a young bull, a good lung shot. He hung behind almost directly after getting the shot, and very soon left his companions, and went off alone, going at a good pace, however, when I came near him. I gave him two more shots, and then seeing that he was very badly wounded, and fearing that the other elephants would scatter—as they nearly always do in Mashunaland—I called to Laer to try to finish him, and at any rate to watch him, and then again took up the spoor of the herd. I had followed it for some distance, and had got about a hundred yards beyond a sort of pass, between a rocky ridge on the one hand and a mass of large granite boulders on the other, when I came face to face with one of the elephants, a large cow, coming straight back towards me on the spoor of the herd she had left. The forest was very open about here, and she saw me as soon as I saw her, and, raising her head and spreading her ears, charged forthwith, screaming loudly. Turning my horse I galloped back for the rocks, but the stallion would not put out any pace, and I could tell from the screams that the elephant was gaining rapidly upon me.

Hastily turning my head I saw she was getting very near, and knew she would soon catch me; so I resolved to dismount and run for the rocks. My stallion was, in some respects, a perfect shooting horse, and immediately I leant forward and seized his mane he stopped dead. I was off and in front of him in an instant, and running for the rocks, which were not twenty yards away. As I got round the first rock I turned, and this is what I saw. The horse was standing absolutely still, with his head up and his fore feet planted firmly in the ground, as if carved in stone, and the elephant, which had then ceased to scream, and was making a curious rumbling noise, was standing alongside of him, smelling about with her trunk. In front of my saddle was tied a leather coat, with a red flannel lining—a present the preceding year from my friend poor Montagu Kerr—and I suppose that the elephant must have touched the horse with her trunk, as he suddenly gave a jump round, throwing the red-lined coat into the air. He then walked slowly to the rocky ridge behind him, and again stood still about fifteen yards away from the elephant. All this time I had been afraid to fire, for fear of exasperating the elephant, and causing it to kill my horse. I now, however, determined to do so, and was thinking of firing for her brain, for she was very near me, when she raised her head and ears and came towards the rocks screaming like a railway engine. She must have got my wind, I fancy, suddenly. However, she could not get at me without going round the other rocks; and as she did so, she gave me a splendid chance at a distance of not more than fifteen yards. I fired into the centre of her shoulder, and immediately the bullet struck her she stopped screaming, and, dropping her ears, swerved off. She only ran a hundred yards or so, and then fell over dead, shot through the large blood-vessels of the upper part of the heart. Directly she fell I ran to my horse and remounted. Prudence whispered to me to give up the hunt, but I could not make up my mind to do so just yet, though I resolved to be cautious and not go too near the elephants in future, as my stallion had evidently not the slightest fear of them, and had made up his mind that nothing should make him really gallop out this day. It was not that he could not do so; he was simply sulky, as he had a very good turn of speed if he liked to exert himself.

I was soon hard on the spoor again, but had not followed it a mile before I found that the elephants had scattered, making it difficult to keep on their line, as they had no longer left a well-defined trail. However, by taking up the spoors of different animals, I got along at a good pace, and before long sighted a few of the hindmost animals. These were, however, with the exception of two, all scattered and diverging rapidly one from the other. The two were going off to the right, walking very quickly in single file, the hindmost animal being followed by a small calf. Riding out to one side of them through the open forest, which was just here quite free from underwood, I saw that they were two fine cows, both having long white tusks, and at once resolved to attack them. I did think of the poor little calf, but consoled myself with the thought that if I destroyed its mother it would follow up the herd and be adopted by another elephant. This is the case, I believe, if they are old enough to live without their mother's milk. These two elephants I ought to have killed very quickly and easily, as the forest through which they first led me was very open, and they kept close together. I was now, however, getting tired, being still very weak, and found it impossible to shoot steadily. Before long I had wounded both the elephants severely, and the one with the calf especially seemed very hard hit. Presently they got into a patch of machabel scrub the soft fern-like leaves of which were, luckily for me, still very thick, and one of them here charged savagely, screaming loudly. I thought I should have had to dismount and run for it again, as I could not get the stallion out of a hand gallop, but by making a quick turn round an immense ant-heap I managed to give her the slip, but I saw that I had to be careful. As soon as she had lost me she rejoined her comrade, and they continued their flight together, before long crossing a small stream of running water.

As they were climbing the farther bank I came down quite close to them and gave the cow with the calf a dead shot, as she only just managed to reach the top when she stopped, and, facing round, fell over backwards, throwing her trunk high in the air as she did so. I ought to have killed the other one here too, as she stopped about a hundred yards on ahead and stood broadside on, waiting probably for her dead comrade. I fired at her, but did not hit her where I ought to have done. She walked on again and went right through a broad open valley covered with long grass, like the place where I had first seen the herd of elephants that morning. As long as she was in the open I dared not go near her, but as soon as she entered the machabel bush on the farther side of the valley I followed as fast as I could get my horse to go. I was still a hundred yards away from the bush, but could see the wounded elephant walking slowly along, skirting just within its edge, when she must have got my wind, for she suddenly

Nach Christus gepurt.1513. Jar. Adi. s. May. Hat man dem grosmechtigen Kunig von Portugall Emanuell gen Lysabona pracht ausz India/ein sollich lebendig Thier. Das nennen s
Rhinocerus.Das ist hye mit aller seiner gestalt Abcondertfet.Es hat ein farb wie ein gespreckelte Schildtkrot.Vnd ist vo dicken Schalen vberlegt fast fest.Vnd ist in der grösz als der Helffant
Aber nydertrechtiger von paynen/vnd fast wehafftig. Es hat ein scharff starck Horn voun auff der nasen/Das begyndt es albeg zu wetzen wo es bey staynen ist. Das dosig Thier ist des Hel
fantz todt seyndt.Der Helffandt furcht es fast vbel/dann wo es Jn ankumbt/so laufft Jm das Thier mit dem kopff zwischen dye foldern payn/vnd reyst den Helffandt vnden am pauch au
vn erwürgt Jn/des mag er sich nit erwern. Dann das Thier ist also gewapent/das Jm der Helffandt nichts kan thün. Sie sagen auch das der Rhynocerus Schnell/ Fraydig vnd Listig sey

1515

RHINOCERVS

swung round, and, raising her head and ears, came out into the open, trumpeting loudly. I had already got my horse's tail towards her, and was doing my best to get him into a gallop, but it was useless, and as it was at least two hundred yards to the other side of the open valley I knew she would catch me long before I reached the shelter of the trees where I might have dodged her. Of course, directly she emerged from the bush she saw me plainly in the open before her and came on two yards to my one, screaming shrilly all the time.

I did not hesitate an instant what to do, but resolved to sacrifice the horse and try to get away myself in the grass. Catching him by the mane, when he instantly stopped dead, I jumped past him and ran forwards through the grass as hard as I could, which was not very hard, as I was now much exhausted. I had got some forty yards beyond him when the elephant suddenly stopped screaming and commenced making the rumbling noise I have spoken of as being made by the first elephant that came up to him. Turning my head I saw that she was standing exactly like the first one, alongside of the horse, who remained perfectly motionless, but that she had not yet touched him. I instantly ducked down in the grass and watched her. I was very much afraid lest she should get my wind and come on after me, and at the same time feared to fire at her, as I felt so terribly shaky after my run that I knew I should only give her a bad shot and let her know where I was. I was very much surprised at her leaving the horse alone. Had she been unwounded, like the first one that came up to him, I should have thought nothing of it, as there are many similar cases on record; but, irritated as the poor brute must have been from the wounds she had received, I made sure she would have killed him instantly. She would most certainly have killed me had she caught me, and I think she showed more magnanimity than sagacity in sparing my horse, for, although he had taken no part in injuring her, he had, at any rate, been instrumental in bringing me within shot of her. However that may be, the fact remains that this wounded and furious elephant ran screaming up to my horse, and, finding his rider gone, stood alongside of him without touching him. After a space of half a minute, perhaps, she turned and walked back into the bush, and I then went back to my horse, who had never moved his feet since I placed my hand on his mane and sprang from the saddle. I mounted again at once, and riding into the bush soon caught sight of the wounded elephant walking very slowly forwards, and constantly stopping. At length she passed one of the enormous ant-heaps common in this part of Africa—ant-heaps twenty yards in circumference, and often with large trees growing on them—and, as soon as she was behind it, I left my horse and ran up to it. Peering round I saw her standing broadside on not fifty yards off, evidently listening and looking very suspicious. I now rested my rifle on the side of the ant-heap and fired into her shoulder. On receiving this shot she moved on for a very short distance and again stood, when I fired once more from the same spot. It was unnecessary, however, as the last bullet must have passed through her heart, I think, and she was just about to fall when I fired again.

I now resolved to give up any further pursuit of the elephants, as it was manifestly tempting fate to follow them up again, and could only end in getting caught myself, or, at any rate, in having my horse killed, who, in spite of his occasional obstinacy, was a valuable animal. Had I had Nelson I should certainly by this time have killed more elephants than I had done, without having tired myself very severely, and I should now have galloped hard round to the right until I had cut the spoor of another of the small herds into which the elephants had broken up, shot several of them before they scattered, and, if the horse had been equal to it, perhaps got round to a third herd. However, as it was, I was already much exhausted, and felt that it would be foolish to follow up the elephants again, and so, with large numbers of these animals still within my reach, in beautiful open forest country, entirely devoid of thick brush, and with my saddle-bags still full of cartridges, I had to give up the hunt. Still it might have been worse. Four animals I knew were dead; the fifth that I had left badly wounded with Laer I hoped he had managed to kill; and I still thought I might find the big bull I had first wounded, as I knew I had hit him about the right place. In going back to the waggons I visited the four elephants I had seen lying dead. The three cows were all pretty good ones, with tusks weighing from 10 lbs. to 14 lbs.; but the bull, although a large animal, had very poor tusks, that proved to weigh only 25 lbs. and 23 lbs. respectively, both of them being slightly broken at the ends.

When I came to the cow that I had killed on the bank of the small stream, I found her little calf still standing beside the carcase. When I approached, the poor little beast, with the pluck always shown by elephant calves, raised its ears, and, screaming shrilly, charged right at me. I did not move, as the poor thing was hardly more than three feet high, and the old stallion never moved or paid the slightest attention to it. It came right up to the horse, but stopped without actually touching him, and, after standing there a few moments, returned to its dead mother. It would, perhaps, have been more merciful to have shot it at once through the brain and ended its troubles, but I had not the heart to do so, and thought it might perhaps escape lions and hyænas and follow up the spoor of its mother's relatives. At any rate, the next morning, when I returned to chop out the tusks, the calf was nowhere to be seen. On reaching the waggons I found Laer there before me, and an elephant's tail hanging from the side of the waggon showed me he had killed the animal I left in his charge. He told me that after I left him, as the wounded animal only walked very slowly forwards, he had dismounted and run round in front of it, and as it came past him had given it a shot in the shoulder with the 10-bore, to which it succumbed almost immediately. This made five elephants at any rate, and eventually I got the big bull too, which had been killed with a single bullet from the 450-bore Metford and had only gone a few hundred yards from where he had been hit. His tusks proved to weigh 41 lbs. and 43 lbs. respectively, and were a nice even pair, quite perfect at the points.

FREDERICK COURTENEY SELOUS
[*Travel and Adventures in South-East Africa* (1893)]

Slaughter of the Innocents

[Not all naturalists are abashed by Emerson's famous question "Hast thou named all the birds without a gun?" Even Thoreau could write: "There is a period in the history of the individual, as of the race, when hunters are 'the best men,' as the Algonquins called them. . . . Such is oftenest the young man's introduction to the forest, and the most original part of himself. He goes thither at first as a hunter and fisher until, at last, if he has the seeds of a better life in him, he distinguishes his proper objects—as a poet or a naturalist maybe—and leaves the gun and the fishpole behind." Despite his friendship with Theodore Roosevelt, John Burroughs felt much the same.]

I have often had occasion to notice how much more intelligence the bird carries in its eye than does the animal or quadruped.

The animal will see you, too, if you are moving, but if you stand quite still even the wary fox will pass within a few yards of you and not know you from a stump, unless the wind brings him your scent.

But a crow or a hawk will discern you when you think yourself quite hidden. His eye is as keen as the fox's sense of smell, and seems fairly to penetrate veils and screens. Most of the water-fowl are equally sharp-eyed.

The chief reliance of the animals for their safety, as well as for their food, is upon the keenness of their scent, while the fowls of the air depend mainly upon the eye.

A hunter out in Missouri relates how closely a deer approached him one day in the woods. The hunter was standing on the top of a log, about four feet from the ground, when the deer bounded playfully into a glade in the forest, a couple of hundred yards away. The animal began to feed and to move slowly toward the hunter. He was on the alert, but did not see or scent his enemy. He never took a bite of grass, says the sportsman, without first putting his nose to it, and then instantly raising his head and looking about.

In about ten minutes the deer had approached within fifty yards of the gunner; then the murderous instinct of the latter began to assert itself. His gun was loaded with fine shot, but he dared not make a move to change his shells lest the deer see him. He had one shell loaded with No. 4 shot in his pocket. Oh! if he could only get that shell into his gun.

The unsuspecting deer kept approaching; presently he passed behind a big tree, and his head was for a moment hidden. The hunter sprang to his work; he got one of the No. 8 shells out of his gun and got his hand into his pocket and a hold of the No. 4. Then the shining eyes of the deer were in view again. The hunter stood in this attitude five minutes. How we wish he had been compelled to stand for five hundred!

Then another tree shut off the buck's gaze for a moment; in went the No. 4 shell into the barrel and the gun was closed quickly, but there was no time to bring it to the shoulder. The animal was now only thirty yards away. His hair was smooth and glossy, and every movement was full of grace and beauty. Time after time he seemed to look straight at the hunter, and once or twice a look of suspicion seemed to cross his face.

The man began to realize how painful it was to stand perfectly still on the top of a log for fifteen minutes. Every muscle ached and seemed about to rebel against his will. If the buck held to his course he would pass not more than fifteen feet to one side of the gun, and the man that held it thought he might almost blow his heart out.

There was one more tree for him to pass behind, when the gun could be raised. He approached the tree, rubbed his nose against it, and for a moment was half hidden behind it. When his head appeared on the other side the gun was pointed straight at his eye—and with only No. 4 shot, which could only wound him, but could not kill him.

The deer stops; he does not expose his body back of the fore leg, as the hunter had wished. The latter begins to be ashamed of himself, and has about made up his mind to let the beautiful creature pass unharmed, when the buck suddenly gets his scent, his head goes up, his nostrils expand, and a look of terror comes over his face. This is too much for the good resolutions of the hunter. Bang! goes the gun, the deer leaps into the air, wheels around a couple of times, recovers himself and is off in a twinkling, no doubt carrying, the narrator says, a hundred No. 4 shot in his face and neck. The man says: "I've always regretted shooting at him."

I should think he would. But a man in the woods, with a gun in his hand, is no longer a man—he is a brute. The devil is in the gun to make brutes of us all.

If the game on this occasion had been, say a wild turkey or a grouse, its discriminating eye would have figured out the hunter there on that log very quickly.

This manly exploit of the Western hunter reminds me of an exploit of a Brooklyn man, who last winter killed a bull moose in Maine. It was a more sportsmanlike proceeding, but my sympathies were entirely with the moose. The hero tells his story in a New York paper. With his guides, all armed with Winchester rifles, he penetrated far into the wilderness till he found a moose yard. It was near the top of a mountain.

They started one of the animals and then took up its trail.

As soon as the moose found it was being followed, it led right off in hopes of outwalking its enemies. But they had snow-shoes and he did not; they had food and he did not. On they went, pursued and pursuers, through the snow-clogged wilderness, day after day. The moose led them the most difficult route he could find.

At night the men would make camp, build a fire, eat and

smoke, and roll themselves in their blankets and sleep. In the morning they would soon come up to the camping place of the poor moose, where the imprint of his great body showed in the snow, and where he had passed a cold, supperless night.

On the fifth day the moose began to show signs of fatigue; he rested often, he also tried to get around and behind his pursuers and let them pass on. Think how inadequate his wit was to cope with the problem—he thought they would pass by him if he went to one side.

On the morning of the sixth day he had made up his mind to travel no farther, but to face his enemies and have it out with them.

As he heard them approach he rose up from his couch of snow, mane erect, his look fierce and determined. Poor creature, he did not know how unequal the contest was. How I wish he could at that moment have had a Winchester rifle too, and had known how to use it. There would have been fair play then.

With such weapons as God had given him he had determined to meet the foe, and if they had had only such weapons as God had given them, he would have been safe. But they had weapons which the devil had given them, and their deadly bullets soon cut him down, and now probably his noble antlers decorate the hall of his murderer.

JOHN BURROUGHS
[*Riverby* (1894)]

Give a Cat a Bad Name . . .

[*The dangerous ferocity of most animals has been wildly exaggerated—sometimes from fear but just as often, perhaps, because it supplies an excuse for killing them. Since there are no tigers in the United States it was necessary to invent one—namely, the puma, cougar, or mountain lion, once common in almost all our forests. Of his character and his fate, Ernest Thompson Seton gives this account: "In North America during 400 years we have reliably recorded six cases of cougars attacking mankind. In only four of these was hu-*

man life lost. Undoubtedly dogs are guilty of as many unprovoked attacks on man every day and destroy more human lives in a year than the cougar during its whole written history. Once it occurred everywhere in the United States where sufficient cover and food was found. In Pennsylvania the woods teemed with them. A bounty was set early. In 1860 a great animal drive in Pennsylvania killed 41 cougars, 114 cats and 111 buffalo. These results tell a story of senseless destruction not surpassed in the annals of America."

No doubt the young Theodore Roosevelt (who was, somewhat incongruously, as much conservationist as big-game hunter) preferred not to consider such facts when he set out enthusiastically to help push the cougar to the wall.]

≈

In January, 1901, I started on a five weeks' cougar hunt from Meeker in Northwest Colorado. My companions were Mr. Philip K. Stewart and Dr. Gerald Webb, of Colorado Springs; Stewart was the captain of the victorious Yale nine of '86. We reached Meeker on January 11th, after a forty mile drive from the railroad, through the bitter winter weather; it was eighteen degrees below zero when we started. At Meeker we met John B. Goff, the hunter, and left town the next morning on horseback for his ranch, our hunting beginning that same afternoon, when after a brisk run our dogs treed a bobcat. After a fortnight Stewart and Webb returned, Goff and I staying out three weeks longer. We did not have to camp out, thanks to the warm-hearted hospitality of the proprietor and manager of the Keystone Ranch, and of the Mathes Brothers and Judge Foreman, both of whose ranches I also visited. The five weeks were spent hunting north of the White River, most of the time in the neighborhood of Coyote Basin and Colorow Mountain.

It is a high, dry country, where the winters are usually very cold, but the snow not under ordinary circumstances very deep. It is wild and broken in character, the hills and low mountains rising in sheer slopes, broken by cliffs and riven by deeply cut and gloomy gorges and ravines. . . . Two of the female cougars we killed were pregnant—in one case the young would have been born almost immediately, that is, in February; and in the other case in March. One, which had a partially grown young one of over fifty pounds with it, still had milk in its teats. At the end of January we found a male and female together, evidently mating. Goff has also found the young just dropped in May, and even June. The females outnumber the males. Of the fourteen we killed, but three were males.

I shot five bobcats: two old males weighing 39 and 31 pounds respectively; and three females, weighing, respectively, 25, 21, and 18 pounds. Webb killed two, a male of 29 pounds and a female of 20; and Stewart two females, one of 22 pounds, and the other a young one of 11 pounds.

I sent the cougar and bobcat skulls to Dr. Merriam, at the Biological Survey, Department of Agriculture, Washington. He wrote me as follows: "The big [cougar] skull is certainly a giant. I have compared it with the largest in our collection from British Columbia and Wyoming, and find it larger than either. It is in fact the largest skull of any member of the *Felis concolor* group I have seen. A hasty preliminary examination indicates that the animal is quite different from the northwest coast form, but that it is the same as my horse-killer from Wyoming—*Felis hippolestes*. In typical *Felis concolor* from Brazil the skull is lighter, the braincase thinner and more smoothly rounded, devoid of the strongly developed sagittal crest; the under jaw straighter and lighter.

"Your series of skulls from Colorado is incomparably the largest, most complete and most valuable series ever brought together from any single locality, and will be of inestimable value in determining the amount of individual variation."

Early the following morning, February 14th, the last day of my actual hunting, we again started for Juniper Mountain, following the same course on which we had started the previous day. Before we had gone a mile, that is, only about half way to where we had come across the cougar track the preceding day, we crossed another, and as we deemed a fresher, trail, which Goff pronounced to belong to a cougar even larger than the one we had just killed. The hounds were getting both weary and footsore, but the scent put heart into them and away they streamed. They followed it across a sage-brush flat, and then worked along under the base of a line of cliffs—cougar being particularly apt thus to travel at the foot of cliffs. The pack kept well together, and it was pleasant, as we cantered over the snowy plain beside them, to listen to their baying, echoed back from the cliffs above. Then they worked over the hill and we spurred ahead and turned to the left, up the same gorge or valley in which we had killed the cougar the day before. The hounds followed the trail straight to the cliff-shoulder where the day before the pack had been puzzled until Boxer struck the fresh scent. Here they seemed to be completely at fault, circling everywhere, and at one time following their track of yesterday over to the pinyon-tree up which the cougar had first gone.

We made our way up the ravine to the head of the plateau, and then, turning, came back along the ridge until we reached the top of the shoulder where the dogs had been; but when we got there they had disappeared. It did not seem likely that the cougar had crossed the ravine behind us—although as a matter of fact this was exactly what had happened—and we did not know what to make of the affair.

We could barely hear the hounds; they had followed their back trail of the preceding day, toward the place where we had first come across the tracks of the cougar we had already killed. We were utterly puzzled, even Goff being completely at fault, and we finally became afraid that the track which the pack had been running was one which, instead of having been made during the night, had been there the previous morning, and had been made by the dead cougar. This meant, of course, that we had passed it without noticing it, both going and coming, on the previous day, and knowing Goff's eye for a track I could not believe this. He, however, thought we might have confused it with some of the big wolf tracks, of which a number had crossed our path. After some hesitation, he said that at any rate we could find out the truth by getting back into the flat and galloping around to where we had begun our hunt the day before; because if the dogs really had a fresh cougar before them he must have so short a start that they were certain to tree him by the time they got across the ridge-crest. Accordingly we scrambled down the precipitous mountain-side, galloped along the flat around the end of the ridge and drew rein at about the place where we had first come across the cougar trail on the previous day. Not a dog was to be heard anywhere, and Goff's belief that the pack was simply running a back track became a certainty both in his mind and mine, when Jim suddenly joined us, evidently having given up the chase. We came to the conclusion that Jim, being wiser than the other dogs, had discovered his mistake while they had not; "He just naturally quit," said Goff.

After some little work we found where the pack had crossed the broad flat valley into a mass of very rough broken country, the same in which I had shot my first big male by moonlight. Cantering and scrambling through this stretch of cliffs and valleys, we began to hear the dogs, and at first were puzzled because once or twice it seemed as though they were barking treed or had something at bay; always, however, as we came nearer we could again hear them running a trail, and when we finally got up tolerably close we found that they were all scattered out. Boxer was far behind, and Nellie, whose feet had become sore, was soberly accompanying him, no longer giving tongue. The others were separated one from the other, and we finally made out Tree'em all by himself, and not very far away. In vain Goff called and blew his horn; Tree'em disappeared up a high hill-side, and with muttered comments on his stupidity we galloped our horses along the valley around the foot of the hill, hoping to intercept him. No sooner had we come to the other side, however, than we heard Tree'em evidently barking treed. We both looked at one another, wondering whether he had come across a bobcat, or whether it had really been a fresh cougar trail after all.

Leaving our horses we scrambled up the cañon until we got in sight of a large pinyon on the hillside, underneath which Tree'em was standing, with his preposterous tail arched like a pump-handle, as he gazed solemnly up in the tree, now and then uttering a bark at a huge cougar, which by this time we could distinctly make out standing in the branches. Turk and Queen had already left us and were running hard to join Tree'em, and in another minute or two all of the hounds, except the belated Boxer and Nellie, had also come up. The cougar having now recovered his wind, jumped down and cantered off. He had been running for three hours before the dogs and evidently had been overtaken again and again, but had either refused to tree, or if he did tree had soon come down and continued his flight, the hounds not venturing to meddle with him, and he paying little heed to them. It was a different matter, however, with Turk and Queen along. He went up the hill and came to bay on the top of the cliffs, where we could see him against the skyline. The hounds surrounded him, but neither they nor Turk came to close quarters. Queen, however, as soon as she arrived rushed straight in, and the cougar knocked her a dozen feet off. Turk tried to seize him as soon as Queen had made her rush; the cougar broke bay, and they all disappeared over the hilltop, while we hurried after them. A quarter of a mile beyond, on the steep hill-side, they again had him up a pinyon-tree. I approached as cautiously as possible so as not to alarm him. He stood in such an awkward position that I could not get a fair shot at the heart, but the bullet broke his back well forward, and the dogs seized him as he struck the ground. There was still any amount of fight in him, and I ran in as fast as possible, jumping and slipping over the rocks and the bushes as the cougar and dogs rolled and slid down the steep mountain-side—for, of course, every minute's delay meant the chance of a dog being killed or crippled. It was a day of misfortunes for Jim, who was knocked completely out of the fight by a single blow. The cougar was too big for the dogs to master, even crippled as he was; but when I came up close Turk ran in and got the great beast by one ear, stretching out the cougar's head, while he kept his own forelegs tucked way back so that the cougar could not get hold of them. This gave me my chance and I drove the knife home, leaping back before the creature could get round at me. Boxer did not come up for half an hour, working out every inch of the trail for himself, and croaking away at short intervals, while Nellie trotted calmly beside him. Even when he saw us skinning the cougar he would not hurry nor take a short cut, but followed the scent to where the cougar had gone up the tree, and from the tree down to where we were; then he meditatively bit the carcass, strolled off, and lay down, satisfied.

It was a very large cougar, fat and heavy, and the men at the ranch believed it was the same one which had at intervals haunted the place for two or three years, killing on one occasion a milch cow, on another a steer, and on yet another a big work horse. Goff stated that he had on two or three occasions killed cougars that were quite as long, and he believed even an inch or two longer, but that he had never seen one as large or as heavy. Its weight was 227 pounds, and as it lay stretched out it looked like a small African lioness. It would be impossible to wish a better ending to a hunt.

The next day Goff and I cantered thirty miles into Meeker, and my holiday was over.

THEODORE ROOSEVELT
[*With the Cougar Hounds* (1901)]

The Wilds Without Firearms

[Enos A. Mills, who wrote extensively about the national parks and other parts of the West, was among the first who conducted a sort of propaganda for the study rather than the slaughter of our wild life.]

Had I encountered the two gray wolves during my first unarmed camping-trip into the wilds, the experience would hardly have suggested to me that going without firearms is the best way to enjoy wild nature. But I had made many unarmed excursions beyond the trail before I had that adventure, and the habit of going without a gun was so firmly fixed and so satisfactory that even a perilous wolf encounter did not arouse any desire for firearms. The habit continued, and to-day the only way I can enjoy the wilds is to leave guns behind.

On that autumn afternoon I was walking along slowly, reflectively, in a deep forest. Not a breath of air moved, and even the aspen's golden leaves stood still in the sunlight. All was calm and peaceful around and within me, when I came to a little sunny frost-tanned grass-plot surrounded by tall, crowding pines. I felt drawn to its warmth and repose and stepped joyfully into it. Suddenly two gray wolves sprang from almost beneath my feet and faced me defiantly. At a few feet distance they made an impressive show of ferocity, standing ready apparently to hurl themselves upon me.

Now the gray wolf is a powerful, savage beast, and directing his strong jaws, tireless muscles, keen scent, and all-seeing eyes are exceedingly nimble wits. He is well equipped to make the severe struggle for existence which his present environment compels. In many Western localities, despite the high price offered for his scalp, he has managed not only to live, but to increase and multiply. I had seen gray wolves pull down big game. On one occasion I had seen a vigorous long-horned steer fall after a desperate struggle with two of these fearfully fanged animals. Many times I had come across scattered bones which told of their triumph; and altogether I was so impressed with their deadliness that a glimpse of one of them usually gave me over to a temporary dread.

The two wolves facing me seemed to have been asleep in the sun when I disturbed them. I realized the danger and was alarmed, of course, but my faculties were under control, were stimulated, indeed, to unusual alertness, and I kept a bold front and faced them without flinching. Their expression was one of mingled surprise and anger, together with the apparent determination to sell their lives as dearly as possible. I gave them all the attention which their appearance and their reputation demanded. Not once did I take my eyes off them. I held them at bay with my eyes. I still have a vivid picture of terribly gleaming teeth, bristling backs, and bulging muscles in savage readiness.

They made no move to attack. I was afraid to attack and I dared not run away. I remembered that some trees I could almost reach behind me had limbs that stretched out toward me, yet I felt that to wheel, spring for a limb, and swing up beyond their reach could not be done quickly enough to escape those fierce jaws.

Both sides were of the same mind, ready to fight, but not at all eager to do so. Under these conditions our nearness was embarrassing, and we faced each other for what seemed, to me at least, a long time. My mind working like lightning, I thought of several possible ways of escaping. I considered each at length, found it faulty, and dismissed it. Meanwhile, not a sound had been made. I had not moved, but something had to be done. Slowly I worked the small folding axe from its sheath, and with the slowest of movements placed it in my right coat-pocket with the handle up, ready for instant use. I did this with studied deliberation, lest a sudden movement should release the springs that held the wolves back. I kept on staring. Statues, almost, we must have appeared to the "camp-bird" whose call from a near-by limb told me we were observed, and whose nearness gave me courage. Then, looking the nearer of the two wolves squarely in the eye, I said to him, "Well, why don't you move?" as though we were playing checkers instead of the game of life. He made no reply, but the spell was broken. I believe that both sides had been bluffing. In attempting to use my kodak while continuing the bluff, I brought matters to a focus. "What a picture you fellows will make," I said aloud, as my right hand slowly worked the kodak out of the case which hung under my left arm. Still keeping up a steady fire of looks, I brought the kodak in front of me ready to focus, and then touched the spring that released the folding front. When the kodak mysteriously, suddenly opened before the wolves, they fled for their lives. In an instant they had cleared the grassy space and vanished into the woods. I did not get their picture.

With a gun, the wolf encounter could not have ended more happily. At any rate, I have not for a moment cared for a gun since I returned enthusiastic from my first delightful trip into the wilds without one. Out in the wilds with nature is one of the safest and most sanitary of places. Bears are not seeking to devour, and the death-list from lions, wolves, snakes, and all other bug-bears combined does not equal the death-list from fire, automobiles, street-cars, or banquets. Being afraid of nature or a rainstorm is like being afraid of the dark.

The time of that first excursion was spent among scenes that I had visited before, but the discoveries I made and the deeper feelings it stirred within me, led me to think it more worth while than any previous trip among the same delightful scenes. The first day, especially, was excitingly crowded with new sights and sounds and fancies. I fear that during the earlier trips the rifle had obscured most of the scenes in which it could not figure, and as a result I missed fairyland and most of the sunsets.

When I arrived at the alpine lake by which I was to camp, evening's long rays and shadows were romantically robing the picturesque wild border of the lake. The crags, the temples, the flower-edged snowdrifts, and the grass-plots of this wild garden seemed half-unreal, as over them the long lights and torn shadows grouped and changed, lingered and vanished, in the last moments of the sun. The deep purple of evening was over all, and the ruined crag with the broken pine on the ridge-top was black against the evening's golden glow, when I hastened to make camp by a pine temple while the beautiful world of sunset's hour slowly faded into the night.

The camp-fire was a glory-burst in the darkness, and the small many-spired evergreen temple before me shone an illuminated cathedral in the night. All that evening I believed in fairies, and by watching the changing camp-fire kept my fancies frolicking in realms of mystery where all the world was young. I lay down without a gun, and while the fire changed and faded to black and gray the coyotes began to howl. But their voices did not seem as lonely or menacing as when I had had a rifle by my side. As I lay listening to them, I thought I detected merriment in their tones, and in a little while their shouts rang as merrily as though they were boys at play. Never before had I realized that coyotes too had enjoyments, and I listened to their shouts with pleasure. At last the illumination faded from the cathedral grove and its templed top stood in charcoal against the clear heavens as I fell asleep beneath the peaceful stars.

The next morning I loitered here and there, getting acquainted with the lake-shore, for without a gun all objects, or my eyes, were so changed that I had only a dim recollection of having seen the place before. From time to time, as I walked about, I stopped to try to win the confidence of the small folk in fur and feathers. I found some that trusted me, and at noon a chipmunk, a camp-bird, a chickadee, and myself were several times busy with the same bit of luncheon at once.

Some years ago mountain sheep often came in flocks to lick the salty soil in a ruined crater on Specimen Mountain. One day I climbed up and hid myself in the crags to watch them. More than a hundred of them came. After licking for a time, many lay down. Some of the rams posed themselves on the rocks in heroic attitudes and looked serenely and watchfully around. Young lambs ran about, and a few occasionally raced up and down smooth, rocky steeps, seemingly without the slightest regard for the laws of falling bodies. I was close to the flock, but luckily they did not suspect my presence. After enjoying their fine wild play for more than two hours, I slipped away and left them in their home among the crags.

One spring day I paused in a whirl of mist and wet snow to look for the trail. I could see only a few yards ahead. As I peered ahead, a bear emerged from the gloom, heading straight for me. Behind her were two cubs. I caught her impatient expression when she beheld me. She stopped, and then, with a growl of anger, she wheeled and boxed cubs right and left like an angry mother. The bears disappeared in the direction from which they had come, the cubs urged on with spanks from behind as all vanished in the falling snow.

The gray Douglas squirrel is one of the most active, audacious, and outspoken of animals. He enjoys seclusion and claims to be monarch of all he surveys, and no trespasser is too big to escape a scolding from him. Many times he has given me a terrible tongue-lashing with a desperate accompaniment of fierce facial expressions, bristling whiskers, and emphatic gestures. I love this brave fellow creature; but if he were only a few inches bigger, I should never risk my life in his woods without a gun.

ENOS A. MILLS
[*Wild Life in the Rockies* (1909)]

Set a Seal to Catch a Seal

[*Nowadays the whale and the seal are, by international agreement, merely "harvested" as a crop rather than pushed into extinction, and the methods of taking them have also been "modernized" by the invention of deadlier mechanical weapons. Vilhjalmur Stefansson, on the other hand, is proud of his ability to survive in the Arctic by the methods which the Eskimos themselves learned to practice.*]

No one should aim to live by hunting on the sea ice without understanding this manner of sealing, called by the Eskimos the "mauttok," or waiting method (in the Greenlandic dialects "maupok"); but in actual practice we have never had to resort to it. We have merely had it as another string to our bow. Our seals are secured either by the (among the Eskimos) nameless way first described where a seal is shot in open water, or by the procedure about to be described, called by the Eskimos the "auktok" or crawling method.

Seals may at any season of the year crawl up on the ice to lie there and sleep, but they do it chiefly in the spring and summer—from March when it still goes down to 30° or 40° Fahrenheit below zero to midsummer when even on the ice the temperature is 40° or 50° above zero and much of the surface is covered with pools of water.

A seal does not crawl unguardedly at any time out on the ice from his hole (enlarged by his teeth, or by the thaw, till it will let him up) or from the lead in which he has been swimming. He is always fearful of polar bears. When he wants to come up and bask, he spies out the situation by bobbing up from the water as high as he can, lifting his head a foot or two above the general ice level. This he does at intervals for some time—perhaps for hours—until he concludes there are no bears around and ventures to hitch himself out on the ice.

Here follows another period of extreme vigilance during which the seal lies beside his hole ready to dive in again at the slightest alarm. Eventually, however, he begins to take the naps that were his desire in coming out of the water. But his sleep is restless through fear of bears. He takes naps of thirty or forty or fifty seconds or perhaps a minute. Then he raises his head ten or fifteen inches from the ice and spends five to twenty seconds in making a complete survey of the horizon before taking another nap. A nap of three minutes is protracted slumber for a seal, although far away from land and in other regions where bears are few or absent I have seen them sleep for five and six minutes.

In rare cases basking seals will be found lying within rifle shot from an ice hummock or land, and can be shot from cover. Ordinarily, however, they select a level expanse of ice. In that case they will see the hunter long before he gets near enough to shoot. An essential of a successful hunt is therefore to convince the seal that you are something that is not dangerous. He may see you move and so you must convince him that you are some harmless animal.

There are only three animals with which seals are familiar—bears, white foxes and other seals. It would not serve the hunter to pretend he is a bear, for that is the one thing the seal fears. This consideration shows you must not wear white clothes for the advantage of "protective coloration" on the white ice. The seal will probably see you, and if he sees something suspicious and white he will think of a bear and dive instantly. You cannot very well pretend to be a fox for they are not much larger than cats, are very agile and continually keep hopping around. That part you would fail in playing. But if you are dressed in dark clothing and are lying flat on the ice you look at a distance much like a seal and you will find by trying it that you can imitate his actions successfully.

You can learn the auktok method of sealing from an Eskimo if you are among some group who practice it, but there are several groups among whom it is not in use. But in any case you can learn from the seals themselves, for your task is but to imitate them. Take your field glass with you and spend a few hours or days in watching basking seals from a safe distance. With seals that is 400 or 500 yards. In the books of the nature fakers animals are sometimes endowed with marvelously keen sight. I think it is true of many birds; and mountain sheep see well, though I doubt that they see as well as a man. Of the remaining "big game" animals known to me, the wolf has the keenest sight and yet conditions of visibility have to be favorable to him if he can see you at much over 500 or 600 yards. Neither a grizzly nor a polar bear is likely to see you at more than half that, nor are polar cattle, while a caribou may see you at 400 or 500 yards. A seal is not likely to see you at much over 300 yards.

Your cue is, then, to begin playing seal when you are about 300 yards away. Up to that point you advance by walking bent while the seal sleeps and dropping on your knees to wait motionless while he is awake. But at less than 300 yards he might notice you on all fours, and as that is not a seal-like posture you must begin to wriggle ahead snake-fashion. You must not crawl head-on, for a man in that position is not so convincingly like a seal as he would be in side view. You must therefore crawl side-on, or crawfish fashion.

You crawl ahead while the seal sleeps and you lie motionless while he is awake. Had you been upright or on all fours he might have noticed you at 300 yards but now he does not till you are perhaps 200 yards away. When he first sees you his actions are plainly interpreted—he becomes tense, raises his head a little higher, crawls a foot or two closer to the water to be ready to dive, and then watches you, intent and suspicious. If you remain motionless, his suspicions increase at the end of the first minute, and before the third or fourth minute is over he plunges into the water, for he knows that no real seal is likely to lie motionless that long. Therefore, before the first minute of his watching is over you should do something seal-like. You are lying flat on the ice like a boy sleeping on a lawn. The easiest seal-like thing to do is to lift your head ten or fifteen inches, spend ten or fifteen seconds looking around, then drop your head on the ice again. By doing this half a dozen times at thirty or fifty-second intervals you will very likely convince your seal that you are another seal.

But some seals are skeptical. If yours seems restive and suspicious it is well to increase the verisimilitude of your acting by not only lifting your head at varying intervals but also going through whatever seal-like antics you have observed while watching the real seals through your field glasses.

It is one of the few unharmful results of the late war that we can now describe freely and discuss openly certain things that were taboo before. Thanks to the war experience and frankness of our soldiers, those of us who lack practical experience have at least theoretical knowledge of the "cooties" which our more familiar ancestors knew as a louse. Seals are lousy, not with our familiar graybacks of course, but with a variety of louse or tick of their own. Being thus infested they itch, itching they want to scratch, and not being restrained by any etiquette in these matters they are continually rubbing and scratching themselves. They rub themselves by rolling on the ice and scratch chiefly with their hind flippers which are long and flexible and armed with admirable claws. It is therefore advisable for the hunter to roll about a little and to flex his legs from the knees frequently as if scratching with hind flippers. These actions make an impression upon the seal which in the long run is convincing and in eight cases out of ten a good hunter is accepted as a fellow seal that has just come out of his hole to bask and sleep. The seals that refuse to be convinced have probably had a narrow escape recently from a bear. Possibly, too, some of them may be getting hungry and may decide not to bother to study the new arrival but to take the occasion for going down and having a feed. That this motive frequently influences seals we judge from the fact that towards midnight a seal usually goes down soon after noticing us. As remarked elsewhere, a seal usually comes up on the ice in the early morning or forenoon and commonly goes down to feed towards midnight.

But if you once get your seal convinced he stays convinced. There is nothing fickle about a seal. He not only does not fear you but even appears to rely on you. He is always alertly on guard against the approach of a bear. I am not very deep in seal psychology, but they appear to me to say to themselves: "Over there is a brother seal, and if a bear approaches from that side he will get him before he gets me. So I can afford to leave that quarter unwatched and can devote myself to guarding against a surprise from the other side." As if he held this view, the seal will give you only a casual glance now and then and you can approach with great confidence. You crawl ahead while he sleeps and stop when he wakes up. If he watches you for more than a few moments you reassure him of your sealship by raising and dropping your head, rolling and wriggling as if itchy, and by flexing your legs from the knees as if scratching with hind flippers—all this lying flat on the ice with your side towards the seal and never allowing him to see your long arms, for a seal's front flippers are short. If you are careful, if the snow is not crusty so it crunches, if a moderate wind from the direction of the seal covers any noises there may be, you can crawl as near him as you like. I have known Eskimos to crawl right up to a seal and seize him by a flipper with one hand while they stab him with a knife with the other. But they do this only rarely, either "for a stunt" or else because they have not the proper hunting gear with them. Ordinarily an Eskimo hurls his harpoon from a distance of from ten to thirty feet. I ordinarily shoot from a distance of twenty-five to seventy-five yards.

An Eskimo, using his native gear, holds the harpooned seal by the harpoon line. With a rifle only a brain shot will serve; for if the seal is not instantly killed he will crawl to the water and dive. The reason why I hardly ever shoot at as much as a hundred yards is that the seal is lying on an incline of ice beside the hole or lead. There are few things so slippery as wet ice and the mere shock of instant death may start him sliding and the blood from his wound may get under him, lubricating the ice and making him slide faster. The seal in most cases has buoyancy enough to float. But in sliding towards the water he acquires momentum enough to take him down diagonally ten or twenty feet. He then comes up diagonally under the thick ice and you can't get him. Fearing this, I always drop my rifle the moment I fire and run as hard as I can towards the seal. In some cases he does not slide at all and I slacken speed on getting nearer; in others he is sliding, gradually gaining headway, and I slide for him like a player stealing a base in baseball. In some cases I have caught the seal by a flipper just as he was disappearing; in others I have been too late and the seal, though stone dead, has been lost.

A good hunter should get sixty or seventy per cent of the seals he goes after. The approach takes on the average about two hours.

Readers of antarctic books may wonder, "Why all this to-do about just the right way to hunt seals?" Their idea is that you can secure a seal any old way. So you can—in the Antarctic. Down South the seal knows no enemy, for there were no predatory animals till the explorers came. Fear is consequently unknown to them and if you walk up to a seal and scratch him he will roll over so you can scratch him better. The Arctic is different. It takes patience and an elaborate technique to get a seal near Prince Patrick Island. In the account of his journey in 1853 to the very place where we were now, McClintock, our only predecessor, said he had seen several seals, "but of course we were unable to secure them." It was formerly supposed that the auktok and mauttok methods described above could be used only by Eskimo hunters. But white men can use them equally.

In the fall hunting seals by the auktok method is often dangerous, for they are lying on ice so thin and treacherous that the hunter may break through, especially while trying to get the seal from the hole after he is killed. In midwinter seals can seldom be secured in this way because they do not crawl out on the ice. From April to June we kill most of our seals by this method. From June to Septem-

ber there is so much water on top of the ice that the auktok neces-
sitates wriggling, snake-fashion, through pools of ice water from a
few inches to a foot or more deep. This is not only disagreeable, but
the almost unavoidable splashing may scare the seals. Therefore this
is essentially a springtime method of hunting. We get about a third of
our seals by it, two thirds by shooting them in open water. As said
above, the mauttok method we keep in our minds merely as a standby.
It is used by Eskimos in midwinter on level, thick bay ice near land.
We would use it on the large expanses of fairly uniform ice found far
from land if any of these proved so extensive that we ran out of food
before we came to open sealing water. This has never happened to us,
though it appears from the narrative of other explorers that it would
be likely to happen. But that is because their travel methods were
different from ours.

VILHJALMUR STEFANSSON
[*The Friendly Arctic* (1921)]

Mark Twain in Eruption

[Like the sportsman, the big-game hunter has been occasionally reviled almost
from the first emergence of the type, but never more vehemently than by
Mark Twain.]

⚓

"Mr. Clemens told me that, because of their explosive and scarifying
character, portions of the autobiography would be held under seal for
long periods before publication. Beside certain sections he would
scribble the notation: 'Not to be published until ten (or twenty-five or
fifty, etc.) years after my death.'

"One day I heard him tell a perfectly blistering story about a
very strenuous American, then bulking very large in the public eye.
The late Theodore Roosevelt had then, only recently, published a
book about himself as a big-game hunter, entitled *African Game
Trails,* and about the same time a Western desperado, Harry Orchard,

had blown up a house with a bomb and also 'liquidated' the only eye-witness to the crime. While indulging in the sulphuric remarks given below, Mr. Clemens was furiously smoking a huge calabash pipe—the largest I ever saw—and occasionally violently gesticulating with it, scattering hot ashes and burning flakes of tobacco in all directions. Mr. Clemens was a man of deep sensitiveness, with a very tender heart. He especially condemned callous people who were cruel to animals and insensitive to their sufferings. Like Saint Francis of Assisi, Mark Twain regarded all animals and birds as his brothers. He was irked by sportsmen who killed harmless, innocent animals for sheer enjoyment. I detected a deadly gleam in his eye; and I divined that the imminent monologue would prove to be a scorcher.

" 'Take this fellow, Harry Orchard, out West,' he ingratiatingly began. 'Now I like a fellow like that: straightforward, downright honest. He blew up the house of an enemy and then shot to death the only eyewitness of the crime. When interrogated by the police captain after the capture, as to why he had killed the eye-witness, Orchard coolly replied: "Why, Cap., it stands to reason. I had to shoot the evidence."

" 'Now,' avowed Mr. Clemens heartily, 'I can't help but like that fellow Orchard. You must hand it to him: he's honest. Cold-blooded, yes; but truthful.'

" 'On the other hand, take Teddy Roosevelt,' he continued with a steely glint in his eye. 'Just read, if you please, this horrible, brutal book about shooting deer and other wild game. *Game!* Teddy is not content with stalking these poor beasts and mercilessly shooting down the lovely, defenceless creatures from ambush—*from ambush!* (he shouted)—with a high powered express rifle. He must go further and tell, with meticulous detail, how he deliberately raised the gun to his shoulder, took careful aim, pulled the trigger, and then—by God! —describes the wave of savage exultation which sweeps through his being as he observed the murderous softnosed bullet tear its jagged way through the tender flesh and sees the poor, bleeding, stricken creature stagger, totter, fall to its pitiful death.'

"These words were shot forth with savage intensity and bitterness. His auditors waited spell-bound, afraid to break the silence with the sound of even a breath. Mark slowly puffed away at the monster calabash pipe and blew out volumes of sulphurous smoke which seemed perfectly attuned to his mood. Then after a long, ruminative pause, he suddenly barked savagely: 'If I had to choose between these two, *give me Harry Orchard every time.*'

"A little later, when calm had been restored to the atmosphere, I gently inquired if that story were going into his autobiography.

" 'Oh yes,' Mark replied emphatically. 'Everything goes in. I make no exceptions. But,' he added emphatically, with the suspicion of a twinkle in his eye, 'I shall insert a note in the manuscript beside the story. Not to be published until one hundred and fifty years after my death.' "

SAMUEL STEVENS HOOD
[*Archibald Henderson: The New Crichton* (1949)]

Death of a Rabbit

[*Sir Walter Scott, Charles Darwin, and Abraham Lincoln are to be numbered among the many who began as hunters but learned in time that, as Thoreau said, the good man will discover "other objects" in the forests. More than a few such have recorded experiences very much like the following, which is described not by a naturalist but by a drama critic.*]

✒

I have gone hunting only once in my life but I think I understand the feeling of these thousands who annually prowl over frozen fields, with a shotgun in their hands, looking for a rabbit or a pheasant.

Some time I may be tempted to try it again for I remember my one day of hunting not altogether unpleasantly.

If you could dissociate the aim and end of hunting from its incidental pleasures it might be wholly delightful. What spoils the adventure is the realization of its purpose in the unpleasant form of a dead bird in the hand or a mangled rabbit.

Or that is the way I remember it. I must have been about fifteen years old. At that age all boys, particularly if they live in a city, dream of hunting, though they often lack a shotgun and a place to hunt.

So I was enraptured when a man of my acquaintance, a red-headed Irish detective, offered to supply firearms and take me with him to a farm on which rabbits were rumored to lurk.

It was a train trip from the city and when we got off the coach we walked into another world. It was snowing and cold, and the woods seemed desolate and ominously quiet. Only the snow underfoot made a pleasant crunching sound in that emptiness.

It was piercingly lonely and forbidding but the strangeness of the environment and the sense of adventure you had were inexpressibly exciting. In the uneasiness you felt, there was mingled something wonderfully satisfying. You were at one with primitive man. You were fifteen years old and you were Daniel Boone and a whole tribe of rugged pioneers romantically and dangerously wresting the means of life from the overflowing resources of a hostile wilderness.

The wind numbed your hands. It didn't matter. The swift, long walk over rough ground set the blood pounding. You were in magnificent health and enormously hungry. You tasted the peace of the philosophers and the ecstasy of the conquerors, for you had got back to primitive nature and you were master of your environment.

We tramped all day. In the late afternoon we found ourselves walking very close together. The Irishman began to talk of banshees that haunted the night woods of County Mayo.

The rumor about the rabbits seemed to have been exaggerated. We hadn't seen one all day.

Denis was sorry and sympathetic.

"There's an empty bottle lying over there," he said. "You might fancy it was a rabbit and see if you can hit it. Be careful now, lad, of the backfire."

The backfire was disappointing. I had been led to believe that it would be paralyzing. There was only a slight jar and an explosion much less thunderous than I had expected. But the bottle was smashed and Denis was proud.

We were ready to quit when a rabbit appeared before us, about a hundred feet away. He sat there on his haunches, as if he had just walked over from a shooting gallery, or stepped out of *Alice in Wonderland*.

"Holy smoke," said Denis, "it's a rabbit."

The tone could not have been more thunderstruck if the animal had been a royal Bengal tiger.

We gazed hypnotized at the apparition. Denis was the first to recover.

"You take it, lad," he said. "It's your first hunt." I can hear the soft brogue now and the rolling of the *r*'s in the word "first."

It was impossible for anybody to miss that conveniently fixed target at such a distance and the rabbit toppled as I fumbled with the trigger. We ran to retrieve the victim.

He was in two parts. The head had been completely blown off. It was a dismaying spectacle. I felt a little sick and ashamed.

So did Denis, though he tried not to show it.

"Fine work, lad," he said, but I noticed that he did not look at the decapitated and bloody creature, still warm, when he put it in the bag.

We walked silently to the train close in comradeship, and further united with a sense of having shared in the reprehensible.

"It will be fine eatin', lad," he said, but when it was cooked he could not touch it. Except for the headless rabbit, it had been a perfect day.

WILLIAM F. MC DERMOTT
[*The Best of McDermott* (1959)]

SECTION THREE

THE WIDE WIDE WORLD

Thank Heaven here is not all the world. The buck-eye does not grow in New England, and the mocking bird is rarely heard here. . . . Yet we think that if rail-fences are pulled down and stone walls piled up on our farms, bounds are henceforth set to our lives and our fates decided. If you are chosen town-clerk-forsooth, you cannot go to Tierra del Fuego this summer.

HENRY DAVID THOREAU
Walden

The voyage of the Beagle *has been by far the most important event in my life and has determined my whole career. . . . I owe to the voyage the first real training of my mind.*

CHARLES DARWIN
Autobiography

Holy Cats

[By long-established convention Herodotus is the father of history, but he was also the first "travel writer"—the first, that is, to visit distant lands for the express purpose of supplying stay-at-homes with a picturesque account of foreign manners, customs, religions, and governments. Though not a naturalist, he took careful note of the cats and the crocodiles in Egypt. He reports also what he had heard of the phoenix but, unlike most subsequent writers during the next two thousand years, he had his doubts.]

Egypt, though it borders upon Libya, is not a region abounding in wild animals. The animals that do exist in the country, whether domesticated or otherwise, are all regarded as sacred. If I were to explain why they are consecrated to the several gods, I should be led to speak of religious matters, which I particularly shrink from mentioning; the points whereon I have touched slightly hitherto have all been introduced for sheer necessity. Their custom with respect to animals is as follows: For every kind there are appointed certain guardians, some male, some female, whose business it is to look after them; and this honour is made to descend from father to son. The inhabitants of the various cities, when they have made a vow to any god, pay it to his animals in the way which I will now explain. At the time of making the vow they shave the head of the child, cutting off all the hair, or else half, or sometimes a third part, which they then weigh in a balance against a sum of silver; and whatever sum the hair weighs is presented to the guardian of the animals, who thereupon cuts up some fish, and gives it to them for food—such being the stuff whereon they are fed. When a man has killed one of the sacred animals, if he did it with malice prepense, he is punished with death; if unwittingly, he has to pay such a fine as the priests choose to impose. When an ibis, however, or a hawk is killed, whether it was done by accident or on purpose, the man must needs die.

The number of domestic animals in Egypt is very great, and would be still greater were it not for what befalls the cats. As the females, when they have kittened, no longer seek the company of the males, these last, to obtain once more their companionship, practise a curious artifice. They seize the kittens, carry them off, and kill them, but do not eat them afterwards. Upon this the females, being deprived of their young, and longing to supply their place, seek the males once more, since they are particularly fond of their offspring. On every occasion of a fire in Egypt the strangest prodigy occurs with the cats. The inhabitants allow the fire to rage as it pleases, while they stand about at intervals and watch these animals, which, slipping by the men or else leaping over them, rush headlong into the flames. When this happens, the Egyptians are in deep affliction. If a cat dies in a private house by a natural death, all the inmates of the house shave their eyebrows; on the death of a dog they shave the head and the whole of the body.

The cats on their decease are taken to the city of Bubastis, where they are embalmed, after which they are buried in certain sacred repositories. The dogs are interred in the cities to which they belong, also in sacred burial-places. The same practice obtains with respect to the ichneumons; the hawks and shrew-mice, on the contrary, are conveyed to the city of Buto for burial, and the ibises to Hermopolis. The bears, which are scarce in Egypt, and the wolves, which are not much bigger than foxes, they bury wherever they happen to find them lying.

The following are the peculiarities of the crocodile: During the four winter months they eat nothing; they are four-footed, and live indifferently on land or in the water. The female lays and hatches her eggs ashore, passing the greater portion of the day on dry land, but at night retiring to the river, the water of which is warmer than the night-air and the dew. Of all known animals this is the one which from the smallest size grows to be the greatest: for the egg of the crocodile is but little bigger than that of the goose, and the young crocodile is in proportion to the egg; yet when it is full grown, the animal measures frequently seventeen cubits and even more. It has the eyes of a pig, teeth large and tusk-like, of a size proportional to its frame; unlike any other animal, it is without a tongue; it cannot move its under jaw, and in this respect too it is singular, being the only animal in the world which moves the upper jaw but not the under. It has strong claws and a scaly skin, impenetrable upon the back. In the water it is blind, but on land it is very keen of sight.

The crocodile is esteemed sacred by some of the Egyptians; by others he is treated as an enemy. Those who live near Thebes, and those who dwell around Lake Mœris, regard them with especial veneration. In each of these places they keep one crocodile in particular, who is taught to be tame and tractable. They adorn his ears with earrings of molten stone or gold, and put bracelets on his fore-paws, giving him daily a set portion of bread, with a certain number of victims; and, after having thus treated him with the greatest possible attention while alive, they embalm him when he dies, and bury him in a sacred repository. The people of Elephantiné, on the other hand, are so far from considering these animals as sacred, that they even eat their flesh. In the Egyptian language they are not called crocodiles, but Champsæ. The name of crocodiles was given them by the Ionians, who remarked their resemblance to the lizards, which in Ionia live in the walls, and are called crocodiles.

They have also a sacred bird called the phœnix, which I myself have never seen, except in pictures. Indeed, it is a great rarity, even in Egypt, only coming there (according to the accounts of the people of Heliopolis) once in 500 years, when the old phœnix dies. Its size and appearance, if it is like the pictures, are as follows: The plumage is partly red, partly golden, while the general make and size are almost exactly that of the eagle. They tell a story of what this bird does, which does not seem to me to be credible: that he comes all the way from Arabia, and brings the parent bird, all plastered over with myrrh, to the temple of the sun, and there buries the body. In order to bring him, they say, he first forms a ball of myrrh as big as he finds that he can carry; then he hollows out the ball, and puts his parent inside, after which he covers over the opening with fresh myrrh, and the ball is then of exactly the same weight as at first; so he brings it to Egypt, plastered over as I have said, and deposits it in the temple of the sun. Such is the story they tell of the doings of this bird.

HERODOTUS
[*History* (5th century B.C.)]

Natural History Notes of a
Practicing Pirate

[Who were those Frank Bucks of Imperial Rome who brought back alive all the rare and improbable beasts slaughtered in the arena or, for that matter, the lions to whom Christian martyrs were fed? Neither they nor anyone else seems to have recorded their adventures, but they must have known their business fairly well and they must have ranged far since menageries and zoos have existed in Europe at least since the beginning of our era. Charlemagne got an elephant from Harun-al-Rashid of Bagdad; St. Louis had lions and elephants. All the royal house of Valois kept a menagerie at the Louvre; even the monastery of St. Gaul boasted bears and badgers in its zoo. Stags, monkeys, and bears were to be seen at the Cathedral of Notre Dame in Paris, and in the thirteenth century a French king sent a spare elephant to his British cousin. The exhibition of animals at the Tower of London goes back at least to the fourteenth century.

Columbus and the other early voyagers to the new world took note of birds and beasts only insofar as they had some bearing on survival, and though Captain John Smith devotes considerable space to the "natural products" of Virginia in the various versions of his autobiographical narrative, it was not until late in the seventeenth century that men began to look with a naturalist's eye at the flora and fauna of the Western Hemisphere. In fact, it has been said that the first such voyager who took an interest in natural history for its own sake was that most extraordinary of pirates, William Dampier, who, in the intervals between raiding ships and ravaging towns, took elaborate notes that would have done credit to a professional zoologist.]

In this River we found a Canoa coming down the stream; and though we went with our Canoas to seek for Inhabitants, yet we found none, but saw in 2 or 3 places signs that Indians had made on the side of the

River. The Canoa which we found was but meanly made for want of Tools, therefore we concluded these Indians have no commerce with the Spaniards, nor with other Indians that have.

While we lay here, our Moskito Men went in their Canoa, and struck us some Manatee, or Sea-Cow. Besides this Blewfields River, I have seen of the Manatee in the Bay of Campeachy, on the Coasts of Bocca del Drago, and Bocco del Toro, in the River of Darien, and among the South Keys or little Islands of Cuba. I have heard of their being found on the North of Jamaica, a few, and in the Rivers of Surinam in great multitudes, which is a very low Land. I have seen of them also at Mindanea one of the Phillippine Islands; and on the Coast of New Holland. This Creature is about the bigness of a Horse, and 10 or 12 foot long. The mouth of it is much like the mouth of a Cow, having great thick Lips. The Eyes are no bigger than a small Pea, the Ears are only two small holes on each side of the Head. The Neck is short and thick, bigger than the Head. The biggest part of this Creature is at the Shoulders, where it hath two large Fins, one on each side of its Belly. Under each of these Fins the Female hath a small Dug to suckle her young. From the Shoulders towards the Tail it retains its bigness for about a foot, then groweth smaller and smaller to the very Tail, which is flat, and about 14 inches broad, and 20 inches long, and in the middle 4 or 5 inches thick, but about the edges of it not above 2 inches thick. From the Head to the Tail it is round and smooth without any Fin but those two before mentioned. I have heard that some have weighed above 1200 *l.* but I never saw any so large. The Manatee delights to live in brackish Water; and they are commonly in Creeks and Rivers near the Sea. 'Tis for this reason possibly they are not seen in the South Seas (that ever I could observe) where the Coast is generally a bold Shore, that is, high Land and deep Water close home by it, with a high Sea or great Surges; except in the Bay of Panama; yet even there is no Manatee. Whereas the West-Indies, being as it were, one great Bay composed of many smaller, are mostly low Land and shoal Water, and afford proper pasture (as I may say) for the Manatee. Sometimes we find them in salt Water, sometimes in fresh; but never far at Sea. And those that live in the Sea at such places where there is no River nor Creek fit for them to enter, yet do commonly come once or twice in 24 hours to the mouth of any fresh water River that is near their place of abode. They live on Grass 7 or 8 inches long, and of a narrow blade, which grows in the Sea in many places, especially among Islands near the Main. This Grass groweth likewise in Creeks, or in great Rivers near the sides of them, in such places where there is but little tide or current. They never come ashore, nor into shallower water than where they can swim. Their Flesh is white, both the fat and the lean, and extraordinary sweet wholesome meat. The tail of a young Cow is most esteem'd; but if old both head and tail are very tough. A Calf that sucks is the most delicate meat; Privateers commonly roast them; as they do also great pieces cut out of the Bellies of the old ones.

The Skin of the Manatee is of great use to Privateers, for they cut them into straps, which they make fast on the sides of their Canoas through which they put their Oars in rowing, instead of tholes or pegs. The Skin of the Bull, or of the Back of the Cow is too thick for this use; but of it they make Horse-whips, cutting them 2 or 3 foot long: at the handle they leave the full substance of the Skin, and from thence cut it away tapering, but very even and square all the four sides. While the Thongs are green they twist them, and hang them to dry: which in a weeks time become as hard as wood. The Moskito-men have always a small Canoa for their use to strike Fish, Tortoise, or Manatee, which they keep usually to themselves, and very neat and clean. They use no Oars but Paddles, the broad part of which doth not go tapering towards the staff, pole or handle of it, as in the Oar; nor do they use it in the same manner, by laying it on the side of the Vessel; but hold it perpendicularly, griping the staff hard with both hands, and putting back the Water by main strength, and very quick strokes. One of the Moskitoes (for there go but two in a Canoa) sits in the stern, the other kneels down in the head, and both paddle till they come to the place where they expect their game. Then they lye still or paddle very softly, looking well about them, and he that is in the head of the Canoa lays down his paddle, and stands up with his striking staff in his hand. This staff is about 8 foot long, almost as big as a mans Arm, at the great end, in which there is a hole to place his Harpoon in. At the other end of his staff there is a piece of light wood called Bobwood, with a hole in it, through which the small end of the staff comes; and on this piece of Bobwood, there is a line of 10 or 12 fathom wound neatly about, and the end of the line made fast to it. The other end of the line is made fast to the Harpoon, which is at the great end of the staff, and the Moskito-man keeps about a fathom of it loose in his hand. When he strikes, the Harpoon presently comes out of the staff, and as the Manatee swims away, the Line runs off from the bob; and altho' at first both staff and bob may be carried under water, yet as the line runs off it will rise again. Then the Moskito-men paddle with all their might to get hold of the bob again, and spend usually a quarter of an hour before they get it. When the Manatee begins to be tired, it lieth still, and then the Moskito-men paddle to the bob and take it up, and begin to hale in the line. When the Manatee feels them he swims away again, with the Canoa after him; then he that steers must be nimble to turn the head of the Canoa that way that his Consort points, who being in the head of the Canoa, and holding the line, both sees and feels which way the Manatee is swimming. Thus the Canoa is towed with a violent motion, till the Manatee's strength decays. Then they gather in the line, which they are often forced to let all go to the very end. At length when the Creature's strength is spent, they hale it up to the Canoas side, and knock it on the Head, and tow it to the nearest shore, where they make it fast, and seek for another; which having taken, they go on shore with it, to put it into their Canoa: For it is so heavy that they cannot lift it in, but they hale it up in shole water, as near the shore as they can, and then overset the Canoa, laying one side close to the Manatee. Then they roll it in, which brings the Canoa upright again, and when they have heav'd out the water, they fasten a line to the other Manatee that lieth afloat, and tow it after them. I have known two Moskito-men for a week every day bring aboard 2 Manatee in this manner; the least of which hath not weighed less than 600 pound, and that in a very small Canoa, that 3 Englishmen would scarce adventure to go in. When they strike a Cow that hath a young one, they seldom miss the Calf, for she commonly takes her young under one of her Fins. But if the Calf is so big that she cannot carry it, or so frightened that she only minds to save her own life, yet the young never leaves her till the Moskito-men have an opportunity to strike her.

The manner of striking Manatee and Tortoise is much the same; only when they seek for Manatee they paddle so gently, that they make no noise, and never touch the side of the Canoa with their paddle; because it is a Creature that hears very well. But they are not so nice when they seek for Tortoise, whose Eyes are better than his Ears. They strike the Tortoise with a square sharp Iron Peg, the other with a Harpoon.

WILLIAM DAMPIER
[*New Voyage Round the World* (1697)]

A French View of the Rattlesnake

[Since the fierce and the dangerous animals of every country get first attention, it is not surprising that the American rattlesnake enjoyed an early fame. The most literary account was written by that French traveler who was a friend of Franklin's and of Jefferson's and who chose to write his somewhat idealized description of American character and habits in the form of letters from an imaginary American farmer. Half of one such letter he devoted to the most famous of our snakes. The concluding anecdote is, by the way, a persistent but probably fictitious tale.]

You insist on my saying something about our snakes; and in relating what I know concerning them, were it not for two singularities, the one of which I saw, and the other I received from an eyewitness, I should have but very little to observe. The southern provinces are the countries where nature has formed the greatest variety of alligators, snakes, serpents; and scorpions, from the smallest size, up to the *pine barren,* the largest species known here. We have but two, whose stings are mortal, which deserve to be mentioned; as for the black one, it is remarkable for nothing but its industry, agility, beauty, and the art of inticing birds by the power of its eyes. I admire it much, and never kill it, though its formidable length and appearance often get the better of the philosophy of some people, particularly of Europeans. The most dangerous one is the *pilot,* or *copperhead;* for the poison of which no remedy has yet been discovered. It bears the first name because it always precedes the rattlesnake; that is, quits its state of torpidity in the spring a week before the other. It bears the second name on account of its head being adorned with many copper-coloured spots. It lurks in rocks near the water, and is extremely active and dangerous. Let man beware of it! I have heard only of one person who was stung by a copperhead in this country. The poor wretch instantly swelled in a most dreadful manner; a multitude of spots of different hues alternately appeared and vanished, on different parts of his body; his eyes were filled with madness and rage, he cast them on all present with the most vindictive looks: he thrust out his tongue as the snakes do; he hissed through his teeth with inconceivable strength, and became an object of terror to all bye-standers. To the lividness of a corpse he united the desperate force of a maniac; they hardly were able to fasten him, so as to guard themselves from his attacks; when in the space of two hours death relieved the poor wretch from his struggles, and the spectators from their apprehensions. The poison of the rattlesnake is not mortal in so short a space, and hence there is more time to procure relief; we are acquainted with several antidotes with which almost every family is provided. They are extremely inactive, and if not touched, are perfectly inoffensive. I once saw, as I was travelling, a great cliff which was full of them; I handled several, and they appeared to be dead; they were all entwined together, and thus they remain until the return of the sun. I found them out, by following the track of some wild hogs which had fed on them; and even the Indians often regale on them. When they find them asleep, they put a small forked stick over their necks, which they keep immoveably fixed on the ground; giving the snake a piece of leather to bite: and this they pull back several times with great force, until they observe their two poisonous fangs torne out. Then they cut off the head, skin the body, and cook it as we do eels; and their flesh is extremely sweet and white. I once saw a *tamed one,* as gentle as you can possibly conceive a reptile to be; it took to the water and swam whenever it pleased; and when the boys to whom it belonged called it back, their summons was readily obeyed. It had been deprived of its fangs by the preceding method; they often stroked it with a soft brush, and this friction seemed to cause the most pleasing sensations, for it would turn on its back to enjoy it, as a cat does before the fire. One of this species was the cause, some years ago, of a most deplorable accident which I shall relate to you, as I had it from the widow and mother of the victims. A Dutch farmer of the Minisink went to mowing, with his Negroes, in his boots, a precaution used to prevent being stung. Inadvertently he trod on a snake, which immediately flew at his legs; and as it drew back in order to renew its blow, one of his Negroes cut it in two with his scythe. They prosecuted their work, and returned home; at night the farmer pulled off his boots and went to bed; and was soon after attacked with a strange sickness at his stomach; he swelled, and before a physician could be sent for, died. The sudden death of this man did not cause much inquiry; the neighbourhood wondered, as is usual in such cases, and without any further examination the corpse was buried. A few days after, the son put on his father's boots, and went to the meadow; at night he pulled them off, went to bed, and was attacked with the same symptoms about the same time, and died in the morning.

MICHEL DE CRÈVECOEUR
[*Letters from an American Farmer* (1782)]

William Bartram Meets the Alligator

[*One of the American farmer's other letters describes his visit (somewhat romanticized, it would appear) to the first accomplished American horticulturist, the self-taught Quaker John Bartram. John's even more famous son William ranged eastern North America as far south as Florida collecting plants, some of which were planted out in his father's Philadelphia garden; also animal as well as plant specimens to be shipped to eager amateurs in England. His account of his travels was widely read there and was a favorite of Coleridge, who wove some memories of it into both "The Ancient Mariner" and "Kubla Khan."*]

❧

At the upper end of this bluff is a fine orange grove. Here my Indian companion requested me to set him on shore, being already tired of rowing under a fervid sun, and having for some time intimated a dislike to his situation. I readily complied with his desire, knowing the impossibility of compelling an Indian against his own inclinations, or even prevailing upon him by reasonable argumets, when labour is in the question. Before my vessel reached the shore, he sprang out of her and landed, when uttering a shrill and terrible whoop, he bounded off like a roebuck, and I lost sight of him. I at first apprehended, that as he took his gun with him, he intended to hunt for some game and return to me in the evening. The day being excessively hot and sultry, I concluded to take up my quarters here until next morning.

The Indian not returning this morning, I sat sail alone. The coasts on each side had much the same appearance as already described. The palm-trees here seem to be of a different species from the cabbage tree; their straight trunks are sixty, eighty, or ninety feet high, with a beautiful taper, of a bright ash colour, until within six or seven feet of the top, where it is a fine green colour, crowned with an orb of rich green plumed leaves: I have measured the stem of these plumes fifteen feet in length, besides the plume, which is nearly of the same length.

The little lake, which is an expansion of the river, now appeared in view; on the east side are extensive marshes, and on the other high forests and orange groves, and then a bay, lined with vast cypress swamps, both coasts gradually approaching each other, to the opening of the river again, which is in this place about three hundred yards wide. Evening now drawing on, I was anxious to reach some high bank of the river, where I intended to lodge; and agreeably to my wishes, I soon after discovered, on the west shore, a little promontory, at the turning of the river, contracting it here to about one hundred and fifty yards in width. This promontory is a peninsula, containing about three acres of high ground, and is one entire orange grove, with a few live oaks, magnolias, and palms. Upon doubling the point, I arrived at the landing, which is a circular harbour, at the foot of the bluff, the top of which is about twelve feet high; the back of it is a large cypress swamp, that spreads each way, the right wing forming the west coast of the little lake, and the left stretching up the river many miles, and encompassing a vast space of low grassy marshes. From this promontory, looking eastward across the river, I beheld a landscape of low country, unparalleled as I think; on the left is the east coast of the little lake, which I had just passed; and from the orange bluff at the lower end, the high forests begin, and increase in breadth from the shore of the lake, making a circular sweep to the right, and contain many hundred thousand acres of meadow; and this grand sweep of high forests encircles, as I apprehend, at least twenty miles of these green fields, interspersed with hommocks or islets of evergreen trees, where the sovereign magnolia and lordly palm stand conspicuous. The islets are high shelly knolls, on the sides of creeks or branches of the river, which wind about and drain off the superabundant waters that cover these meadows during the winter season.

The evening was temperately cool and calm. The crocodiles began to roar and appear in uncommon numbers along the shores and in the river. I fixed my camp in an open plain, near the utmost projection of the promontory, under the shelter of a large live oak, which stood on the highest part of the ground, and but a few yards from my boat. From this open, high situation, I had a free prospect of the river, which was a matter of no trivial consideration to me, having good reason to dread the subtle attacks of the alligators, who were crowding about my harbour. Having collected a good quantity of wood for the purpose of keeping up a light and smoke during the night, I began to think of preparing my supper, when, upon examining my stores, I found but a scanty provision. I thereupon determined, as the most expeditious way of supplying my necessities, to take my bob and try for some trout. About one hundred yards above my harbour began a cove or bay of the river, out of which opened a large lagoon. The mouth or entrance from the river to it was narrow, but the waters soon after spread and formed a little lake, extending into the marshes: its entrance and shores within I observed to be verged with floating lawns of the pistia and nymphea and other aquatic plants; these I knew were excellent haunts for trout.

The verges and islets of the lagoon were elegantly embellished with flowering plants and shrubs; the laughing coots with wings half spread were tripping over the little coves, and hiding themselves in the tufts of grass; young broods of the painted summer teal, skimming the still surface of the waters, and following the watchful parent unconscious of danger, were frequently surprised by the voracious trout; and he, in turn, as often by the subtle greedy alligator. Behold him rushing forth from the flags and reeds. His enormous body swells. His plaited tail brandished high, floats upon the lake. The waters like a cataract descend from his opening jaws. Clouds of smoke issue from his dilated nostrils. The earth trembles with his thunder. When immediately from the opposite coast of the lagoon, emerges from the deep his rival champion. They suddenly dart upon each other. The boiling surface of the lake marks their rapid course, and a terrific conflict commences. They now sink to the bottom folded together in horrid wreaths. The water becomes thick and discoloured. Again they rise, their jaws clap together, re-echoing through the deep surrounding forests. Again they sink, when the contest ends at the muddy bottom of the lake, and the vanquished makes a hazardous escape, hiding himself in the muddy turbulent waters and sedge on a distant shore. The proud victor exulting returns to the place of action.

The shores and forests resound his dreadful roar, together with the triumphing shouts of the plaited tribes around, witnesses of the horrid combat.

My apprehensions were highly alarmed after being a spectator of so dreadful a battle. It was obvious that every delay would but tend to increase my dangers and difficulties, as the sun was near setting, and the alligators gathered around my harbour from all quarters. From these considerations I concluded to be expeditious in my trip to the lagoon, in order to take some fish. Not thinking it prudent to take my fusee with me, lest I might lose it overboard in case of a battle, which I had every reason to dread before my return, I therefore furnished myself with a club for my defence, went on board, and penetrating the first line of those which surrounded my harbour, they gave way; but being pursued by several very large ones, I kept strictly on the watch, and paddled with all my might towards the entrance of the lagoon, hoping to be sheltered there from the multitude of my assailants; but ere I had half-way reached the place, I was attacked on all sides, several endeavouring to overset the canoe. My situation now became precarious to the last degree: two very large ones attacked me closely, at the same instant, rushing up with their heads and part of their bodies above the water, roaring terribly and belching floods of water over me. They struck their jaws together so close to my ears, as almost to stun me, and I expected every moment to be dragged out of the boat and instantly devoured. But I applied my weapons so effectually about me, though at random, that I was so successful as to beat them off a little; when, finding that they designed to renew the battle, I made for the shore, as the only means left me for my preservation; for, by keeping close to it, I should have my enemies on one side of me only, whereas I was before surrounded by them; and there was a probability, if pushed to the last extremity, of saving myself, by jumping out of the canoe on shore, as it is easy to outwalk them on land, although comparatively as swift as lightning in the water. I found this last expedient alone could fully answer my expectations, for as soon as I gained the shore, they drew off and kept aloof. This was a happy relief, as my confidence was, in some degree, recovered by it. On recollecting myself, I discovered that I had almost reached the entrance of the lagoon, and determined to venture in, if possible, to take a few fish, and then return to my harbour, while day-light continued; for I could now, with caution and resolution, make my way with safety along shore; and indeed there was no other way to regain my camp, without leaving my boat and making my retreat through the marshes

and reeds, which, if I could even effect, would have been in a manner throwing myself away, for then there would have been no hopes of
ever recovering my bark, and returning in safety to any settlements of
men. I accordingly proceeded, and made good my entrance into the
lagoon, though not without opposition from the alligators, who
formed a line across the entrance, but did not pursue me into it, nor
was I molested by any there, though there were some very large ones
in a cove at the upper end. I soon caught more trout than I had present occasion for, and the air was too hot and sultry to admit of their
being kept for many hours, even though salted or barbecued. I now
prepared for my return to camp, which I succeeded in with but little
trouble, by keeping close to the shore; yet I was opposed upon re-
entering the river out of the lagoon, and pursued near to my landing
(though not closely attacked), particularly by an old daring one, about
twelve feet in length, who kept close after me; and when I stepped on
shore and turned about, in order to draw up my canoe, he rushed up
near my feet, and lay there for some time, looking me in the face, his
head and shoulders out of water. I resolved he should pay for his temerity, and having a heavy load in my fusee, I ran to my camp, and
returning with my piece, found him with his foot on the gunwale of
the boat, in search of fish. On my coming up he withdrew sullenly and
slowly into the water, but soon returned and placed himself in his
former position, looking at me, and seeming neither fearful nor any
way disturbed. I soon dispatched him by lodging the contents of my
gun in his head, and then proceeded to cleanse and prepare my fish for
supper; and accordingly took them out of the boat, laid them down
on the sand close to the water, and began to scale them; when, raising
my head, I saw before me, through the clear water, the head and
shoulders of a very large alligator, moving slowly towards me. I instantly stepped back, when, with a sweep of his tail, he brushed off
several of my fish. It was certainly most providential that I looked up
at that instant, as the monster would probably, in less than a minute,
have seized and dragged me into the river. This incredible boldness
of the animal disturbed me greatly, supposing there could now be no
reasonable safety for me during the night, but by keeping continually
on the watch: I therefore, as soon as I had prepared the fish, proceeded to secure myself and effects in the best manner I could. In the
first place, I hauled my bark upon the shore, almost clear out of the
water, to prevent their oversetting or sinking her; after this, every
moveable was taken out and carried to my camp, which was but a few
yards off; then ranging some dry wood in such order as was the most

convenient, I cleared the ground round about it, that there might be no impediment in my way, in case of an attack in the night, either from the water or the land; for I discovered by this time, that this small isthmus, from its remote situation and fruitfulness, was resorted to by bears and wolves. Having prepared myself in the best manner I could, I charged my gun, and proceeded to reconnoitre my camp and the adjacent grounds; when I discovered that the peninsula and grove, at the distance of about two hundred yards from my encampment, on the land side, were invested by a cypress swamp, covered with water, which below was joined to the shore of the little lake, and above to the marshes surrounding the lagoon; so that I was confined to an islet exceedingly circumscribed, and I found there was no other retreat for me, in case of an attack, but by either ascending one of the large oaks, or pushing off with my boat.

It was by this time dusk, and the alligators had nearly ceased their roar, when I was again alarmed by a tumultuous noise that seemed to be in my harbour, and therefore engaged my immediate attention. Returning to my camp, I found it undisturbed, and then continued on to the extreme point of the promontory, where I saw a scene, new and surprising, which at first threw my senses into such a tumult, that it was some time before I could comprehend what was the matter; however, I soon accounted for the prodigious assemblage of crocodiles at this place, which exceeded every thing of the kind I had ever heard of.

How shall I express myself so as to convey an adequate idea of it to the reader, and at the same time avoid raising suspicions of my veracity? Should I say, that the river (in this place) from shore to shore, and perhaps near half a mile above and below me, appeared to be one solid bank of fish, of various kinds, pushing through this narrow pass of St. Juan's into the little lake, on their return down the river, and that the alligators were in such incredible numbers, and so close together from shore to shore, that it would have been easy to have walked across on their heads, had the animals been harmless? What expressions can sufficiently declare the shocking scene that for some minutes continued, whilst this mighty army of fish were forcing the pass? During this attempt, thousands, I may say hundreds of thousands, of them were caught and swallowed by the devouring alligators. I have seen an alligator take up out of the water several great fish at a time, and just squeeze them betwixt his jaws, while the tails of the great trout flapped about his eyes and lips, ere he had swallowed them. The horrid noise of their closing jaws, their plunging amidst the broken banks of fish, and rising with their prey some feet upright above the water, the floods of water and blood rushing out of their mouths, and the clouds of vapour issuing from their wide nostrils, were truly frightful. This scene continued at intervals during the night, as the fish came to the pass. After this sight, shocking and tremendous as it was, I found myself somewhat easier and more reconciled to my situation; being convinced that their extraordinary assemblage here was owing to the annual feast of fish; and that they were so well employed in their own element, that I had little occasion to fear their paying me a visit.

It being now almost night, I returned to my camp, where I had left my fish broiling, and my kettle of rice stewing; and having with me oil, pepper, and salt, and excellent oranges hanging in abundance over my head (a valuable substitute for vinegar) I sat down and regaled myself cheerfully. Having finished my repast, I rekindled my fire for light, and whilst I was revising the notes of my past day's journey, I was suddenly roused with a noise behind me toward the main land. I sprang up on my feet, and listening, I distinctly heard some creature wading the water of the isthmus. I seized my gun and went cautiously from my camp, directing my steps towards the noise: when I had advanced about thirty yards, I halted behind a coppice of orange trees, and soon perceived two very large bears, which had made their way through the water, and had landed in the grove, about one hundred yards distance from me, and were advancing towards me. I waited until they were within thirty yards of me: they there began to snuff and look towards my camp: I snapped my piece, but it flashed, on which they both turned about and galloped off, plunging through the water and swamp, never halting, as I suppose, until they reached fast land, as I could hear them leaping and plunging a long time. They did not presume to return again, nor was I molested by any other creature, except being occasionally awakened by the whooping of owls, screaming of bitterns, or the wood-rats running amongst the leaves.

The wood-rat is a very curious animal. It is not half the size of the domestic rat; of a dark brown or black colour; its tail slender and shorter in proportion, and covered thinly with short hair. It is singular with respect to its ingenuity and great labour in the construction of its habitation, which is a conical pyramid about three or four feet high, constructed with dry branches, which it collects with great labour and perseverance, and piles up without any apparent order; yet they are so interwoven with one another, that it would take a bear or wild-cat some time to pull one of these castles to pieces, and allow the animals sufficient time to secure a retreat with their young.

The noise of the crocodiles kept me awake the greater part of the night; but when I arose in the morning, contrary to my expectations, there was perfect peace; very few of them to be seen, and those were sleep on the shore. Yet I was not able to suppress my fears and apprehensions of being attacked by them in future; and indeed yesterday's combat with them, notwithstanding I came off in a manner victorious, or at least made a safe retreat, had left sufficient impression on my mind to damp my courage; and it seemed too much for one of my strength, being alone in a very small boat, to encounter such collected danger. To pursue my voyage up the river, and be obliged every evening to pass such dangerous defiles, appeared to me as perilous as running the gauntlet betwixt two rows of Indians armed with knives and firebrands. I however resolved to continue my voyage one day longer, if I possibly could with safety, and then return down the river, should I find the like difficulties to oppose. Accordingly I got every thing on board, charged my gun, and set sail, cautiously, along shore. . . .

WILLIAM BARTRAM
[*Travels* (1791)]

Humboldt in South America

[*The most princely and magisterial of all travelers was certainly the German baron Alexander von Humboldt—philosopher, physicist, botanist, zoologist, and mining engineer—who was more nearly master of all the science of his day than it has been possible for anyone since to become. Having traveled as far east as the Urals, he then spent five years in South America, where his inclusive observations of every sort of natural phenomenon make it possible to call him the first to conceive of what we now call "geophysics." He was greatly fascinated by the electric eel.*]

I was impatient, from the time of my arrival at Cumana [in Venezuela], to procure electrical eels. We had been promised them often, but our hopes had always been disappointed. Money loses its value as you withdraw from the coast; and how is the imperturbable apathy of the ignorant people to be vanquished, when they are not excited by the desire of gain?

The Spaniards confound all electric fishes under the name of *tembladores*. There are some of these in the Caribbean Sea, on the coast of Cumana. The Guayquerie Indians, who are the most skilful and active fishermen in those parts, brought us a fish, which, they said, benumbed their hands. This fish ascends the little river Manzanares. It is a new species of ray, the lateral spots of which are scarcely visible, and which much resembles the torpedo. The torpedos, which are furnished with an electric organ externally visible, on account of the transparency of the skin, form a genus or subgenus different from the rays properly so called. The torpedo of Cumana was very lively, very energetic in its muscular movements, and yet the electric shocks it gave us were extremely feeble. They became stronger on galvanizing the animal by the contact of zinc and gold. Other *tembladores*, real gymnoti or electric eels, inhabit the Rio Colorado, the Guarapiche, and several little streams which traverse the Missions of the Chayma Indians. They abound also in the large rivers of America, the Orinoco, the Amazon, and the Meta; but the force of the currents and the depth of the water, prevent them from being caught by the Indians. They see these fish less frequently than they feel shocks from them when swimming or bathing in the river. In the Llanos, particularly in the environs of Calabozo, between the farms of Morichal and the Upper and Lower Missions, the basins of stagnant water and the confluents of the Orinoco (the Rio Guarico and the *caños* Rastro, Berito, and Paloma) are filled with electric eels. We at first wished to make our experiments in the house we inhabited at Calabozo; but the dread of the shocks caused by the gymnoti is so great, and so exaggerated among the common people, that during three days we could not obtain one, though they are easily caught, and we had promised the Indians two piastres for every strong and vigorous fish. This fear of the Indians is the more extraordinary, as they do not attempt to adopt precautions in which they profess to have great confidence. When interrogated on the effect of the *tembladores*, they never fail to tell the Whites, that they may be touched with impunity while you are chewing tobacco. This supposed influence of tobacco on animal electricity is as general on the continent of South America, as the belief among mariners of the effect of garlic and tallow on the magnetic needle.

Impatient of waiting, and having obtained very uncertain results from an electric eel which had been brought to us alive, but much enfeebled, we repaired to the Caño de Bera, to make our experiments in the open air, and at the edge of the water. We set off on the 19th of March, at a very early hour, for the village of Rastro; thence we were conducted by the Indians to a stream, which, in the time of drought, forms a basin of muddy water, surrounded by fine trees, the clusia, the amyris, and the mimosa with fragrant flowers. To catch the gymnoti with nets is very difficult, on account of the extreme agility of the fish, which bury themselves in the mud. We would not employ the *barbasco,* that is to say, the roots of the Piscidea erithyrna, the Jacquinia armillaris, and some species of phyllanthus, which thrown into the pool, intoxicate or benumb the eels. These methods have the effect of enfeebling the gymnoti. The Indians therefore told us that they would "fish with horses" (*embarbascar con caballos*). We found it difficult to form an idea of this extraordinary manner of fishing; but we soon saw our guides return from the savannah, which they had been scouring for wild horses and mules. They brought about thirty with them, which they forced to enter the pool.

The extraordinary noise caused by the horses' hoofs, makes the fish issue from the mud, and excites them to the attack. These yellowish and livid eels, resembling large aquatic serpents, swim on the surface of the water, and crowd under the bellies of the horses and mules. A contest between animals of so different an organization presents a very striking spectacle. The Indians, provided with harpoons and long slender reeds, surround the pool closely; and some climb up the trees, the branches of which extend horizontally over the surface of the water. By their wild cries, and the length of their reeds, they prevent the horses from running away and reaching the bank of the pool. The eels, stunned by the noise, defend themselves by the repeated discharge of their electric batteries. For a long interval they seem likely to prove victorious. Several horses sink beneath the violence of the invisible strokes which they receive from all sides, in organs the most essential to life; and stunned by the force and frequency of the shocks, they disappear under the water. Others, panting, with mane erect, and haggard eyes expressing anguish and dismay, raise themselves, and endeavour to flee from the storm by which they are overtaken. They are driven back by the Indians into the middle of the water; but a small number succeed in eluding the active vigilance of the fishermen. These regain the shore, stumbling at every step, and stretch themselves on the sand, exhausted with fatigue, and with limbs benumbed by the electric shocks of the gymnoti.

In less than five minutes two of our horses were drowned. The eel being five feet long, and pressing itself against the belly of the horses, makes a discharge along the whole extent of its electric organ. It attacks at once the heart, the intestines, and the cæliac fold of the abdominal nerves. It is natural that the effect felt by the horses should be more powerful than that produced upon man by the touch of the same fish at only one of his extremities. The horses are probably not killed, but only stunned. They are drowned from the impossibility of rising amid the prolonged struggle between the other horses and the eels.

We had little doubt that the fishing would terminate by killing successively all the animals engaged; but by degrees the impetuosity of this unequal combat diminished, and the wearied gymnoti dispersed. They require a long rest, and abundant nourishment, to repair the galvanic force which they have lost. The mules and horses appear less frightened; their manes are no longer bristled, and their eyes express less dread. The gymnoti approach timidly the edge of the marsh, where they are taken by means of small harpoons fastened to long cords. When the cords are very dry the Indians feel no shock in raising the fish into the air. In a few minutes we had five large eels, most of which were but slightly wounded. Some others were taken, by the same means, towards evening.

The temperature of the waters in which the gymnoti habitually live, is from 26° to 27°. Their electric force diminishes, it is said, in colder waters; and it is remarkable that, in general, animals endowed with electromotive organs, the effects of which are sensible to man, are not found in the air, but in a fluid that is a conductor of electricity. The gymnotus is the largest of electrical fishes. I measured some that were from five feet to five feet three inches long; and the Indians assert that they have seen them still larger. We found that a fish of three feet ten inches long weighed twelve pounds. The transverse diameter of the body, without reckoning the anal fin, which is elongated in the form of a keel, was three inches and a half. The gymnoti of the Caño de Bera are of a fine olive-green. The under part of the head is yellow mingled with red. Two rows of small yellow spots are placed symmetrically along the back, from the head to the end of the tail. Every spot contains an excretory aperture. In consequence, the skin of the animal is constantly covered with a mucous matter, which, as Volta has proved, conducts electricity twenty or thirty times better than pure water. It is in general somewhat remarkable, that no electric fish yet discovered in the different parts of the world is covered with scales.

The gymnoti, like our eels, are fond of swallowing and breathing air on the surface of the water; but we must not thence conclude that the fish would perish if it could not come up to breathe the air. The European eel will creep during the night upon the grass; but I have seen a very vigorous gymnotus that had sprung out of the water, die on the ground. M. Provençal and myself have proved by our researches on the respiration of fishes, that their humid bronchiæ perform the double function of decomposing the atmospheric air, and of appropriating the oxygen contained in water. They do not suspend their respiration in the air; but they absorb the oxygen like a reptile furnished with lungs. It is known that carp may be fattened by being fed, out of the water, if their gills are wet from time to time with humid moss, to prevent them from becoming dry. Fish separate their gill-covers wider in oxygen gas than in water. Their temperature however, does not rise; and they live the same length of time in pure vital air, and in a mixture of ninety parts nitrogen and ten oxygen. We found that tench placed under inverted jars filled with air, absorb half a cubic centimetre of oxygen in an hour. This action takes place in the gills only; for fishes on which a collar of cork has been fastened, and leaving their head out of the jar filled with air, do not act upon the oxygen by the rest of their body.

The swimming-bladder of the gymnotus is two feet five inches long in a fish of three feet ten inches. It is separated by a mass of fat from the external skin; and rests upon the electric organs, which occupy more than two-thirds of the animal's body. The same vessels which penetrate between the plates or leaves of these organs, and which cover them with blood when they are cut transversely, also send out numerous branches to the exterior surface of the air-bladder. I found in a hundred parts of the air of the swimming-bladder four of oxygen and ninety-six of nitrogen. The medullary substance of the brain displays but a feeble analogy with the albuminous and gelatinous matter of the electric organs. But these two substances have in common the great quantity of arterial blood which they receive, and which is deoxidated in them. We may again remark, on this occasion, that an extreme activity in the functions of the brain causes the blood to flow more abundantly towards the head, as the energy of the movement of the muscles accelerates the deoxidation of the arterial blood. What a contrast between the multitude and the diameter of the blood-vessels of the gymnotus, and the small space occupied by its muscular system! This contrast reminds the observer, that three functions of animal life, which appear in other respects sufficiently distinct,—the functions of

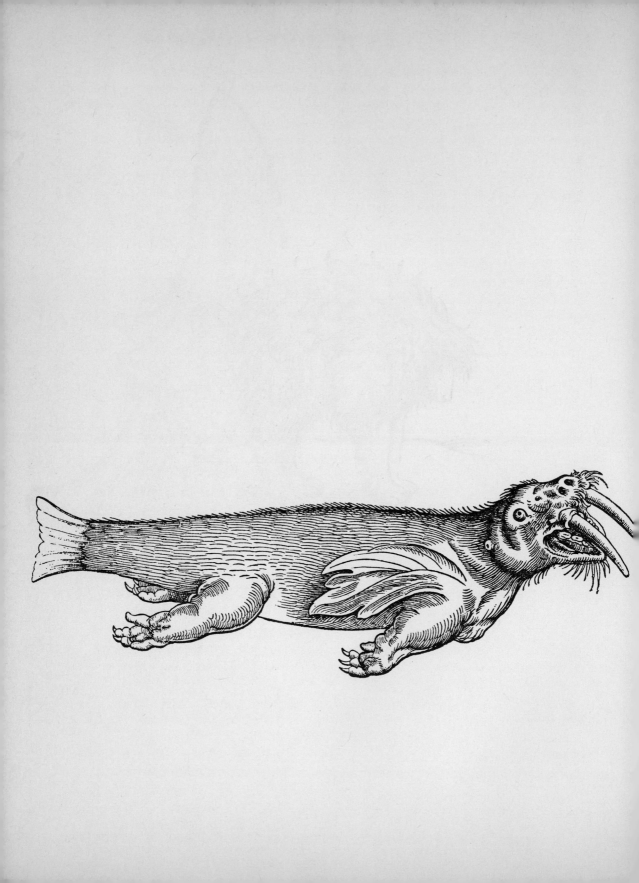

the brain, those of the electrical organ, and those of the muscles, all require the afflux and concourse of arterial or oxygenated blood.

It would be temerity to expose ourselves to the first shocks of a very large and strongly irritated gymnotus. If by chance a stroke be received before the fish is wounded or wearied by long pursuit, the pain and numbness are so violent that it is impossible to describe the nature of the feeling they excite. I do not remember having ever received from the discharge of a large Leyden jar, a more dreadful shock than that which I experienced by imprudently placing both my feet on a gymnotus just taken out of the water. I was affected during the rest of the day with a violent pain in the knees, and in almost every joint. To be aware of the difference that exists between the sensation produced by the Voltaic battery and an electric fish, the latter should be touched when they are in a state of extreme weakness. The gymnoti and the torpedos then cause a twitching of the muscles, which is propagated from the part that rests on the electric organs, as far as the elbow. We seem to feel at every stroke, an internal vibration, which lasts two or three seconds, and is followed by a painful numbness. Accordingly, the Tamanac Indians call the gymnotus, in their expressive language, *arimna,* which means "something that deprives of motion."

The sensation caused by the feeble shocks of an electric eel appeared to me analogous to that painful twitching with which I have been seized at each contact of two heterogeneous metals applied to wounds which I had made on my back by means of cantharides. This difference of sensation between the effects of electric fishes and those of a Voltaic battery or a Leyden jar feebly charged has struck every observer; there is, however, nothing in this contrary to the supposition of the identity of electricity and the galvanic action of fishes. The electricity may be the same; but its effects will be variously modified by the disposition of the electrical apparatus, by the intensity of the fluid, by the rapidity of the current, and by the particular mode of action.

In Dutch Guiana, at Demerara for instance, electric eels were formerly employed to cure paralytic affections. At a time when the physicians of Europe had great confidence in the effects of electricity, a surgeon of Essequibo, named Van der Lott, published in Holland a treatise on the medical properties of the gymnotus. These electric remedies are practised among the savages of America, as they were among the Greeks. We are told by Scribonius Largus, Galen, and Dioscorides, that torpedos cure the headache and the gout. I did not hear of this mode of treatment in the Spanish colonies which I visited; and I can assert that, after having made experiments during four hours successively with gymnoti, M. Bonpland and myself felt, till the next day, a debility in the muscles, a pain in the joints, and a general uneasiness, the effect of a strong irritation of the nervous system.

The gymnotus is neither a charged conductor, nor a battery, nor an electromotive apparatus, the shock of which is received every time they are touched with one hand, or when both hands are applied to form a conducting circle between the opposite poles. The electric action of the fish depends entirely on its will; because it does not keep its electric organs always charged, or whether by the secretion of some fluid, or by any other means alike mysterious to us, it be capable of directing the action of its organs to an external object. We often tried, both insulated and otherwise, to touch the fish, without feeling the least shock. When M. Bonpland held it by the head, or by the middle of the body, while I held it by the tail, and, standing on the moist ground, did not take each other's hand, one of us received shocks, which the other did not feel. It depends upon the gymnotus to direct its action towards the point where it finds itself most strongly irritated. The discharge is then made at one point only, and not at the neighbouring points. If two persons touch the belly of the fish with their fingers, at an inch distance, and press it simultaneously, sometimes one, sometimes the other, will receive the shock. In the same manner, when one insulated person holds the tail of a vigorous gymnotus, and another pinches the gills or pectoral fin, it is often the first only by whom the shock is received. It did not appear to us that these differences could be attributed to the dryness or moisture of our hands, or to their unequal conducting power. The gymnotus seemed to direct its strokes sometimes from the whole surface of its body, sometimes from one point only. This effect indicates less a partial discharge of the organ composed of an innumerable quantity of layers, than the faculty which the animal possesses (perhaps by the instantaneous secretion of a fluid spread through the cellular membrane), of establishing the communication between its organs and the skin only, in a very limited space.

Nothing proves more strongly the faculty, which the gymnotus possesses, of darting and directing its stroke at will, than the observations made at Philadelphia and Stockholm, on gymnoti rendered extremely tame. When they had been made to fast a long time, they killed small fishes put into the tub. They acted from a distance; that is to say, their electrical shock passed through a very thick stratum of water. We need not be surprised that what was observed in Sweden, on a single gymnotus only, we could not perceive in a great number of individuals in their native country. The electric action of animals being a vital action, and subject to their will, it does not depend solely on their state of health and vigour. A gymnotus that has been kept a long time in captivity, accustoms itself to the imprisonment to which is it reduced; it resumes by degrees the same habits in the tub, which it had in the rivers and marshes. An electrical eel was brought to me at Calabozo: it had been taken in a net, and consequently had no wound. It ate meat, and terribly frightened the little tortoises and frogs which, not aware of their danger, placed themselves on its back. The frogs did not receive the stroke till the moment when they touched the body of the gymnotus. When they recovered, they leaped out of the tub; and when replaced near the fish, they were frightened at the mere sight of it. We then observed nothing that indicated an action at a distance; but our gymnotus, recently taken, was not yet sufficiently tame to attack and devour frogs. On approaching the finger, or the metallic points, very close to the electric organs, no shock was felt. Perhaps the animal did not perceive the proximity of a foreign body; or, if it did, we must suppose that in the commencement of its captivity, timidity prevented it from darting forth its energetic strokes except when strongly irritated by an immediate contact. The gymnotus being immersed in water, I placed my hand, both armed and unarmed with metal, within a very small distance from the electric organs; yet the strata of water transmitted no shock, while M. Bonpland irritated the animal strongly by an immediate contact, and received some very violent shocks. Had we placed a very delicate electroscope in the contiguous strata of water, it might possibly have been influenced at the moment when the gymnotus seemed to direct its stroke elsewhere. Prepared frogs, placed immediately on the body of a torpedo, experience, according to Galvani, a strong contraction at every discharge of the fish.

The electrical organ of the gymnoti acts only under the immediate influence of the brain and the heart. On cutting a very vigorous fish through the middle of the body, the fore part alone gave shocks. These are equally strong in whatever part of the body the fish is touched; it is most disposed, however, to omit them when the pectoral fin, the electrical organ, the lips, the eyes, or the gills, are pinched. Sometimes the animal struggles violently with a person holding it by the tail without communicating the least shock. Nor did I feel any when I made a slight incision near the pectoral fin of the fish, and galvanized the wound by the contact of two pieces of zinc and silver. The gymnotus bent itself convulsively, and raised its head out of the water, as if terrified by a sensation altogether new; but I felt no vibration in the hands which held the two metals. The most violent muscular movements are not always accompanied by electric discharges. . . .

Though employing the most delicate electrometers in various ways, insulating them on a plate of glass, and receiving very strong shocks which passed through the electrometer, I could never discover any phenomenon of attraction or repulsion. The same observation was made by M. Fahlberg at Stockholm. That philosopher, however, has seen an electric spark, as Walsh and Ingenhousz had before him, in London, by placing the gymnotus in the air, and interrupting the conducting chain by two gold leaves pasted upon glass, and a line distant from each other. No person, on the contrary, has ever perceived a spark issue from the body of the fish itself. We irritated it for a long time during the night, at Calabozo, in perfect darkness, without observing any luminous appearance. Having placed four gymnoti, of unequal strength, in such a manner as to receive the shocks of the most vigorous fish by contact, that is to say, by touching only one of the other fishes, I did not observe that these last were agitated at the moment when the current passed their bodies. Perhaps the current did not penetrate below the humid surface of the skin. We will not, however, conclude from this, that the gymnoti are insensible to electricity; and that they cannot fight with each other at the bottom of the pools. Their nervous system must be subject to the same agents as the nerves of other animals. I have indeed seen, that, on laying open their nerves, they undergo muscular contractions at the mere contact of two opposite metals; and M. Fahlberg, of Stockholm, found that his gymnotus was convulsively agitated when placed in a copper vessel, and feeble discharges from a Leyden jar passed through its skin.

After the experiments I had made on gymnoti, it became highly interesting to me, on my return to Europe, to ascertain with precision the various circumstances in which another electric fish, the torpedo of our seas, gives or does not give shocks. Though this fish had been examined by numerous men of science, I found all that had been published on its electrical effects extremely vague. It has been very arbitrarily supposed, that this fish acts like a Leyden jar, which may be discharged at will, by touching it with both hands; and this supposition appears to have led into error observers who have devoted themselves to researches of this kind. M. Gay-Lussac and myself, dur-

ing our journey to Italy, made a great number of experiments on torpedos taken in the gulf of Naples. These experiments furnish many
results somewhat different from those I collected on the gymnoti. It is
probable that the cause of these anomalies is owing rather to the in-
equality of electric power in the two fishes, than to the different disposition of their organs. . . .

The gymnoti, which are objects of curiosity and of the deepest
interest to the philosophers of Europe, are at once dreaded and detested by the natives. They furnish, indeed, in their muscular flesh,
pretty good aliment; but the electric organ fills the greater part of
their body, and this organ is slimy, and disagreeable to the taste; it is
accordingly separated with care from the rest of the eel. The presence
of gymnoti is also considered as the principal cause of the want of fish
in the ponds and pools of the Llanos. They, however, kill many more
than they devour: and the Indians told us, that when young alligators and gymnoti are caught at the same time in very strong nets, the
latter never show the slightest trace of a wound, because they disable
the young alligators before they are attacked by them. All the inhabitants of the waters dread the society of the gymnoti. Lizards, tortoises,
and frogs, seek pools where they are secure from the electric action. It
became necessary to change the direction of a road near Uritucu, because the electric eels were so numerous in one river, that they every
year killed a great number of mules, as they forded the water with
their burdens.

Though in the present state of our knowledge we may flatter ourselves with having thrown some light on the extraordinary effects of
electric fishes, yet a vast number of physical and physiological researches still remain to be made. The brilliant results which chemistry
has obtained by means of the Voltaic battery, have occupied all observers, and turned attention for some time from the examinations of
the phenomena of vitality. Let us hope that these phenomena, the
most awful and the most mysterious of all, will in their turn occupy
the earnest attention of natural philosophers. This hope will be easily
realized if they succeed in procuring anew living gymnoti in some
one of the great capitals of Europe. The discoveries that will be made
on the electromotive apparatus of these fish, much more energetic, and
more easy of preservation, than the torpedos, will extend to all the phenomena of muscular motion subject to volition. It will perhaps be
found that, in most animals, every contraction of the muscular fibre is
preceded by a discharge from the nerve into the muscle; and that the
mere simple contact of heterogeneous substances is a source of move-

ment and of life in all organized beings. Did an ingenious and lively people, the Arabians, guess from remote antiquity that the same force which inflames the vault of Heaven in storms is the living and invisible weapon of inhabitants of the waters? It is said that the electric fish of the Nile bears a name in Egypt that signifies *thunder*. . . .

ALEXANDER VON HUMBOLDT
[*Personal Narrative* (1807)]

Why the Sloth Is Slothful

[*If Humboldt was the most magisterial of travelers, Charles Waterton was probably the most eccentric. Born to a comfortable fortune, he was one of the first of the many nineteenth-century Britishers who preferred the discomforts and dangers of Africa, India, or South America to England's green and pleasant land. Anxious to be on as intimate terms as possible with the animals he loved, he once took a fourteen-foot boa constrictor to bed with him just to see what it would be like, and in South America, where he wandered for eight years, he repeatedly slept with his toes outside the tent in the hope (always disappointed) that a vampire bat would bite him. After he retired to his English estate, he lived in, rather than kept, a private zoo which included a sloth that shared his bedroom and a chimpanzee he never failed to kiss good night. Probably, however, his contemporaries found none of these eccentricities quite so odd as the fact that, during his travels in eastern North America he formed a very favorable opinion of the country, its institutions, and people. Scientists refuse to take him very seriously as a naturalist, but the flavor of the man comes through amusingly in the following exposé of the great Buffon's absurd theory that the South American sloth was designed by nature to be miserable.*]

ᕬ

Let us now turn our attention to the sloth, whose native haunts have hitherto been so little known, and probably little looked into. Those who have written on this singular animal, have remarked that he is in a perpetual state of pain, that he is proverbially slow in his movements, that he is a prisoner in space, and that as soon as he has consumed all the leaves of the tree upon which he had mounted, he rolls himself up in the form of a ball, and then falls to the ground. This is not the case.

If the naturalists who have written the history of the sloth had gone into the wilds, in order to examine his haunts and economy, they would not have drawn the foregoing conclusions; they would have learned, that though all other quadrupeds may be described while resting upon the ground, the sloth is an exception to this rule, and that his history must be written while he is in the tree.

This singular animal is destined by nature to be produced, to live and to die in the trees; and to do justice to him, naturalists must examine him in this his upper element. He is a scarce and solitary animal, and being good food, he is never allowed to escape. He inhabits remote and gloomy forests, where snakes take up their abode, and where cruelly stinging ants and scorpions, and swamps, and innumerable thorny shrubs and bushes, obstruct the step of civilized man. Were you to draw your own conclusions from the descriptions which have been given of the sloth, you would probably suspect, that no naturalist has actually gone into the wilds with the fixed determination to find him out and examine his haunts and see whether nature has committed any blunder in the formation of this extraordinary creature, which appears to us so forlorn and miserable, so ill put together, and so totally unfit to enjoy the blessings which have been so bountifully given to the rest of animated nature; for, as it has formerly been remarked, he has no soles to his feet, and he is evidently ill at ease when he tries to move on the ground, and it is then that he looks up in your face with a countenance that says, "Have pity on me, for I am in pain and sorrow."

It mostly happens that Indians and Negroes are the people who catch the sloth, and bring it to the white man: hence it may be conjectured that the erroneous accounts we have hitherto had of the sloth, have not been penned down with the slightest intention to mislead the reader, or give him an exaggerated history, but that these errors have naturally arisen by examining the sloth in those places where nature never intended that he should be exhibited.

However, we are now in his own domain. Man but little frequents these thick and noble forests, which extend far and wide on every side of us. This, then, is the proper place to go in quest of the sloth. We will first take a near view of him. By obtaining a knowledge of his anatomy, we shall be enabled to account for his movements, hereafter, when we see him in his proper haunts. His fore-legs, or, more correctly speaking, his arms, are apparently much too long, while his hind-legs are very short, and look as if they could be bent almost to the shape of a corkscrew. Both the fore and hind legs, by their form, and by the manner in which they are joined to the body, are quite incapacitated from acting in a perpendicular direction, or in supporting it on the earth, as the bodies of other quadrupeds are supported, by their legs. Hence, when you place him on the floor, his belly touches the ground. Now, granted that he supported himself on his legs like other animals, nevertheless he would be in pain, for he has no soles to his feet, and his claws are very sharp and long, and curved; so that, were his body supported by his feet it would be by their extremities, just as your body would be, were you to throw yourself on all fours, and try to support it on the ends of your toes and fingers—a trying position. Were the floor of glass, or of a polished surface, the sloth would actually be quite stationary; but as the ground is generally rough, with little protuberances upon it, such as stones, or roots of grass, &c., this just suits the sloth, and he moves his fore-legs in all directions, in order to find something to lay hold of; and when he has succeeded, he pulls himself forward, and is thus enabled to travel onwards, but at the same time in so tardy and awkward a manner, as to acquire him the name of Sloth.

Indeed his looks and his gestures evidently betray his uncomfortable situation; and as a sigh every now and then escapes him, we may be entitled to conclude that he is actually in pain.

Some years ago I kept a sloth in my room for several months. I often took him out of the house and placed him upon the ground, in order to have an opportunity of observing his motions. If the ground were rough, he would pull himself forwards, by means of his fore-legs, at a pretty good pace; and he invariably immediately shaped his course towards the nearest tree. But if I put him upon a smooth and well-trodden part of the road, he appeared to be in trouble and distress: his favourite abode was the back of a chair: and after getting all his legs in a line upon the topmost part of it, he would hang there for hours together, and often with a low and inward cry, would seem to invite me to take notice of him.

The sloth, in its wild state, spends its whole life in trees, and never leaves them but through force or by accident. An all-ruling Providence has ordered man to tread on the surface of the earth, the eagle to soar in the expanse of the skies, and the monkey and squirrel to inhabit the trees: still these may change their relative situations without feeling much inconvenience: but the sloth is doomed to spend his whole life in the trees; and, what is more extraordinary, not *upon* the branches, like the squirrel and the monkey, but *under* them. He moves suspended from the branch, he rests suspended from it, and he sleeps suspended from it. To enable him to do this, he must have a very different formation from that of any other known quadruped.

Hence his seemingly bungled conformation is at once accounted for; and in lieu of the sloth leading a painful life and entailing a melancholy and miserable existence on its progeny, it is but fair to surmise that it just enjoys life as much as any other animal, and that its extraordinary formation and singular habits are but further proofs to engage us to admire the wonderful works of Omnipotence.

It must be observed, that the sloth does not hang head-downwards like the vampire. When asleep, he supports himself from a branch parallel to the earth. He first seizes the branch with one arm, and then with the other; and after that, brings up both his legs, one by one, to the same branch; so that all four are in a line: he seems perfectly at rest in this position. Now, had he a tail, he would be at a loss to know what to do with it in this position: were he to draw it up within his legs, it would interfere with them; and were he to let it hang down, it would become the sport of the winds. Thus his deficiency of tail is a benefit to him; it is merely an apology for a tail, scarcely exceeding an inch and a half in length.

I observed, when he was climbing, he never used his arms both together, but first one and then the other, and so on alternately. There is a singularity in his hair, different from that of all other animals, and, I believe, hitherto unnoticed by naturalists; his hair is thick and coarse at the extremity, and gradually tapers to the root, where it becomes fine as a spider's web. His fur has so much the hue of the moss which grows on the branches of the trees, that it is very difficult to make him out when he is at rest.

The male of the three-toed sloth has a longitudinal bar of very fine black hair on his back, rather lower than the shoulder-blades; on each side of this black bar there is a space of yellow hair, equally fine; it has the appearance of being pressed into the body, and looks exactly as if it had been singed. If we examine the anatomy of his forelegs, we shall immediately perceive by their firm and muscular texture, how very capable they are of supporting the pendent weight of his body, both in climbing and at rest; and, instead of pronouncing them a bungled composition, as a celebrated naturalist has done, we shall consider them as remarkably well calculated to perform their extraordinary functions.

As the sloth is an inhabitant of forests within the tropics, where the trees touch each other in the greatest profusion, there seems to be no reason why he should confine himself to one tree alone for food, and entirely strip it of its leaves. During the many years I have ranged the forests, I have never seen a tree in such a state of nudity; indeed, I would hazard a conjecture, that, by the time the animal had finished the last of the old leaves, there would be a new crop on the part of the tree he had stripped first, ready for him to begin again, so quick is the process of vegetation in these countries.

There is a saying amongst the Indians, that when the wind blows, the sloth begins to travel. In calm weather he remains tranquil, probably not liking to cling to the brittle extremity of the branches, lest they should break with him in passing from one tree to another; but as soon as the wind rises, the branches of the neighbouring trees become interwoven, and then the sloth seizes hold of them, and pursues his journey in safety. There is seldom an entire day of calm in these forests. The trade-wind generally sets in about ten o'clock in the morning, and thus the sloth may set off after breakfast, and get a considerable way before dinner. He travels at a good round pace; and were you to see him pass from tree to tree, as I have done, you would never think of calling him a sloth.

Thus, it would appear that the different histories we have of this quadruped are erroneous on two accounts: first, that the writers of them, deterred by difficulties and local annoyances, have not paid sufficient attention to him in his native haunts; and secondly, they have described him in a situation in which he was never intended by nature to cut a figure; I mean on the ground. The sloth is as much at a loss to proceed on his journey upon a smooth and level floor, as a man would be who had to walk a mile in stilts upon a line of feather beds.

One day, as we were crossing the Essequibo, I saw a large two-toed sloth on the ground upon the bank; how he had got there nobody could tell: the Indian said he had never surprised a sloth in such a situation before: he would hardly have come there to drink, for both above and below the place, the branches of the trees touched the water, and afforded him an easy and safe access to it. Be this as it may, though the trees were not above twenty yards from him, he could not make his way through the sand in time enough to escape before we landed. As soon as we got up to him he threw himself upon his back, and defended himself in gallant style with his fore-legs. "Come, poor fellow," said I to him, "if thou hast got into a hobble to-day, thou shalt not suffer for it: I'll take no advantage of thee in misfortune; the forest is large enough both for thee and me to rove in: go thy ways up above, and enjoy thyself in these endless wilds: it is more than probable thou wilt never have another interview with man. So fare thee well." On saying this, I took a long stick which was lying there, held it for him to hook on, and then conveyed him to a high and stately mora. He ascended with wonderful rapidity, and in about a minute he was almost at the top of the tree. He now went off in a side direction, and caught hold of the branch of a neighbouring tree; he then proceeded towards the heart of the forest. I stood looking on, lost in amazement at his singular mode of progress. I followed him with my eye till the intervening branches closed in betwixt us; and then I lost sight for ever of the two-toed sloth. I was going to add, that I never saw a sloth take to his heels in such earnest; but the expression will not do, for the sloth has no heels.

That which naturalists have advanced of his being so tenacious of life is perfectly true. I saw the heart of one beat for half an hour after it was taken out of the body. The wourali-poison seems to be the only thing that will kill it quickly. On reference to a former part of these wanderings, it will be seen that a poisoned arrow killed the sloth in about ten minutes.

So much for this harmless, unoffending animal. He holds a conspicuous place in the catalogue of the animals of the world. Though naturalists have made no mention of what follows, still it is not less true on that account. The sloth is the only quadruped known, which spends its whole life from the branch of a tree, suspended by his feet. I have paid uncommon attention to him in his native haunts. The monkey and squirrel will seize a branch with their fore-feet, and pull themselves up, and rest or run upon it; but the sloth, after seizing it, still remains suspended, and suspended moves along under the branch, till he can lay hold of another. Whenever I have seen him in his native woods, whether at rest, or asleep, or on his travels, I have always observed that he was suspended from the branch of a tree. When his form and anatomy are attentively considered, it will appear evident that the sloth cannot be at ease in any situation, where his body is higher, or above his feet.

CHARLES WATERTON
[*Wanderings in South America* (1828)]

The Great Beast of the Plains

[Naturalists are fond of reminding us that the American robin isn't a robin, that the American elk isn't an elk, and that the American buffalo isn't a buffalo. Be that as it may, the latter was an imposing beast and represented what may well have been the greatest concentration of large animals that had existed anywhere on earth since the beginning of historical times. Not much more than a generation was needed to reduce the species almost to extinction, but it had been in the meantime so often described that a whole buffalo anthology might be compiled. An obligatory item would undoubtedly be the account of firsthand observation written by Francis Parkman, that delicate and delicately nurtured New Englander who risked everything to see for himself the great American wilderness so soon to disappear.]

Four days on the Platte, and yet no buffalo! Last year's signs of them were provokingly abundant; and wood being extremely scarce, we found an admirable substitute in the *bois de vache,* which burns like peat, producing no unpleasant effects. The wagons one morning had left the camp; Shaw and I were already on horseback, but Henry Chatillon still sat cross-legged by the dead embers of the fire, playing pensively with the lock of his rifle, while his sturdy Wyandot pony stood quietly behind him, looking over his head. At last he got up, patted the neck of the pony (which, from an exaggerated appreciation of his merits, he had christened "Five Hundred Dollar"), and then mounted, with a melancholy air.

"What is it, Henry?"

"Ah, I feel lonesome; I never been here before but I see away yonder over the buttes, and down there on the prairie, black—all black with buffalo."

In the afternoon he and I left the party in search of an antelope, until, at the distance of a mile or two on the right, the tall white
wagons and the little black specks of horsemen were just visible, so
slowly advancing that they seemed motionless; and far on the left rose
the broken line of scorched, desolate sand-hills. The vast plain waved
with tall rank grass, that swept our horses' bellies; it swayed to and fro
in billows with the light breeze, and far and near antelope and wolves
were moving through it, the hairy backs of the latter alternately appearing and disappearing as they bounded awkwardly along; while
the antelope, with the simple curiosity peculiar to them, would often
approach us closely, their little horns and white throats just visible
above the grass-tops, as they gazed eagerly at us with their round
black eyes.

I dismounted, and amused myself with firing at the wolves.
Henry attentively scrutinized the surrounding landscape; at length he
gave a shout, and called on me to mount again, pointing in the direction of the sand-hills. A mile and a half from us two black specks
slowly traversed the bare glaring face of one of them, and disappeared
behind the summit. "Let us go!" cried Henry, belaboring the sides of
"Five Hundred Dollar;" and I following in his wake, we galloped
rapidly through the rank grass toward the base of the hills.

From one of their openings descended a deep ravine, widening
as it issued on the prairie. We entered it, and galloping up, in a moment were surrounded by the bleak sand-hills. Half of their steep
sides were bare; the rest were scantily clothed with clumps of grass,
and various uncouth plants, conspicuous among which appeared the
reptile-like prickly-pear. They were gashed with numberless ravines;
and as the sky had suddenly darkened, and a cold gusty wind arisen,
the strange shrubs and the dreary hills looked doubly wild and desolate. But Henry's face was all eagerness. He tore off a little hair from
the piece of buffalo-robe under his saddle, and threw it up, to show
the course of the wind. It blew directly before us. The game were
therefore to leeward, and it was necessary to make our best speed to
get round them.

We scrambled from this ravine, and, galloping away through
the hollows, soon found another, winding like a snake among the hills,
and so deep that it completely concealed us. We rode up the bottom of
it, glancing through the bushes at its edge, till Henry abruptly jerked
his rein, and slid out of his saddle. Full a quarter of a mile distant,
on the outline of the farthest hill, a long procession of buffalo were
walking, in Indian file, with the utmost gravity and deliberation; then

more appeared, clambering from a hollow not far off, and ascending, one behind the other, the grassy slope of another hill; then a shaggy head and a pair of short broken horns issued out of a ravine close at hand, and with a slow, stately step, one by one, the enormous brutes came into view, taking their way across the valley, wholly unconscious of an enemy. In a moment Henry was worming his way, lying flat on the ground, through grass and prickly-pears, towards his unsuspecting victims. He had with him both my rifle and his own. He was soon out of sight, and still the buffalo kept issuing into the valley. For a long time all was silent; I sat holding his horse, and wondering what he was about, when suddenly, in rapid succession, came the sharp reports of the two rifles, and the whole line of buffalo, quickening their pace into a clumsy trot, gradually disappeared over the ridge of the hill. Henry rose to his feet, and stood looking after them.

"You have missed them," said I.

"Yes," said Henry; "let us go." He descended into the ravine, loaded the rifles, and mounted his horse.

We rode up the hill after the buffalo. The herd was out of sight when we reached the top, but lying on the grass, not far off, was one quite lifeless, and another violently struggling in the death-agony.

"You see I miss him!" remarked Henry. He had fired from a distance of more than a hundred and fifty yards, and both balls had passed through the lungs, the true mark in shooting buffalo.

The darkness increased, and a driving storm came on. Tying our horses to the horns of the victims, Henry began the bloody work of dissection, slashing away with the science of a connoisseur, while I vainly tried to imitate him. Old Hendrick recoiled with horror and indignation when I endeavored to tie the meat to the strings of raw hide, always carried for this purpose, dangling at the back of the saddle. After some difficulty we overcame his scruples; and, heavily burdened with the more eligible portions of the buffalo, we set out on our return. Scarcely had we emerged from the labyrinth of gorges and ravines, and issued upon the open prairie, when the prickling sleet came driving, gust upon gust, directly in our faces. It was strangely dark, though wanting still an hour of sunset. The freezing storm soon penetrated to the skin, but the uneasy trot of our heavy-gaited horses kept us warm enough, as we forced them unwillingly in the teeth of the sleet and rain, by the powerful suasion of our Indian whips. The prairie in this place was hard and level. A flourishing colony of prairie-dogs had burrowed into it in every direction, and the little mounds of fresh earth around their holes were about as numerous as the hills in a cornfield; but not a yelp was to be heard; not the nose of a single citizen was visible; all had retired to the depths of their burrows, and we envied them their dry and comfortable habitations. An hour's hard riding showed us our tent dimly looming through the storm, one side puffed out by the force of the wind, and the other collapsed in proportion, while the disconsolate horses stood shivering close around, and the wind kept up a dismal whistling in the boughs of three old half-dead trees above. Shaw, like a patriarch, sat on his saddle in the entrance, with a pipe in his mouth and his arms folded, contemplating, with cool satisfaction, the piles of meat that we flung on the ground before him. A dark and dreary night succeeded; but the sun rose, with a heat so sultry and languid that the captain excused himself on that account from waylaying an old buffalo bull, who with stupid gravity was walking over the prairie to drink at the river. So much for the climate of the Platte.

But it was not the weather alone that had produced this sudden abatement of the sportsman-like zeal which the captain had always professed. He had been out on the afternoon before, together with several members of his party; but their hunting was attended with no other result than the loss of one of their best horses, severely injured by Sorel, in vainly chasing a wounded bull. The captain, whose ideas of hard riding were all derived from transatlantic sources, expressed the utmost amazement at the feats of Sorel, who went leaping ravines, and dashing at full speed up and down the sides of precipitous hills, lashing his horse with the recklessness of a Rocky Mountain rider. Unfortunately for the poor animal, he was the property of R——, against whom Sorel entertained an unbounded aversion. The captain himself, it seemed, had also attempted to "run" a buffalo, but though a good and practised horseman, he had soon given over the attempt, being astonished and utterly disgusted at the nature of the ground he was required to ride over. . . .

"Buffalo! buffalo!" It was but a grim old bull, roaming the prairie by himself in misanthropic seclusion; but there might be more behind the hills. Dreading the monotony and languor of the camp, Shaw and I saddled our horses, buckled our holsters in their places, and set out with Henry Chatillon in search of the game. Henry, not intending to take part in the chase, but merely conducting us, carried his rifle with him, while we left ours behind as encumbrances. We rode for some five or six miles, and saw no living thing but wolves, snakes, and prairie-dogs.

"This won't do at all," said Shaw.

"What won't do?"

"There's no wood about here to make a litter for the wounded man: I have an idea that one of us will need something of the sort before the day is over."

There was some foundation for such an idea, for the ground was none of the best for a race, and grew worse continually as we proceeded; indeed, it soon became desperately bad, consisting of abrupt hills and deep hollows, cut by frequent ravines not easy to pass. At length, a mile in advance, we saw a band of bulls. Some were scattered grazing over a green declivity, while the rest were crowded together in the wide hollow below. Making a circuit, to keep out of sight, we rode towards them, until we ascended a hill, within a furlong of them, beyond which nothing intervened that could possibly screen us from their view. We dismounted behind the ridge, just out of sight, drew our saddle-girths, examined our pistols, and mounting again, rode over the hill, and descended at a canter towards them, bending close to our horses' necks. Instantly they took the alarm: those on the hill descended, those below gathered into a mass, and the whole got into motion, shouldering each other along at a clumsy gallop. We followed, spurring our horses to full speed; and as the herd rushed, crowding and trampling in terror through an opening in the hills, were close at their heels, half suffocated by the clouds of dust. But as we drew near, their alarm and speed increased; our horses, being new to the work, showed signs of the utmost fear, bounding violently aside as we approached, and refusing to enter among the herd. The buffalo now broke into several small bodies, scampering over the hills in different directions, and I lost sight of Shaw; neither of us knew where the other had gone. Old Pontiac ran like a frantic elephant up hill and down hill, his ponderous hoofs striking the prairie like sledge-hammers. He showed a curious mixture of eagerness and terror, straining to overtake the panic-stricken herd, but constantly recoiling in dismay as we drew near. The fugitives, indeed, offered no very attractive spectacle, with their shaggy manes and the tattered remnants of their last winter's hair covering their backs in irregular shreds and patches, and flying off in the wind as they ran. At length I urged my horse close behind a bull, and after trying in vain, by blows and spurring, to bring him alongside, I fired from this disadvantageous position. At the report Pontiac swerved so much that I was again thrown a little behind the game. The bullet, entering too much in the rear, failed to disable the bull; for a buffalo requires to be shot at particular points, or he will certainly escape. The herd ran up a hill, and I followed in pursuit. As Pontiac rushed headlong down on the other side, I saw Shaw and Henry descending the hollow on the right, at a leisurely gallop; and in front, the buffalo were just disappearing behind the crest of the next hill, their short tails erect, and their hoofs twinkling through a cloud of dust.

At that moment I heard Shaw and Henry shouting to me; but the muscles of a stronger arm than mine could not have checked at once the furious course of Pontiac, whose mouth was as insensible as leather. Added to this, I rode him that morning with a snaffle, having the day before, for the benefit of my other horse, unbuckled from my bridle the curb which I commonly used. A stronger and hardier brute never trod the prairie; but the novel sight of the buffalo filled him with terror, and when at full speed he was almost incontrollable. Gaining the top of the ridge, I saw nothing of the buffalo; they had all vanished amid the intricacies of the hills and hollows. Reloading my pistols, in the best way I could, I galloped on until I saw them again scuttling along at the base of the hill, their panic somewhat abated. Down went old Pontiac among them, scattering them to the right and left; and then we had another long chase. About a dozen bulls were before us, scouring over the hills, rushing down the declivities with tremendous weight and impetuosity, and then laboring with a weary gallop upward. Still Pontiac, in spite of spurring and beating, would not close with them. One bull at length fell a little behind the rest, and by dint of much effort, I urged my horse within six or eight yards of his side. His back was darkened with sweat: he was panting heavily, while his tongue lolled out a foot from his jaws. Gradually I came up abreast of him, urging Pontiac with leg and rein nearer to his side, when suddenly he did what buffalo in such circumstances will always do: he slackened his gallop, and turning towards us, with an aspect of mingled rage and distress, lowered his huge, shaggy head for a charge. Pontiac, with a snort, leaped aside in terror, nearly throwing me to the ground, as I was wholly unprepared for such an evolution. I raised my pistol in a passion to strike him on the head, but thinking better of it, fired the bullet after the bull, who had resumed his flight; then drew rein, and determined to rejoin my companions. It was high time. The breath blew hard from Pontiac's nostrils, and the sweat rolled in big drops down his sides; I myself felt as if drenched in warm water. Pledging myself to take my revenge at a future opportunity, I looked about for some indications to show me where I was, and what course I ought to pursue; I might as well have looked for landmarks in the midst of the ocean. How many miles I had run, or in what direction, I had no idea; and around me the prairie was rolling in steep swells and pitches, without a single distinctive feature to guide me. I had a little compass hung at my neck; and, ignorant that the Platte at this point diverged considerably from its easterly course, I thought that by keeping to the northward I should certainly reach it. So I turned and rode about two hours in that direction. The prairie changed as I advanced, softening away into easier undulations, but nothing like the Platte appeared, nor any sign of a human being: the same wild endless expanse lay around me still; and to all appearance I was as far from my object as ever. I began now to think myself in danger of being lost, and, reining in my horse, summoned the scanty share of woodcraft that I possessed (if that term is applicable upon the prairie) to extricate me. It occurred to me that the buffalo might prove my best guides. I soon found one of the paths made by them in their passage to the river: it ran nearly at right angles to my course; but turning my horse's head in the direction it indicated, his freer gait and erected ears assured me that I was right.

But in the mean time my ride had been by no means a solitary one. The face of the country was dotted far and wide with countless hundreds of buffalo. They tropped along in files and columns, bulls, cows, and calves, on the green faces of the declivities in front. They scrambled away over the hills to the right and left; and far off, the pale blue swells in the extreme distance were dotted with innumerable specks. Sometimes I surprised shaggy old bulls grazing alone, or sleeping behind the ridges I ascended. They would leap up at my approach, stare stupidly at me through their tangled manes, and then gallop heavily away. The antelope were very numerous; and as they are always bold when in the neighborhood of buffalo, they would approach to look at me, gaze intently with their great round eyes, then suddenly leap aside, and stretch lightly away over the prairie, as swiftly as a race-horse. Squalid, ruffian-like wolves sneaked through the hollows and sandy ravines. Several times I passed through villages of prairie-dogs, who sat, each at the mouth of his burrow, holding his paws before him in a supplicating attitude, and yelping away most vehemently, whisking his little tail with every squeaking cry he uttered. Prairie-dogs are not fastidious in their choice of companions; various long checkered snakes were sunning themselves in the midst of the village, and demure little gray owls, with a large white ring around each eye, were perched side by side with the rightful inhabitants. The prairie teemed with life. Again and again I looked toward the crowded hillsides, and was sure I saw horsemen; and riding near, with a mixture of hope and dread, for Indians were abroad, I found them transformed into a group of buffalo. There was nothing in human shape amid all this vast congregation of brute forms.

When I turned down the buffalo path the prairie seemed changed; only a wolf or two glided by at intervals, like conscious felons, never looking to the right or left. Being now free from anxiety, I was at leisure to observe minutely the objects around me; and here, for the first time, I noticed insects wholly different from any of the varieties found farther to the eastward. Gaudy butterflies fluttered about my horse's head; strangely formed beetles, glittering with metallic lustre, were crawling upon plants that I had never seen before; multitudes of lizards, too, were darting like lightning over the sand.

I had run to a great distance from the river. It cost me a long ride on the buffalo path, before I saw, from the ridge of a sand-hill, the pale surface of the Platte glistening in the midst of its desert valley, and the faint outline of the hills beyond waving along the sky. From where I stood, not a tree nor a bush nor a living thing was visible throughout the whole extent of the sun-scorched landscape. In half an hour I came upon the trail, not far from the river; and seeing that the party had not yet passed, I turned eastward to meet them, old Pontiac's long swinging trot again assuring me that I was right in doing so. Having been slightly ill on leaving camp in the morning, six or seven hours of rough riding had fatigued me extremely. I soon stopped, therefore, flung my saddle on the ground, and with my head resting on it, and my horse's trail-rope tied loosely to my arm, lay waiting the arrival of the party, speculating meanwhile on the extent of the injuries Pontiac had received. At length the white wagon coverings rose from the verge of the plain. By a singular coincidence, almost at the same moment two horsemen appeared coming down from the hills. They were Shaw and Henry, who had searched for me awhile in the morning, but well knowing the futility of the attempt in such a broken country, had placed themselves on the top of the highest hill they could find, and picketing their horses near them, as a signal to me, had lain down and fallen asleep. The stray cattle had been recovered, as the emigrants told us, about noon. Before sunset, we pushed forward eight miles farther.

"June 7, 1846.—Four men are missing: R———, Sorel, and two emigrants. They set out this morning after buffalo, and have not yet made their appearance; whether killed or lost, we cannot tell."

I find the above in my note-book, and well remember the council held on the occasion. Our fire was the scene of it; for the superiority of Henry Chatillon's experience and skill made him the resort of the whole camp upon every question of difficulty. He was moulding bullets at the fire, when the captain drew near, with a perturbed and careworn expression of countenance, faithfully reflected on the heavy features of Jack, who followed close behind. Then the emigrants came straggling from their wagons towards the common centre. Various suggestions were made, to account for the absence of the four men, and one or two of the emigrants declared that, when out after the cattle, they had seen Indians dogging them, and crawling like wolves along the ridges of the hills. At this the captain slowly shook his head with double gravity, and solemnly remarked,—

"It's a serious thing to be travelling through this cursed wilderness;" an opinion in which Jack immediately expressed a thorough coincidence. Henry would not commit himself by declaring any positive opinion.

"Maybe he only followed the buffalo too far; maybe Indian kill him; maybe he got lost; I cannot tell."

With this the auditors were obliged to rest content; the emigrants, not in the least alarmed, though curious to know what had become of their comrades, walked back to their wagons, and the captain betook himself pensively to his tent. Shaw and I followed his example.

FRANCIS PARKMAN
[The California and Oregon Trail (1849)]

Meditation on a Tortoise

[Not many years after Darwin considered the puzzle of the giant Galápagos tortoise and long before he startled the world with the theories they had helped him to form, the young Herman Melville contemplated the same antediluvian reptiles. Since Melville was a man to whom nature was an allegory rather than a mechanism, he thought very different thoughts.]

✿

TWO SIDES TO A TORTOISE

Most ugly shapes and horrible aspects,
Such as Dame Nature selfe mote feare to see,
Or shame, that ever should so fowle defects
From her most cunning hand escaped bee;
All dreadfull pourtraicts of deformitee:
Ne wonder, if these do a man appall;
For all that here at home we dreadfull hold,
Be but as bugs to fearen babes withall,
Compared to the creatures in these isles' entrall.

"Feare nought," then saide the Palmer well aviz'd,
"For these same monsters are not these in deed,
But are into these fearfull shapes disguiz'd."
And lifting up his vertuous staffe on hye,
Then all that dreadfull armie fast can flye
Into great Tethys bosome, where they hidden lye.

In view of the description given, may one be gay upon the Encantadas? Yes: that is, find one the gaiety, and he will be gay. And, indeed, sackcloth and ashes as they are, the isles are not perhaps unmitigated gloom. For while no spectator can deny their claims to a most solemn and superstitious consideration, no more than my firmest resolutions can decline to behold the spectre-tortoise when emerging from its shadowy recess; yet even the tortoise, dark and melancholy as it is upon the back, still possesses a bright side; its calipee or breast-plate being sometimes of a faint yellowish or golden tinge. Moreover, every one knows that tortoises as well as turtles are of such a make, that if you but put them on their backs you thereby expose their bright sides without the possibility of their recovering themselves, and turning into view the other. But after you have done this, and because you have done this, you should not swear that the tortoise has no dark side. Enjoy the bright, keep it turned up perpetually if you can, but be honest, and don't deny the black. Neither should he, who cannot turn the tortoise from its natural position so as to hide the darker and expose his livelier aspect, like a great October pumpkin in the sun, for that cause declare the creature to be one total inky blot. The tortoise is both black and bright. But let us to particulars.

Some months before my first stepping ashore upon the group, my ship was cruising in its close vicinity. One noon we found ourselves off the South Head of Albermarle, and not very far from the land. Partly by way of freak, and partly by way of spying out so strange a country, a boat's crew was sent ashore, with orders to see all they could, and besides, bring back whatever tortoises they could conveniently transport.

It was after sunset, when the adventurers returned. I looked down over the ship's high side as if looking down over the curb of a well, and dimly saw the damp boat deep in the sea with some unwonted weight. Ropes were dropt over, and presently three huge antediluvian-looking tortoises, after much straining, were landed on deck. They seemed hardly of the seed of earth. We had been abroad upon the waters for five long months, a period amply sufficient to make all things of the land wear a fabulous hue to the dreamy mind. Had three Spanish custom-house officers boarded us then, it is not unlikely that I should have curiously stared at them, felt of them, and stroked them much as savages serve civilized guests. But instead of three custom-house officers, behold these really wondrous tortoises— none of your schoolboy mud-turtles—but black as widower's weeds, heavy as chests of plate, with vast shells medallioned and orbed like shields, and dented and blistered like shields that have breasted a battle, shaggy, too, here and there, with dark green moss, and slimy with the spray of the sea. These mystic creatures, suddenly translated by night from unutterable solitudes to our peopled deck, affected me in a manner not easy to unfold. They seemed newly crawled forth from beneath the foundations of the world. Yea, they seemed the identical tortoises whereon the Hindoo plants this total sphere. With a lantern I inspected them more closely. Such worshipful venerableness of aspect! Such furry greenness mantling the rude peelings and healing the fissures of their shattered shells. I no more saw three tortoises. They expanded—became transfigured. I seemed to see three Roman Coliseums in magnificent decay.

Ye oldest inhabitants of this, or any other isle, said I, pray, give me the freedom of your three walled towns.

The great feeling inspired by these creatures was that of age:— dateless, indefinite endurance. And, in fact, that any other creature can live and breathe as long as the tortoise of the Encantadas, I will not readily believe. Not to hint of their known capacity of sustaining life, while going without food for an entire year, consider that impregnable armor of their living mail. What other bodily being possesses such a citadel wherein to resist the assaults of Time?

As lantern in hand, I scraped among the moss and beheld the ancient scars of bruises received in many a sullen fall among the marly mountains of the isle—scars strangely widened, swollen, half obliterate, and yet distorted like those sometimes found in the bark of very hoary trees, I seemed an antiquary of a geologist, studying the bird-tracks and ciphers upon the exhumed slates trod by incredible creatures whose very ghosts are now defunct.

As I lay in my hammock that night, overhead I heard the slow weary draggings of the three ponderous strangers along the encumbered deck. Their stupidity or their resolution was so great, that they never went aside for any impediment. One ceased his movements altogether just before the mid-watch. At sunrise I found him butted like a battering-ram against the immovable foot of the foremast, and still striving, tooth and nail, to force the impossible passage. That these tortoises are the victims of a penal, or malignant, or perhaps a downright diabolical enchanter, seems in nothing more likely than in that strange infatuation of hopeless toil which so often possesses them. I have known them in their journeyings ram themselves heroically against rocks, and long abide there, nudging, wriggling, wedging, in order to displace them, and so hold on their inflexible path. Their crowning curse is their drudging impulse to straightforwardness in a belittered world.

Meeting with no such hinderance as their companion did, the other tortoises merely fell foul of small stumbling-blocks—buckets, blocks, and coils of rigging—and at times in the act of crawling over them would slip with an astounding rattle to the deck. Listening to these draggings and concussions, I thought me of the haunt from which they came; an isle full of metallic ravines and gulches, sunk bottomlessly into the hearts of splintered mountains, and covered for many miles with inextricable thickets. I then pictured these three straightforward monsters, century after century, writhing through the shades, grim as blacksmiths; crawling so slowly and ponderously, that not only did toad-stools and all fungous things grow beneath their feet, but a sooty moss sprouted upon their backs. With them I lost myself in volcanic mazes; brushed away endless boughs of rotting thickets; till finally in a dream I found myself sitting cross-legged upon the foremost, a Brahmin similarly mounted upon either side, forming a tripod of foreheads which upheld the universal cope.

Such was the wild nightmare begot by my first impression of the Encantadas tortoise. But next evening, strange to say, I sat down with my shipmates, and made a merry repast from tortoise steaks and tortoise stews; and supper over, out knife, and helped convert the three mighty concave shells into three fanciful soup-tureens, and polished the three flat yellowish calipees into three gorgeous salvers.

HERMAN MELVILLE
[*The Encantadas* (1854)]

The River and the Jungle

[*Inspired by nothing except a love of natural history, Henry Walter Bates set sail from England for the Amazon. He was twenty-three years old and without financial resources but he traveled 1,400 miles up the Amazon and for eleven years supported himself by collections (including 8,000 new species of insects) sent back to scientific institutions. Darwin called him "second only to Humboldt in describing a tropical forest," and it was at Darwin's insistence that he wrote the book from which the following account of monkeys, vampire bats, and that absurd bird, the toucan, is taken.*]

As may have been gathered from the remarks already made, the neighbourhood of Ega was a fine field for a Natural History collector. With the exception of what could be learnt from the new specimens brought home, after transient visits, by Spix and Martius and the Count de Castelnau, whose acquisitions have been deposited in the public museums of Munich and Paris, very little was known in Europe of the animal tenants of this region; the collections that I had the opportunity of making and sending home attracted, therefore, considerable attention. Indeed, the name of my favourite village has become quite a household word amongst a numerous class of Naturalists, not only in England but abroad, in consequence of the very large number of new species (upwards of 3000) which they have had to describe, with the locality "Ega" attached to them. The discovery of new species, however, forms but a small item in the interest belonging to the study of the living creation. The structure, habits, instincts, and geographical distribution of some of the oldest-known forms supply inexhaustible materials for reflection. The few remarks I have to make on the animals of Ega will relate to the mammals, birds, and insects, and will sometimes apply to the productions of the whole Upper Amazons region. We will begin with the monkeys, the most interesting, next to man, of all animals.

Scarlet-faced Monkeys. Early one sunny morning, in the year 1855, I saw in the streets of Ega a number of Indians, carrying on their shoulders down to the port, to be embarked on the Upper Amazons steamer, a large cage made of strong lianas, some twelve feet in length and five in height, containing a dozen monkeys of the most grotesque appearance. Their bodies (about eighteen inches in height, exclusive of limbs) were clothed from neck to tail with very long, straight, and shining whitish hair; their heads were nearly bald, owing to the very short crop of thin grey hairs, and their faces glowed with the most vivid scarlet hue. As a finish to their striking physiognomy, they had bushy whiskers of a sandy colour, meeting under the chin, and reddish-yellow eyes. These red-faced apes belonged to a species called by the Indians Uakari, which is peculiar to the Ega district, and the cage with its contents was being sent as a present by Senhor Chrysostomo, the Director of Indians of the Japurá, to one of the Government officials at Rio Janeiro, in acknowledgment of having been made colonel of the new national guard. They had been obtained with great difficulty in the forests which cover the lowlands, near the principal mouth of the Japurá, about thirty miles from Ega. It was the first time I had seen this most curious of all the South American monkeys, and one that appears to have escaped the notice of Spix and Martius. I afterwards made a journey to the district inhabited by it, but did not then succeed in obtaining specimens; before leaving the country, however, I acquired two individuals, one of which lived in my house for several weeks.

Owl-faced Night Apes. A third interesting genus of monkeys, found near Ega, are the Nyctipitheci, or night apes, called Ei-á by the Indians. Of these I found two species, closely related to each other but nevertheless quite distinct, as both inhabit the same forests, namely, those of the higher and drier lands, without mingling with each other or intercrossing. They sleep all day long in hollow trees, and come forth to prey on insects and eat fruits only in the night. They are of small size, the body being about a foot long, and the tail fourteen inches, and are thickly clothed with soft grey and brown fur, similar in substance to that of the rabbit. Their physiognomy reminds one of an owl, or tiger-cat: the face is round and encircled by a ruff of whitish fur; the muzzle is not at all prominent; the mouth and chin are small; the ears are very short, scarcely appearing above the hair of the head; and the eyes are large and yellowish in colour, imparting the staring expression of nocturnal animals of prey. The forehead is whitish, and decorated with three black stripes, which in one of the species (Nyctipithecus trivirgatus) continue to the crown, and in the other (N. felinus) meet on the top of the forehead. N. trivirgatus was first described by Humboldt, who discovered it on the banks of the Cassiquiare, near the head waters of the Rio Negro.

I kept a pet animal of the N. trivirgatus for many months, a young one having been given to me by an Indian *compadre,* as a present from my newly-baptised godson. These monkeys, although sleeping by day, are aroused by the least noise; so that, when a person passes by a tree in which a number of them are concealed, he is startled by the sudden apparition of a group of little striped faces crowding a hole in the trunk. It was in this way that my compadre discovered the colony from which the one given to me was taken. I was obliged to keep my pet chained up; it therefore never became thoroughly familiar. I once saw, however, an individual of the other species (N. felinus) which was most amusingly tame. It was as lively and nimble as the Cebi, but not so mischievous and far more confiding in its disposition, delighting to be caressed by all persons who came into the house. But its owner, the Municipal Judge of Ega, Dr. Carlos Mariana, had treated it for many weeks with the greatest kindness, allowing it to sleep with him at night in his hammock, and to nestle in his bosom half the day as he lay reading. It was a great favourite with everyone, from the cleanliness of its habits and the prettiness of its features and ways. My own pet was kept in a box, in which was placed a broad-mouthed glass jar; into this it would dive, head foremost, when any one entered the room, turning round inside, and thrusting forth its inquisitive face an instant afterwards to stare at the intruder. It was very active at night, venting at frequent intervals a hoarse cry, like the suppressed barking of a dog, and scampering about the room, to the length of its tether, after cockroaches and spiders. In climbing between the box and the wall, it straddled the space, resting its hands on the palms and tips of the out-stretched fingers with the knuckles bent at an acute angle, and thus mounted to the top with the greatest facility. Although seeming to prefer insects, it ate all kinds of fruit, but would not touch raw or cooked meat, and was very seldom thirsty. I was told by persons who had kept these monkeys loose about the house, that they cleared the chambers of bats as well as insect vermin. When approached gently, my Ei-á allowed itself to be caressed; but when handled roughly, it always took alarm, biting severely, striking out its little hands, and making a hissing noise like a cat. As already related, my pet was killed by a jealous Caiarára monkey, which was kept in the house at the same time.

Barrigudo Monkeys. Ten other species of monkeys were found, in addition to those already mentioned, in the forests of the Upper Amazons. All were strictly arboreal and diurnal in their habits, and lived in flocks, travelling from tree to tree, the mothers with their children on their backs; leading, in fact, a life similar to that of the Parárauáte Indians, and, like them, occasionally plundering the plantations which lie near their line of march.

The Vampire Bat. The little grey blood-sucking Phyllostoma, mentioned in a former chapter as found in my chamber at Caripí, was not uncommon at Ega, where everyone believes it to visit sleepers and bleed them in the night. But the vampire was here by far the most abundant of the family of leaf-nosed bats. It is the largest of all the South American species, measuring twenty-eight inches in expanse of wing. Nothing in animal physiognomy can be more hideous than the countenance of this creature when viewed from the front; the large, leathery ears standing out from the sides and top of the head, the erect spear-shaped appendage on the tip of the nose, the grin and the glistening black eye, all combining to make up a figure that reminds one of some mocking imp of fable. No wonder that imaginative people have inferred diabolical instincts on the part of so ugly an animal. The vampire, however, is the most harmless of all bats, and its inoffensive character is well known to residents on the banks of the Amazons. I found two distinct species of it, one having the fur of a blackish colour, the other of a ruddy hue, and ascertained that both feed chiefly on fruits. The church at Ega was the headquarters of both kinds; I used to see them, as I sat at my door during the short evening twilights, trooping forth by scores from a large open window at the back of the altar, twittering cheerfully as they sped off to the borders of the forest. They sometimes enter houses; the first time I saw one in my chamber, wheeling heavily round and round, I mistook it for a pigeon, thinking that a tame one had escaped from the premises of one of my neighbours. I opened the stomachs of several of these bats, and found them to contain a mass of pulp and seeds of fruits mingled with a few remains of insects. The natives say they devour ripe cajús and guavas on trees in the gardens, but on comparing the seeds taken from their stomachs with those of all cultivated trees at Ega, I found they were unlike any of them; it is therefore probable that they generally resort to the forest to feed, coming to the village in the morning to sleep, because they find it more secure from animals of prey than their natural abodes in the woods.

Toucans. Cuvier's Toucan. Of this family of birds, so conspicuous from the great size and light structure of their beaks, and so characteristic of tropical American forests, five species inhabit the woods of Ega. The commonest is Cuvier's Toucan, a large bird, distinguished from its nearest relatives by the feathers at the bottom of the back being of a saffron hue, instead of red. It is found more or less numerously throughout the year, as it breeds in the neighbourhood, laying its eggs in holes of trees, at a great height from the ground. During most months of the year, it is met with in single individuals or small flocks, and the birds are then very wary. Sometimes one of these little bands of four or five is seen perched, for hours together, amongst the topmost branches of high trees, giving vent to their remarkably loud, shrill, yelping cries, one bird, mounted higher than the rest, acting, apparently, as leader of the inharmonious chorus; but two of them are often heard yelping alternately, and in different notes. These cries have a vague resemblance to the syllables Tocáno, Tocáno, and hence the Indian name of this genus of birds. At these times it is difficult to get a shot at Toucans, for their senses are so sharpened that they descry the hunter before he gets near the tree on which they are perched, although he may be half-concealed amongst the underwood, 150 feet below them. They stretch their necks downwards to look beneath, and on espying the least movement amongst the foliage, fly off to the more inaccessible parts of the forest. Solitary Toucans are sometimes met with at the same season, hopping silently up and down the larger boughs, and peering into crevices of the tree-trunks. They moult in the months from March to June, some individuals earlier, others later. This season of enforced quiet being passed, they make their appearance suddenly in the dry forest, near Ega, in large flocks, probably assemblages of birds gathered together from the neighbouring Ygapó forests, which are then flooded and cold. The birds have now become exceedingly tame and the troops travel with heavy laborious flight from bough to bough amongst the lower trees. They thus become an easy prey to hunters, and every one at Ega, who can get a gun of any sort and a few charges of powder and shot, or a blow-pipe, goes daily to the woods to kill a few brace for dinner; for, as already observed, the people of Ega live almost exclusively on stewed and roasted Toucans during the months of June and July; the birds being then very fat, and the meat exceedingly sweet and tender.

No one, on seeing a Toucan, can help asking what is the use of the enormous bill, which, in some species, attains a length of seven inches, and a width of more than two inches. A few remarks on this subject may be here introduced. The early naturalists, having seen only the bill of a Toucan, which was esteemed as a marvellous production by the *virtuosi* of the sixteenth and seventeenth centuries, concluded that the bird must have belonged to the aquatic and web-footed order, as this contains so many species of remarkable development of beak, adapted for seizing fish. Some travellers also related fabulous stories of Toucans resorting to the banks of rivers to feed on fish, and these accounts also encouraged the erroneous views of the habits of the birds which for a long time prevailed. Toucans, however, are now well known to be eminently arboreal birds, and to belong to a group (including trogons, parrots, and barbets), all of whose members are fruit-eaters. On the Amazons, where these birds are very common, no one pretends ever to have seen a Toucan walking on the ground in its natural state, much less acting the part of a swimming or wading bird. Professor Owen found, on dissection, that the gizzard in Toucans is not so well adapted for the trituration of food as it is in other vegetable feeders, and concluded, therefore, as Broderip had observed the habit of chewing the cud in a tame bird, that the great toothed bill was useful in holding and remasticating the food. The bill can scarcely be said to be a very good contrivance for seizing and crushing small birds, or taking them from their nests in crevices of trees, habits which have been imputed to Toucans by some writers. The hollow, cellular structure of the interior of the bill, its curved and clumsy shape, and the deficiency of force and precision when it is used to seize objects, suggest a want of fitness, if this be the function of the member. But fruit is undoubtedly the chief food of Toucans, and it is in reference to their mode of obtaining it that the use of their uncouth bills is to be sought.

Flowers and fruit on the crowns of the large trees of South American forests grow, principally, towards the end of slender twigs which will not bear any considerable weight; all animals, therefore, which feed upon fruit, or on insects contained in flowers, must, of course, have some means of reaching the ends of the stalks from a distance. Monkeys obtain their food by stretching forth their long arms and, in some instances, their tails, to bring the fruit near to their mouths. Humming-birds are endowed with highly-perfected organs of flight, with corresponding muscular development, by which they are enabled to sustain themselves on the wing before blossoms whilst rifling them of their contents. These strong-flying creatures, however, will, whenever they can get near enough, remain on their perches whilst probing neighbouring flowers for insects. Trogons have feeble wings, and a dull, inactive temperament. Their mode of obtaining food is to station themselves quietly on low branches in the gloomy shades of the forest, and eye the fruits on the surrounding trees darting off, as if with an effort, every time they wish to seize a mouthful, and returning to the same perch. Barbets (Capitoninæ) seem to have no especial endowment, either of habits or structure, to enable them to seize fruits; and in this respect they are similar to the Toucans, if we leave the bill out of question, both tribes having heavy bodies, with feeble organs of flight, so that they are disabled from taking their food on the wing. The purpose of the enormous bill here becomes evident. It is to enable the Toucan to reach and devour fruit whilst remaining seated, and thus to counterbalance the disadvantage which its heavy body and gluttonous appetite would otherwise give it in the competition with allied groups of birds. The relation between the extraordinarily lengthened bill of the Toucan and its mode of obtaining food, is therefore precisely similar to that between the long neck and lips of the Giraffe and the mode of browsing of the animal. The bill of the Toucan can scarcely be considered a very perfectly-formed instrument for the end to which it is applied, as here explained; but nature appears not to invent organs at once for the functions to which they are now adapted, but avails herself, here of one already-existing structure or instinct, there of another, according as they are handy when need for their further modification arises.

One day, whilst walking along the principal pathway in the woods near Ega, I saw one of these Toucans seated gravely on a low branch close to the road, and had no difficulty in seizing it with my hand. It turned out to be a runaway pet bird; no one, however, came to own it, although I kept it in my house for several months.

The bird was in a half-starved and sickly condition, but after a few days of good living it recovered health and spirits, and became one of the most amusing pets imaginable. Many excellent accounts of the habits of tame Toucans have been published, and therefore I need not describe them in detail, but I do not recollect to have seen any notice of their intelligence and confiding disposition under domestication, in which qualities my pet seemed to be almost equal to parrots.

HENRY WALTER BATES
[*The Naturalist on the Amazons* (1863)]

The Old Man of the Woods

[A century before Darwin published The Descent of Man, Lord Monboddo, a learned and eccentric Scottish lawyer, argued at great length that, zoologically considered, man was one of the primates. He settled on the orangutan (or "man of the woods" as the name means in the Malay language) as our closest living relative and got only ridicule for his pains. Curiously enough, one of the earliest and best firsthand accounts of the orangutan was written about a hundred years later by that Alfred Russel Wallace who spent many years in the remotest jungles of South America and the southeastern islands of the Pacific and who, while lying ill of a fever in the Moluccas, suddenly realized (as Darwin had a few years earlier) that the Malthusian Law might explain how the evolution of animals had come about. Darwin's shock upon receiving from Wallace a letter which anticipated the publication of his own theories is one of the classic moments of drama in the history of science.]

❧

One of my chief objects in coming to stay at Simunjon was to see the Orang-utan (or great man-like ape of Borneo) in his native haunts, to study his habits, and obtain good specimens of the different varieties and species of both sexes, and of the adult and young animals. In all these objects I succeeded beyond my expectations, and will now give some account of my experience in hunting the Orang-utan, or "Mias," as it is called by the natives; and as this name is short, and easily pronounced, I shall generally use it in preference to Simia satyrus, or Orang-utan.

Just a week after my arrival at the mines, I first saw a Mias. I was out collecting insects, not more than a quarter of a mile from the house, when I heard a rustling in a tree near, and, looking up, saw a large red-haired animal moving slowly along, hanging from the branches by its arms. It passed on from tree to tree till it was lost in the jungle, which was so swampy that I could not follow it. This mode of progression was, however, very unusual, and is more characteristic of the Hylobates than of the Orang. I suppose there was some individual peculiarity in this animal, or the nature of the trees just in this place rendered it the most easy mode of progression.

About a fortnight afterwards I heard that one was feeding in a tree in the swamp just below the house, and, taking my gun, was fortunate enough to find it in the same place. As soon as I approached, it tried to conceal itself among the foliage; but I got a shot at it, and the second barrel caused it to fall down almost dead, the two balls having entered the body. This was a male, about half-grown, being scarcely three feet high. On April 26th, I was out shooting with two Dyaks, when we found another about the same size. It fell at the first shot, but did not seem much hurt, and immediately climbed up the nearest tree, when I fired, and it again fell, with a broken arm and a wound in the body. The two Dyaks now ran up to it, and each seized hold of a hand, telling me to cut a pole, and they would secure it. But although one arm was broken, and it was only a half-grown animal, it was too strong for these young savages, drawing them up towards its mouth notwithstanding all their efforts, so that they were again obliged to leave go, or they would have been seriously bitten. It now began climbing up the tree again; and, to avoid trouble, I shot it through the heart.

On May 2nd, I again found one on a very high tree, when I had only a small 80-bore gun with me. However, I fired at it, and on seeing me, it began howling in a strange voice like a cough, and seemed in a great rage, breaking off branches with its hands and throwing them down, and then soon made off over the tree-tops. I did not care to follow it, as it was swampy, and in parts dangerous, and I might easily have lost myself in the eagerness of pursuit.

On the 12th of May I found another, which behaved in a very similar manner, howling and hooting with rage, and throwing down branches. I shot at it five times, and it remained dead on the top of the tree, supported in a fork in such a manner that it would evidently not fall. I therefore returned home, and luckily found some Dyaks, who came back with me, and climbed up the tree for the animal. This was the first full-grown specimen I had obtained; but it was a female, and not nearly so large or remarkable as the full-grown males. It was, however, 3 ft. 6 in. high, and its arms stretched out to a width of 6 ft. 6 in. I preserved the skin of this specimen in a cask of arrack, and prepared a perfect skeleton, which was afterwards purchased for the Derby Museum.

Only four days afterwards some Dyaks saw another Mias near the same place, and came to tell me. We found it to be a rather large one, very high up on a tall tree. At the second shot it fell rolling over, but almost immediately got up again and began to climb. At a third shot it fell dead. This was also a full-grown female, and while preparing to carry it home, we found a young one face downwards in the bog. This little creature was only about a foot long, and had evidently been hanging to its mother when she first fell. Luckily it did not appear to have been wounded, and after we had cleaned the mud out of its mouth it began to cry out, and seemed quite strong and active. While carrying it home it got its hands in my beard, and grasped so tightly that I had great difficulty in getting free, for the fingers are habitually bent inwards at the last joint so as to form complete hooks. At this time it had not a single tooth, but a few days afterwards it cut its two lower front teeth. Unfortunately, I had no milk to give it, as neither Malays, Chinese, nor Dyaks ever use the article, and I in vain inquired for any female animal that could suckle my little infant. I was therefore obliged to give it rice-water from a bottle with a quill in the cork, which after a few trials it learned to suck very well. This was a very meagre diet, and the little creature did not thrive well on it, although I added sugar and cocoa-nut milk occasionally, to make it more nourishing. When I put my finger in its mouth it sucked with great vigour, drawing in its cheeks with all its might in the vain effort to extract some milk, and only after persevering a long time would it give up in disgust, and set up a scream very like that of a baby in similar circumstances.

When handled or nursed, it was very quiet and contented, but when laid down by itself would invariably cry; and for the first few nights was very restless and noisy. I fitted up a little box for a cradle, with a soft mat for it to lie upon, which was changed and washed every day; and I soon found it necessary to wash the little Mias as well. After I had done so a few times, it came to like the operation, and as soon as it was dirty would begin crying, and not leave off till I took it out and carried it to the spout, when it immediately became quiet, although it would wince a little at the first rush of the cold water and make ridiculously wry faces while the stream was running over its head. It enjoyed the wiping and rubbing dry amazingly, and when I brushed its hair seemed to be perfectly happy, lying quite still with its arms and legs stretched out while I thoroughly brushed the long hair of its back and arms. For the first few days it clung desperately with all four hands to whatever it could lay hold of, and I had to be careful to keep my beard out of its way, as its fingers clutched hold of hair more tenaciously than anything else, and it was impossible to free myself without assistance. When restless it would struggle about with its hands up in the air trying to find something to take hold of, and, when it had got a bit of stick or rag in two or three of its hands, seemed quite happy. For want of something else, it would often seize its own feet, and after a time it would constantly cross its arms and grasp with each hand the long hair that grew just below the opposite shoulder. The great tenacity of its grasp soon diminished, and I was obliged to invent some means to give it exercise and strengthen its limbs. For this purpose I made a short ladder of three or four rounds, on which I put it to hang for a quarter of an hour at a time. At first it seemed much pleased, but it could not get all four hands in a comfortable position, and, after changing about several times, would leave hold of one hand after the other, and drop on to the floor. Sometimes, when hanging only by two hands, it would loose one, and cross it to the opposite shoulder, grasping its own hair; and, as this seemed much more agreeable than the stick, it would then loose the other and tumble down, when it would cross both and lie on its back quite contentedly, never seeming to be hurt by its numerous tumbles. Finding it so fond of hair, I endeavoured to make an artificial mother, by wrapping up a piece of buffalo-skin into a bundle, and suspending it about a foot from the floor. At first this seemed to suit it admirably, as it could sprawl its legs about and always find some hair, which it grasped with the greatest tenacity. I was now in hopes that I had made the little orphan quite happy; and so it seemed for some time, till it began to remember its lost parent, and try to suck. It would pull itself up close to the skin, and try about everywhere for a likely place; but, as it only succeeded in getting mouthfuls of hair and wool, it would be greatly disgusted, and scream violently, and after two or three attempts, let go altogether.

One day it got some wool into its throat, and I thought it would have choked, but after much gasping it recovered, and I was obliged to take the imitation mother to pieces again, and give up this last attempt to exercise the little creature.

After the first week I found I could feed it better with a spoon, and give it a little more varied and more solid food. Well-soaked biscuit mixed with a little egg and sugar, and sometimes sweet potatoes, were readily eaten; and it was a never-failing amusement to observe the curious changes of countenance by which it would express its approval or dislike of what was given to it. The poor little thing would lick its lips, draw in its cheeks, and turn up its eyes with an expression of the most supreme satisfaction when it had a mouthful particularly to its taste. On the other hand, when its food was not sufficiently sweet or palatable, it would turn the mouthful about with its tongue for a moment as if trying to extract what flavour there was, and then push it out between its lips. If the same food was continued, it would set up a scream and kick about violently, exactly like a baby in a passion.

After I had had the little Mias about three weeks, I fortunately obtained a young hare-lip monkey (*Macacus cynomolgus*), which, though small, was very active, and could feed itself. I placed it in the same box with the Mias, and they immediately became excellent friends, neither exhibiting the least fear of the other. The little monkey would sit upon the other's stomach, or even on its face, without the least regard to its feelings. While I was feeding the Mias, the monkey would sit by, picking up all that was spilt, and occasionally putting out its hands to intercept the spoon; and as soon as I had finished would pick off what was left sticking to the Mias's lips, and then pull open its mouth and see if any still remained inside; afterwards lying down on the poor creature's stomach as on a comfortable cushion. The little helpless Mias would submit to all these insults with the most exemplary patience only too glad to have something warm near it, which it could clasp affectionately in its arms. It sometimes, however, had its revenge; for when the monkey wanted to go away, the Mias would hold on as long as it could by the loose skin of its back or head, or by its tail, and it was only after many vigorous jumps that the monkey could make his escape.

It was curious to observe the different actions of these two animals, which could not have differed much in age. The Mias, like a very young baby, lying on its back quite helpless, rolling lazily from side to side, stretching out all four hands into the air, wishing to grasp something, but hardly able to guide its fingers to any definite object; and when dissatisfied, opening wide its almost toothless mouth, and expressing its wants by a most infantine scream. The little monkey, on the other hand, in constant motion; running and jumping about wherever it pleased, examining everything around it, seizing hold of the smallest objects with the greatest precision, balancing itself on the edge of the box, or running up a post, and helping itself to anything eatable that came in its way. There could hardly be a greater contrast, and the baby Mias looked more baby-like by the comparison.

When I had had it about a month, it began to exhibit some signs of learning to run alone. When laid upon the floor it would push itself along by its legs, or roll itself over, and thus make an unwieldy progression. When lying in the box it would lift itself up to the edge into almost an erect position, and once or twice succeeded in tumbling out. When left dirty, or hungry, or otherwise neglected, it would scream violently till attended to, varied by a kind of coughing or pumping noise, very similar to that which is made by the adult animal. If no one was in the house, or its cries were not attended to, it would be quiet after a little while, but the moment it heard a footstep would begin again harder than ever.

After five weeks it cut its two upper front teeth, but in all this time it had not grown the least bit, remaining both in size and weight the same as when I first procured it. This was no doubt owing to the want of milk or other equally nourishing food. Rice-water, rice, and biscuits were but a poor substitute, and the expressed milk of the cocoa-nut which I sometimes gave it did not quite agree with its stomach. To this I imputed an attack of diarrhœa from which the poor little creature suffered greatly, but a small dose of castor-oil operated well, and cured it. A week or two afterwards it was again taken ill, and this time more seriously. The symptoms were exactly those of intermittent fever, accompanied by watery swellings on the feet and head. It lost all appetite for its food, and, after lingering for a week a most pitiable object, died, after being in my possession nearly three months. I much regretted the loss of my little pet, which I had at one time looked forward to bringing up to years of maturity, and taking home to England. For several months it had afforded me daily amusement by its curious ways and the inimitably ludicrous expression of its little countenance. Its weight was three pounds nine ounces, its height fourteen inches, and the spread of its arm twenty-three inches. I preserved its skin and skeleton, and in doing so found that when it fell from the tree it must have broken an arm and a leg, which had, however, united so rapidly that I had only noticed the hard swellings on the limbs where the irregular junction of the bones had taken place.

Exactly a week after I had caught this interesting little animal I succeeded in shooting a full grown male Orang-utan. I had just come home from an entomologizing excursion when Charles rushed in out of breath with running and excitement, and exclaimed, interrupted by gasps. "Get the gun, sir—be quick—such a large Mias!" "Where is it?" I asked, taking hold of my gun as I spoke, which happened luckily to have one barrel loaded with ball. "Close by, sir—on the path to the mines—he can't get away." Two Dyaks chanced to be in the house at the time, so I called them to accompany me, and started off, telling Charley to bring all the ammunition after me as soon as possible. The path from our clearing to the mines led along the side of the hill a little way up its slope, and parallel with it at the foot a wide opening had been made for a road, in which several Chinamen were working, so that the animal could not escape into the swampy forests below without descending to cross the road or ascending to get round the clearings. We walked cautiously along, not making the least noise, and listening attentively for any sound which might betray the presence of the Mias, stopping at intervals to gaze upwards. Charley soon joined us at the place where he had seen the creature, and having taken the ammunition and put a bullet in the other barrel we dispersed a little, feeling sure that it must be somewhere near, as it had probably descended the hill, and would not be likely to return again. After a short time I heard a very slight rustling sound overhead, but on gazing up could see nothing. I moved about in every direction to get a full view into every part of the tree under which I had been standing, when I again heard the same noise but louder, and saw the leaves shaking as if caused by the motion of some heavy animal which moved off to an adjoining tree. I immediately shouted for all of them to come up and try to get a view, so as to allow me to have a shot. This was not an easy matter, as the Mias had a knack of selecting places with dense foliage beneath. Very soon, however, one of the Dyaks called me and pointed upwards, and on looking I saw a great red hairy body and a huge black face gazing down from a great height, as if wanting to know what was making such a disturbance below. I instantly fired, and he made off at once, so that I could not then tell whether I had hit him.

A L F R E D   R U S S E L   W A L L A C E
[*The Malay Archipelago* (1869)]

The Communist Achievement

[Thomas Belt, a Victorian mining engineer who spent years in South America, employed his spare time making natural-history observations, some of which were of first-rate importance. Like many another, he was struck by the perfected communism of the ants.]

The Ecitons are singular amongst the ants in this respect, that they have no fixed habitations, but move on from one place to another, as they exhaust the hunting grounds around them. I think *Eciton hamata* does not stay more than four or five days in one place. I have sometimes come across the migratory columns; they may easily be known by all the common workers moving in one direction, many of them carrying the larvae and pupae carefully in their jaws. Here and there one of the light-coloured officers moves backwards and forwards directing the columns. Such a column is of enormous length, and contains many thousands if not millions of individuals. I have sometimes followed them up for two or three hundred yards without getting to the end.

They make their temporary habitations in hollow trees, and sometimes underneath large fallen trunks that offer suitable hollows. A nest that I came across in the latter situation was open at one side. The ants were clustered together in a dense mass, like a great swarm of bees, hanging from the roof, but reaching to the ground below. Their innumerable long legs looked like brown threads binding together the mass, which must have been at least a cubic yard in bulk, and contained hundreds of thousands of individuals, although many columns were outside, some bringing in the pupae of ants, others the legs and dissected bodies of various insects. I was surprised to see in this living nest tubular passages leading down to the centre of the mass, kept open just as if it had been formed of inorganic materials. Down these holes the ants who were bringing in booty passed with their prey. I thrust a long stick down to the centre of the cluster, and brought out clinging to it many ants holding larvae and pupae, which probably were kept warm by the crowding together of the ants. Besides the common dark-coloured workers and light-coloured officers, I saw here many still larger individuals with enormous jaws. These they go about holding wide open in a threatening manner, and I found, contrary to my expectation, that they could give a severe bite with them, and that it was difficult to withdraw the jaws from the skin again.

One day when watching a small column of these ants, I placed a little stone on one of them to secure it. The next that approached, as soon as it discovered its situation, ran backwards in an agitated manner, and soon communicated the intelligence to the others. They rushed to the rescue, some bit at the stone and tried to move it, others seized the prisoner by the legs, and tugged with such force that I thought the legs would be pulled off, but they persevered until they got the captive free. I next covered one up with a piece of clay, leaving only the ends of its antennae projecting. It was soon discovered by its fellows, which set to work immediately, and by biting off pieces of the clay, soon liberated it. Another time I found a very few of them passing along at intervals. I confined one of these under a piece of clay, at a little distance from the line, with his head projecting. Several ants passed it, but at last one discovered it and tried to pull it out, but could not. It immediately set off at a great rate, and I thought it had deserted its comrade, but it had only gone for assistance, for in a short time about a dozen ants came hurrying up, evidently fully informed of the circumstances of the case, for they made directly for their imprisoned comrade, and soon set him free. I do not see how this action could be instinctive. It was sympathetic help, such as man only among the higher mammalia shows. The excitement and ardour with which they carried on their unflagging exertions for the rescue of their comrade could not have been greater if they had been human beings, and this to meet a danger that can be only of the rarest occurrence. Amongst the ants of Central America I place Eciton as the first in intelligence, and as such at the head of the Articulata. Wasps and bees come next, and then others of the Hymenoptera. Between ants and the lower forms of insects there is a greater difference in reasoning powers than there is between man and the lowest mammalian. A recent writer has argued that of all animals ants approach nearest to man in their social condition. Perhaps if we could learn their wonderful language we should find that even in their mental condition they also rank next to humanity.

I shall relate two more instances of the use of a reasoning faculty in these ants. I once saw a wide column trying to pass along a crumbling, nearly perpendicular, slope. They would have got very slowly over it, and many of them would have fallen, but a number having secured their hold, and reaching to each other, remained stationary, and over them the main column passed. Another time they were crossing a water-course along a small branch, not thicker than a goose-quill. They widened this natural bridge to three times its width by a number of ants clinging to it and to each other on each side, over which the column passed three or four deep; whereas excepting for this expedient they would have had to pass over in single file, and treble the time would have been consumed. Can it be contended that such insects are not able to determine by reasoning powers which is the best way of doing a thing, or that their actions are not guided by thought and reflection? This view is much strengthened by the fact that the cerebral ganglia in ants are more developed than in any other insects, and that in all the Hymenoptera, at the head of which they stand, "they are many times larger than in the less intelligent orders, such as beetles" (Darwin).

The Hymenoptera standing at the head of the Articulata, and the Mammalia at the head of the Vertebrata, it is curious to mark how in zoological history the appearance and development of these two orders (culminating in the one in the Ants, and in the other in the Primates) run parallel. The Hymenoptera and the Mammalia both make their first appearance early in the secondary period, and it is not until the commencement of the tertiary epoch that ants and monkeys appear upon the scene. There the parallel ends; no one species of ant has attained any great superiority above all its fellows, whilst man is very far in advance of all the other Primates.

When we see these intelligent insects dwelling together in orderly communities of many thousands of individuals, their social instincts developed to a high degree of perfection, making their marches with the regularity of disciplined troops, showing ingenuity in the crossing of difficult places, assisting each in danger, defending their nests at the risk of their own lives, communicating information rapidly to a great distance, making a regular division of work, the whole community taking charge of the rearing of the young, and all imbued with the stronger sense of industry, each individual labouring not for itself alone but for all its fellows—we may imagine that Sir Thomas More's description of Utopia might have been applied with greater justice to such a community than to any human society. "But in Utopia, where every man has a right to everything, they do all know that if care is taken to keep the public stores full, no private man can want anything; for among them there is no unequal distribution, so that no man is poor, nor in any necessity, and though no man has anything, yet they are all rich; for what can make a man so rich as to lead a serene and cheerful life, free from anxieties, neither apprehending want himself, nor vexed with the endless complaints of his wife? He is not afraid of the misery of his children, nor is he contriving how to raise a portion for his daughters, but is secure in this, that both he and his wife, his children and grandchildren, to as many generations as he can fancy, will all live both plentifully and happily."

THOMAS BELT
[*The Naturalist in Nicaragua* (1874)]

Far Away and Long Ago

[*W. H. Hudson was only twenty-nine years old when he sailed back to England from the South America he was never to see again but which was to remain the home of his imagination. Much of his best writing is tinged with nostalgia and softened by distance, but there is a surprising immediacy in his account of the southern puma, a very close relative of the cougar whose character Ernest Thompson Seton also defended vigorously.*]

🙠

The puma is, with the exception of some monkeys, the most playful animal in existence. The young of all the Felidæ spend a large portion of their time in characteristic gambols; the adults, however, acquire a grave and dignified demeanour, only the female playing on occasions with her offspring; but this she always does with a certain formality of manner, as if the relaxation were indulged in not spontaneously, but for the sake of the young and as being a necessary part of their education. Some writer has described the lion's assumption of gaiety as more grim than its most serious moods. The puma at heart is always a kitten, taking unmeasured delight in its frolics, and when, as often happens, one lives alone in the desert, it will amuse itself by the hour fighting mock battles or playing at hide-and-seek with imaginary companions, and lying in wait and putting all its wonderful strategy in practice to capture a passing butterfly. Azara kept a young male for four months, which spent its whole time playing with the slaves. This animal, he says, would not refuse any food offered to it; but when not hungry it would bury the meat in the sand, and when inclined to eat dig it up, and, taking it to the water-trough, wash it clean. I have only known one puma kept as a pet, and this animal, in seven or eight years had never shown a trace of ill-temper. When approached, he would lie down, purring loudly, and twist himself about a person's legs, begging to be caressed. A string or handkerchief drawn about was sufficient to keep him in a happy state of excitement for an hour; and when one person was tired of playing with him he was ready for a game with the next comer.

I was told by a person who had spent most of his life on the pampas that on one occasion, when travelling in the neighbourhood of Cape Corrientes, his horse died under him, and he was compelled to continue his journey on foot, burdened with his heavy native horse-gear. At night he made his bed under the shelter of a rock, on the slope of a stony sierra; a bright moon was shining, and about nine o'clock in the evening four pumas appeared, two adults with their two half-grown young. Not feeling the least alarm at their presence, he did not stir; and after a while they began to gambol together close to him, concealing themselves from each other among the rocks, just as kittens do, and frequently while pursuing one another leaping over him. He continued watching them until past midnight, then fell asleep, and did not wake until morning, when they had left him.

This man was an Englishman by birth, but having gone very young to South America he had taken kindly to the semi-barbarous life of the gauchos, and had imbibed all their peculiar notions, one of which is that human life is not worth very much. "What does it matter?" they often say, and shrug their shoulders, when told of a comrade's death; "so many beautiful horses die!" I asked him if he had ever killed a puma, and he replied that he had killed only one and had sworn never to kill another. He said that while out one day with another gaucho looking for cattle a puma was found. It sat up with its back against a stone, and did not move even when his companion threw the noose of his lasso over its neck. My informant then dismounted, and, drawing his knife, advanced to kill it: still the puma made no attempt to free itself from the lasso, but it seemed to know, he said, what was coming, for it began to tremble, the tears ran from its eyes, and it whined in the most pitiful manner. He killed it as it sat there unresisting before him, but after accomplishing the deed felt that he had committed a murder. It was the only thing he had ever done in his life, he added, which filled him with remorse when he remembered it. This I thought a rather startling declaration, as I knew that he had killed several individuals of his own species in duels, fought with knives, in the fashion of the gauchos.

All who have killed or witnessed the killing of the puma—and I have questioned scores of hunters on this point—agree that it resigns itself in this unresisting, pathetic manner to death at the hands of man. Claudio Gay, in his *Natural History of Chile,* says, "When attacked by man its energy and daring at once forsake it, and it becomes a weak, inoffensive animal, and trembling, and uttering piteous moans, and shedding abundant tears, it seems to implore compassion from a generous enemy." The enemy is not often generous; but many gauchos have assured me, when speaking on this subject, that although they kill the puma readily to protect their domestic animals, they consider it an evil thing to take its life in desert places, where it is man's only friend among the wild animals.

When the hunter is accompanied by dogs, then the puma, instead of drooping and shedding tears, is roused to a sublime rage: its hair stands erect; its eyes shine like balls of green flame; it spits and snarls like a furious tom cat. The hunter's presence seems at such times to be ignored altogether, its whole attention being given to the dogs and its rage directed against them. In Patagonia a sheep-farming Scotchman, with whom I spent some days, showed me the skulls of five pumas which he had shot in the vicinity of his ranch. One was of an exceptionally large individual, and I here relate what he told me of his encounter with this animal, as it shows just how the puma almost invariably behaves when attacked by man and dogs. He was out on foot with his flock, when the dogs discovered the animal concealed among the bushes. He had left his gun at home, and having no weapon, and finding that the dogs dared not attack it where it sat in a defiant attitude with its back against a thorny bush, he looked about and found a large dry stick, and going boldly up to it tried to stun it with a violent blow on the head. But though it never looked at him, its fiery eyes gazing steadily at the dogs all the time, he could not hit it, for with a quick side movement it avoided every blow. The small heed the puma paid him, and the apparent ease with which it avoided his best-aimed blows, only served to rouse his spirit, and at length striking with increased force his stick came to the ground and was broken to pieces. For some moments he now stood within two yards of the animal perfectly defenceless and not knowing what to do. Suddenly it sprang past him, actually brushing against his arm with its side, and began pursuing the dogs round and round among the bushes. In the end my informant's partner appeared on the scene with his rifle, and the puma was shot.

In encounters of this kind the most curious thing is that the puma steadfastly refuses to recognize an enemy in man, although it finds him acting in concert with its hated canine foe, about whose hostile intentions it has no such delusion.

It is said that when taken adult pumas invariably pine away and die; when brought up in captivity they invariably make playful, affectionate pets, and are gentle towards all human beings, but very seldom overcome their instinctive animosity towards the dog.

I shall, in conclusion, relate here the story of Maldonada, which is not generally known, although familiar to Buenos Ayreans as the story of Lady Godiva's ride through Coventry is to the people of that town. The case of Maldonada is circumstantially narrated by Rui Diaz de Guzman, in his history of the colonization of the Plata: he was a person high in authority in the young colonies, and is regarded by students of South American history as an accurate and sober-minded chronicler of the events of his own times. He relates that in the year 1536 the settlers at Buenos Ayres, having exhausted their provisions, and being compelled by hostile Indians to keep within their pallisades, were reduced to the verge of starvation. The Governor Mendoza went off to seek help from the other colonies up the river, deputing his authority to one Captain Ruiz, who, according to all accounts, displayed an excessively tyrannous and truculent disposition while in power. The people were finally reduced to a ration of six ounces of flour per day for each person; but as the flour was putrid and only made them ill, they were forced to live on any small animals they could capture, including snakes, frogs and toads. Some horrible details are given by Rui Diaz, and other writers; one, Del Barco Centenera, affirms that of two thousand persons in the town eighteen hundred

perished of hunger. During this unhappy time, beasts of prey in large numbers were attracted to the settlement by the effluvium of the corpses, buried just outside the pallisades; and this made the condition of the survivors more miserable still, since they could venture into the neighbouring woods only at the risk of a violent death. Nevertheless, many did so venture, and among these was the young woman Maldonada, who, losing herself in the forest, strayed to a distance, and was eventually found by a party of Indians, and carried by them to their village.

Some months later, Captain Ruiz discovered her whereabouts, and persuaded the savages to bring her to the settlement; then, accusing her of having gone to the Indian village in order to betray the colony, he condemned her to be devoured by wild beasts. She was taken to a wood at a distance of a league from the town, and left there, tied to a tree, for the space of two nights and a day. A party of soldiers then went to the spot, expecting to find her bones picked clean by the beasts, but were greatly astonished to find Maldonada still alive, without hurt or scratch. She told them that a puma had come to her aid, and had kept at her side, defending her life against all the other beasts that approached her. She was instantly released, and taken back to the town, her deliverance through the action of the puma probably being looked on as a direct interposition of Providence to save her.

Rui Diaz concludes with the following paragraph, in which he affirms that he knew the woman Maldonada, which may be taken as proof that she was among the few that survived the first disastrous settlement and lived on to more fortunate times: his pius pun on her name would be lost in a translation: *"De esta manera quedó libre la que ofrecieron a las fieras: la cual mujer yo la conocí, y la llamaban la Maldonada, que mas bien se le podia llamar la* BIENDONADA; *pues por este suceso se ha de ver no haber merecido el castigo á que la ofrecieron."*

If such a thing were to happen now, in any portion of southern South America, where the puma's disposition is best known, it would not be looked on as a miracle, as it was, and that unavoidably, in the case of Maldonada.

W. H. HUDSON
[*The Naturalist in La Plata* (1892)]

Sheep Without Shepherds

[Among all the naturalists of Europe and America John Muir experienced most vividly and described most convincingly an instinctive delight in vastness, solitude, and that "wilderness" of which Thoreau could only dream in his tamed New England. That is why, no doubt, the ousel was his favorite bird and the mountaineering bighorn sheep his favorite mammal.]

The wild sheep ranks highest among the animal mountaineers of the Sierra. Possessed of keen sight and scent, and strong limbs, he dwells secure amid the loftiest summits, leaping unscathed from crag to crag, up and down the fronts of giddy precipices, crossing foaming torrents and slopes of frozen snow, exposed to the wildest storms, yet maintaining a brave, warm life, and developing from generation to generation in perfect strength and beauty.

Nearly all the lofty mountain-chains of the globe are inhabited by wild sheep, most of which, on account of the remote and all but inaccessible regions where they dwell, are imperfectly known as yet.

While engaged in the work of exploring high regions where they delight to roam I have been greatly interested in studying their habits. In the months of November and December, and probably during a considerable portion of midwinter, they all flock together, male and female, old and young. I once found a complete band of this kind numbering upward of fifty, which, on being alarmed, went bounding away across a jagged lava-bed at admirable speed, led by a majestic old ram, with the lambs safe in the middle of the flock.

In spring and summer, the full-grown rams form separate bands of from three to twenty, and are usually found feeding along the edges of glacier meadows, or resting among the castle-like crags of the high summits; and whether quietly feeding, or scaling the wild cliffs, their noble forms and the power and beauty of their movements never fail to strike the beholder with lively admiration.

Their resting-places seem to be chosen with reference to sunshine and a wide outlook, and most of all to safety. Their feeding-grounds are among the most beautiful of the wild gardens, bright with daisies and gentians and mats of purple bryanthus, lying hidden away on rocky headlands and cañon sides, where sunshine is abundant, or down in the shady glacier valleys, along the banks of the streams and lakes, where the plushy sod is greenest. Here they feast all summer, the happy wanderers, perhaps relishing the beauty as well as the taste of the lovely flora on which they feed.

When the winter storms set in, loading their highland pastures with snow, then, like the birds, they gather and go to lower climates, usually descending the eastern flank of the range to the rough, volcanic table-lands and treeless ranges of the Great Basin adjacent to the Sierra. They never make haste, however, and seem to have no dread of storms, many of the strongest only going down leisurely to bare, wind-swept ridges, to feed on bushes and dry bunch-grass, and then returning up into the snow. Once I was snow-bound on Mount Shasta for three days, a little below the timber line. It was a dark and stormy time, well calculated to test the skill and endurance of mountaineers. The snow-laden gale drove on night and day in hissing, blinding floods, and when at length it began to abate, I found that a small band of wild sheep had weathered the storm in the lee of a clump of Dwarf Pines a few yards above my storm-nest, where the snow was eight or ten feet deep. I was warm back of a rock, with blankets, bread, and fire. My brave companions lay in the snow, without food, and with only the partial shelter of the short trees, yet they made no sign of suffering or faint-heartedness.

In the months of May and June, the wild sheep bring forth their young in solitary and almost inaccessible crags, far above the nesting-rocks of the eagle. I have frequently come upon the beds of the ewes and lambs at an elevation of from 12,000 to 13,000 feet above sea-level. These beds are simply oval-shaped hollows, pawed out among loose, disintegrating rock-chips and sand, upon some sunny spot commanding a good outlook, and partially sheltered from the winds that sweep those lofty peaks almost without intermission. Such is the cradle of the little mountaineer, aloft in the very sky; rocked in storms, curtained in clouds, sleeping in thin, icy air; but, wrapped in his hairy coat, and nourished by a strong, warm mother, defended from the talons of the eagle and the teeth of the sly coyote, the bonny lamb grows apace. He soon learns to nibble the tufted rockgrasses and leaves of the white spiræa; his horns begin to shoot, and before summer is done he is strong and agile, and goes forth with the flock, watched by the same divine love that tends the more helpless human lamb in its cradle by the fireside.

Nothing is more commonly remarked by noisy, dusty trail-travelers in the Sierra than the want of animal life—no song-birds, no deer, no squirrels, no game of any kind, they say. But if such could only go away quietly into the wilderness, sauntering afoot and alone with natural deliberation, they would soon learn that these mountain mansions are not without inhabitants, many of whom, confiding and gentle, would not try to shun their acquaintance.

The gray, boulder-chafed river was singing loudly through the valley, but above its massy roar I heard the booming of a waterfall, which drew me eagerly on; and just as I emerged from the tangled groves and brier-thickets at the head of the valley, the main fork of the river came in sight, falling fresh from its glacier fountains in a snowy cascade, between granite walls 2000 feet high. The steep incline down which the glad waters thundered seemed to bar all farther progress. It was not long, however, before I discovered a crooked seam in the rock, by which I was enabled to climb to the edge of a terrace that crosses the cañon, and divides the cataract nearly in the middle. Here I sat down to take breath and make some entries in my note-book, taking advantage, at the same time, of my elevated position above the trees to gaze back over the valley into the heart of the noble landscape, little knowing the while what neighbors were near.

After spending a few minutes in this way, I chanced to look across the fall, and there stood three sheep quietly observing me. Never did the sudden appearance of a mountain, or fall, or human friend more forcibly seize and rivet my attention. Anxiety to observe accurately held me perfectly still. Eagerly I marked the flowing undulations of their firm, braided muscles, their strong legs, ears, eyes, heads, their graceful rounded necks, the color of their hair, and the bold, up-sweeping curves of their noble horns. When they moved I watched every gesture, while they, in no wise disconcerted either by my attention or by the tumultuous roar of the water, advanced deliberately alongside the rapids, between the two divisions of the cataract, turning now and then to look at me. Presently they came to a steep, ice-burnished acclivity, which they ascended by a succession of quick, short, stiff-legged leaps, reaching the top without a struggle. This was the most startling feat of mountaineering I had ever witnessed, and, considering only the mechanics of the thing, my astonishment could hardly have been greater had they displayed wings and taken to flight. "Sure-footed" mules on such ground would have fallen and rolled like loosened boulders. Many a time, where the slopes are far lower, I have been compelled to take off my shoes and stockings, tie them to my belt, and creep barefooted, with the utmost caution. No wonder then, that I watched the progress of these animal mountaineers with keen sympathy, and exulted in the boundless sufficiency of wild nature displayed in their invention, construction, and keeping. A few minutes later I caught sight of a dozen more in one band, near the foot of the upper fall. They were standing on the same side of the river with me, only twenty-five or thirty yards away, looking as unworn and perfect as if created on the spot. It appeared by their tracks, which I had seen in the Little Yosemite, and by their present position, that when I came up the cañon they were all feeding together down in the valley, and in their haste to reach high ground, where they could look about them to ascertain the nature of the strange disturbance, they were divided, three ascending on one side the river, the rest on the other.

The main band, headed by an experienced chief, now began to cross the wild rapids between the two divisions of the cascade. This was another exciting feat; for, among all the varied experiences of mountaineers, the crossing of boisterous, rock-dashed torrents is found to be one of the most trying to the nerves. Yet these fine fellows walked fearlessly to the brink, and jumped from boulder to boulder, holding themselves in easy poise above the whirling, confusing current, as if they were doing nothing extraordinary.

In the immediate foreground of this rare picture there was a fold of ice-burnished granite, traversed by a few bold lines in which rock-ferns and tufts of bryanthus were growing, the gray cañon walls on the sides, nobly sculptured and adorned with brown cedars and pines; lofty peaks in the distance, and in the middle ground the snowy fall, the voice and soul of the landscape; fringing bushes beating time to its thunder-tones, the brave sheep in front of it, their gray forms slightly obscured in the spray, yet standing out in good, heavy relief against the close white water, with their huge horns rising like the upturned roots of dead pine-trees, while the evening sunbeams streaming up the cañon colored all the picture a rosy purple and made it glorious. After crossing the river, the dauntless climbers, led by their chief, at once began to scale the cañon wall, turning now right, now left, in long, single file, keeping well apart out of one another's way, and leaping in regular succession from crag to crag, now ascending slippery dome-curves, now walking leisurely along the edges of precipices, stopping at times to gaze down at me from some flat-topped rock, with heads held aslant, as if curious to learn what I thought about it, or whether I was likely to follow them. After reaching the top of the wall, which, at this place, is somewhere between 1500 and 2000 feet high, they were still visible against the sky as they lingered, looking down in groups of twos or threes.

Throughout the entire ascent they did not make a single awkward step, or an unsuccessful effort of any kind. I have frequently seen tame sheep in mountains jump upon a sloping rock-surface, hold on tremulously a few seconds, and fall back baffled and irresolute. But in the most trying situations, where the slightest want or inaccuracy would have been fatal, these always seemed to move in comfortable reliance on their strength and skill, the limits of which they never appeared to know. Moreover, each one of the flock, while following the guidance of the most experienced, yet climbed with intelligent independence as a perfect individual, capable of separate existence whenever it should wish or be compelled to withdraw from the little clan. The domestic sheep, on the contrary, is only a fraction of an animal, a whole flock being required to form an individual, just as numerous flowerets are required to make one complete sunflower.

Those shepherds who, in summer, drive their flocks to the mountain pastures, and, while watching them night and day, have seen them frightened by bears and storms, and scattered like wind-driven chaff, will, in some measure, be able to appreciate the self-reliance and strength and noble individuality of Nature's sheep.

Like the Alp-climbing ibex of Europe, our mountaineer is said to plunge headlong down the faces of sheer precipices, and alight on his big horns. I know only two hunters who claim to have actually witnessed this feat; I never was so fortunate. They describe the act as a diving head-foremost. The horns are so large at the base that they cover the upper portion of the head down nearly to a level with the eyes, and the skull is exceedingly strong. I struck an old, bleached specimen on Mount Ritter a dozen blows with my ice-ax without breaking it. Such skulls would not fracture very readily by the wildest rock-diving, but other bones could hardly be expected to hold together in such a performance; and the mechanical difficulties in the way of controlling their movements, after striking upon an irregular surface, are, in themselves, sufficient to show this boulder-like method of progression to be impossible, even in the absence of all other evidence on the subject; moreover the ewes follow wherever the rams may lead, although their horns are mere spikes. I have found many pairs of the horns of the old rams considerably battered, doubtless a result of fighting. I was particularly interested in the question, after witnessing the performances of this San Joaquin band upon the glaciated rocks at the foot of the falls; and as soon as I procured specimens and examined their feet, all the mystery disappeared. The secret, considered in connection with exceptionally strong muscles, is simply this: the wide posterior portion of the bottom of the foot, instead of wearing down and becoming flat and hard, like the feet of tame sheep and horses, bulges out in a soft, rubber-like pad or cushion, which not only grips and holds well on smooth rocks, but fits into small cavities, and down upon or against slight protuberances. Even the hardest portions of the edge of the hoof are comparatively soft and elastic; furthermore, the toes admit of an extraordinary amount of both lateral and vertical movement, allowing the foot to accommodate itself still more perfectly to the irregularities of rock surfaces, while at the same time increasing the gripping power.

At the base of Sheep Rock, one of the winter strongholds of the Shasta flocks, there lives a stock-raiser who has had the advantage of observing the movements of wild sheep every winter; and, in the course of a conversation with him on the subject of their diving habits, he pointed to the front of a lava headland about 150 feet high, which is only eight or ten degrees out of the perpendicular. "There," said he, "I followed a band of them fellows to the back of that rock yonder, and expected to capture them all, for I thought I had a dead thing on them. I got behind them on a narrow bench that runs along the face of the wall near the top and comes to an end where they couldn't get away without falling and being killed; but they jumped off, and landed all right, as if that were the regular thing with them."

"What!" said I. "Jumped 150 feet perpendicular! Did you see them do it?"

"No," he replied, "I didn't see them going down, for I was behind them; but I saw them go off over the brink, and then I went below and found their tracks where they struck on the loose rubbish at the bottom. They just *sailed right off,* and landed on their feet right side up. That is the kind of animal *they* is—beats anything else that goes on four legs."

On another occasion, a flock that was pursued by hunters retreated to another portion of this same cliff where it is still higher, and, on being followed, they were seen jumping down in perfect order, one behind another, by two men who happened to be chopping where they had a fair view of them and could watch their progress from top to bottom of the precipice. Both ewes and rams made the frightful descent without evincing any extraordinary concern, hugging the rock closely, and controlling the velocity of their half falling, half leaping movements by striking at short intervals and holding back with their cushioned, rubber feet upon small ledges and roughened inclines until near the bottom, when they "sailed off," into the free air and alighted on their feet, but with their bodies so nearly in a vertical position that they appeared to be diving.

It appears, therefore, that the methods of this wild mountaineering become clearly comprehensible as soon as we make ourselves acquainted with the rocks, and the kind of feet and muscles brought to bear upon them.

JOHN MUIR
[*The Mountains of California* (1894)]

CRUELTY AND FELLOW FEELING

The life of animals and plants is preserved not for themselves but for man.

THOMAS AQUINAS
Summa Theologica

Plants and animals are mere machines . . . Brutes . . . act by force of nature and by springs like a clock.

RENÉ DESCARTES
Letter to the Marquis of Newcastle

The question is not, can they reason. Nor, can they talk, but, can they suffer.

JEREMY BENTHAM
The Principles of Morals and Legislation

Kill not the moth nor butterfly
For the Last Judgment draweth nigh.

WILLIAM BLAKE
Auguries of Innocence

He prayeth best, who loveth best
All things both great and small;

SAMUEL TAYLOR COLERIDGE
The Ancient Mariner

When a man wants to murder a tiger he calls it sport; when the tiger wants to murder him he calls it ferocity.

BERNARD SHAW
The Revolutionist's Handbook

I am not the sloppy sentimental type that thinks it terrible to shoot birds and animals. What else are they good for?

Reply of a Florida lady to a questionnaire

Man's Best Friend

[Though the Greeks were not conspicuous animal lovers they built no arenas, and the fidelity of the dog must have been already a familiar theme—as witness the famous passage in the Odyssey where the home-coming Odysseus, unrecognized by any human being, is greeted by his dog.]

🐕

Meantime Odysseus and the noble swineherd halted as they drew near, while round them came notes of the hollow lyre; for Phemius lifted up his voice to sing before the suitors. And taking the swineherd by the hand, Odysseus said:

"Surely, Eumaeus, this is the goodly palace of Odysseus, easy to notice even among many. Building joins building here. The court is built with wall and cornice, and a double gate protects. No man may scorn it. I notice too that a great company are banqueting within; for the savory steam mounts up, and in the house resounds the lyre, made by the gods the fellow of the feast."

And, swineherd Eumaeus, you answered him and said: "You notice quickly, dull of thought in nothing. Come then and let us plan what we must do. You enter the stately buildings first and mingle with the suitors, while I stay here behind; or if you like, wait you, and I will go. But do not linger long, or somebody may spy you at the door and throw a stone or strike you. Take care, I say!"

Then long-tried royal Odysseus answered: "I see, I understand; you speak to one who knows. But go you on before, I will stay here behind: for I am not unused to blows and missiles. Stanch is my soul; for many dangers have I borne from waves and war. To those let this be added. Yet I cannot disregard a gnawing belly, the pest which brings so many ills to men. To ease it, timbered ships are fitted and carry woe to foemen over barren seas."

So they conversed together. But a dog lying near lifted his head and ears. Argos it was, the dog of hardy Odysseus, whom long ago he reared but never used. Before the dog was grown, Odysseus went to sacred Ilios. In the times past young men would take him on the chase, for wild goats, deer, and hares; but now he lay neglected, his master gone away, upon the pile of dung which had been dropped before the door by mules and oxen, and which lay there in a heap for slaves to carry off and dung the broad lands of Odysseus. Here lay the dog, this Argos, full of fleas. Yet even now, seeing Odysseus near, he wagged his tail and dropped both ears, but toward his master he had not strength to move. Odysseus turned aside and wiped away a tear, swiftly concealing from Eumaeus what he did; then straightway thus he questioned:

"Eumaeus, it is strange this dog lies on the dung-hill. His form is good; but I am not sure if he has speed of foot to match his beauty, or if he is merely what the table-dogs become which masters keep for show."

And, swineherd Eumaeus, you answered him and said: "Aye truly, that is the dog of one who died afar. If he were as good in form and action as when Odysseus left him and went away to Troy, you would be much surprised to see his speed and strength. For nothing could escape him in the forest-depths, no creature that he started; he was keen upon the scent. Now he has come to ill. In a strange land his master perished, and the slack women give him no more care; for slaves, when masters lose control, will not attend to duties. Ah, half the value of a man far-seeing Zeus destroys when the slave's lot befalls him!"

HOMER
[*The Odyssey*]

The Little Brothers of St. Francis

[During the Middle Ages interest in animals (except insofar as a moral could be drawn from their supposed behavior) seems to have been generally frowned upon by the severer moralists, but there are exceptions to all generalizations, and if St. Francis was not typical he was at least not condemned.]

It befell on a day that a certain young man had caught many turtle-doves: and as he was carrying them for sale, Saint Francis, who had ever a tender pity for gentle creatures, met him, and looking on those turtle-doves with pitying eyes, said to the youth: "I pray thee give them me, that birds so gentle, unto which the Scripture likeneth chaste and humble and faithful souls, may not fall into the hands of cruel men that would kill them." Forthwith, inspired of God, he gave them all to Saint Francis; and he receiving them into his bosom, began to speak tenderly unto them: "O my sisters, simple-minded turtle-doves, innocent and chaste, why have you let yourselves be caught? Now would I fain deliver you from death and make you nests, that ye may be fruitful and multiply, according to the commandments of your Creator." And Saint Francis went and made nests for them all: and they abiding therein, began to lay their eggs and hatch them before the eyes of the brothers: and so tame were they, they dwelt with Saint Francis and all the other brothers as though they had been fowls that had always fed from their hands, and never did they go away until Saint Francis with his blessing gave them leave to go.

And as with great fervor he was going on the way, he lifted up his eyes and beheld some trees hard by the road whereon sat a great company of birds well-nigh without number; whereat Saint Francis marvelled, and said to his companions: "Ye shall wait for me here upon the way and I will go to preach unto my little sisters, the birds." And he went unto the field and began to preach unto the birds that were upon the ground; and immediately those that were on the trees flew down to him, and they all of them remained still and quiet together, until Saint Francis made an end of preaching: and not even then did they depart, until he had given them his blessing. And according to what Brother Masseo afterwards related unto Brother Jacques da Massa, Saint Francis went among them touching them with his cloak, howbeit none moved from out his place. The sermon that Saint Francis preached unto them was after this fashion: "My little sisters, the birds, much bounden ye are to God, your Creator, and always in every place ought ye to praise Him, for that He hath given you liberty to fly about everywhere, and hath also given you double and triple raiment; moreover He preserved your seed in the ark of Noah, that your race might not perish out of the world; still more are ye beholden to Him for the element of the air which He hath appointed for you; beyond all this, ye sow not, neither do ye reap; and God feedeth you, and giveth you the streams and fountains for your drink; the mountains and the valleys for your refuge and the high trees whereon to make your nests; and because ye know not how to spin or sew, God clotheth you, you and your children; wherefore your Creator loveth you much, seeing He hath bestowed on you so many benefits; and therefore, my little sisters, beware of the sin of ingratitude, and study always to give praises unto God." Whenas Saint Francis spake these words to them, those birds began all of them to open their beaks, and stretch their necks, and spread their wings, and reverently bend their heads down to the ground, and by their acts and by their songs to show that the holy Father gave them joy exceeding great. And Saint Francis rejoiced with them, and was glad, and marvelled much at so great a company of birds and their most beautiful diversity and their good heed and sweet friendliness, for which cause he devoutly praised their Creator in them. At the last, having ended the preaching, Saint Francis made over them the sign of the cross, and gave them leave to go away; and thereby with wondrous singing all the birds rose up in the air; and then, in the fashion of the cross that Saint Francis had made over them, divided themselves into four parts; and the one part flew toward the East, and the other toward the West, and the other toward the South, and the fourth towards the North, and each flight went on its way singing wondrous songs.

ANONYMOUS
[*The Little Flowers of St. Francis of Assisi* (14th century)]

No Pets Permitted

[*Chaucer's medieval nun was close enough to St. Francis to weep if anyone was harsh with her little dog, but there is documentary evidence that many authorities regarded animal pets as an intolerable frivolity.*]

✒

Whereas we have convinced ourselves by clear proofs that some of the nuns of your house bring with them to church birds, rabbits, hounds, and such like frivolous things, whereunto they give more heed than to the office of the church, with frequent hindrance to their own psalmody, and that of their fellow nuns, and to the grevious peril of their souls—therefore we strictly forbid you and all several, in virtue of the obedience due unto Us, that ye presume henceforth to bring to church no birds, hounds, rabbits or other frivolous things that promote indiscipline."

WILLIAM OF WYKEHAM
[14th Century]
[Quoted in "The Love of Animals" by Dix Harwood]

Mr. Pepys Is Not Amused

[Sporadic protests against sadistic pleasure go back at least to the fifteenth century and they continued with increasing frequency until compassion became a cardinal virtue during the eighteenth-century enlightenment. Here are three significant passages, one from the fifteenth, the other two from the late seventeenth century.]

When God forbade man to eat flesh, He forbade him to slay beasts in any cruel way, or out of any liking for shrewness. Therefore, He said, "Eat ye no flesh with blood [Gen. IX], that is to say, with cruelty: for I shall seek the blood of your souls, at the hands of all beasts." That is to say: I shall take vengeance for all the beasts that are slain only out of cruelty of soul and a liking for shrewness. For God that made all hath care of all, and He will take vengeance upon all that misuse His creatures. Therefore, Solomon saith, "that He will arm creatures in vengeance on their enemies" [Wisd. V]; and so men should have thought for birds and beasts and not harm them without cause, in taking regard they are God's creatures. Therefore, they that out of cruelty and vanity behead beasts, and torment beasts or fowl, more than is proper for men's living, they sin in case full grievously.

ANONYMOUS
[*Dives et Pauper* (15th century)]

🐎

But, Lord, to see the strange variety of people—from Parliament man, by name Wildes, that was Deptuy-Governor of the Tower when Robinson was Lord Mayor, to the poorest 'prentices, bakers, brewers, butchers, draymen, and what not—and all these fellows one with another in swearing, cursing, and betting, and yet I would not but have seen it once. I soon had enough of it, it being strange to observe the natures of these poor creatures; how they will fight till they drop down dead upon the table and strike after they are ready to give up the ghost, not offering to run away when they are weary or wounded past doing further, whereas when a dunghill brood comes, he will, after a sharp stroke that pricks him, run off the stage, and then they wring his neck without much more ado. Whereas the other they preserve, though their eyes be both out, for breed only of a true cock of the game. Sometimes a cock that has had ten to one against him will by chance give an unlucky blow, and will strike the other stark dead in a moment, that he never stirs more; but the common rule is that though a cock neither runs nor dies, yet if any man will bet £10 to a crown and nobody take the bet, the game is given over, and not sooner. One thing more, it is strange to see how people of this poor rank, that look as if they had not bread to put in their mouths, shall bet three or four pounds at one bet and lose it, and yet bet as much the next battle (so they call every match of two cocks), so that one of them will lose £10 or £20 at a meeting; thence having had enough of it.

SAMUEL PEPYS
[*Diary* (December 21, 1663)]

🐎

. . . so home and dined, and after dinner, with my wife and Mercer to the Beare-garden, where I have not been, I think, of many years, and saw some good sport of the bull's tossing of the dogs: one into the very boxes. But it is a very rude and nasty pleasure. We had a great many hectors in the same box with us (and one very fine went into the pit and played the dogs for a wager, which was a strange sport for a gentleman) . . . Then home, well enough satisfied, however, with the variety of the afternoon's exercise.

SAMUEL PEPYS
[*Diary* (August 14, 1665)]

Sweet Reason

[*Far ahead of his time in his compassion for the animal world was the 16th century writer-philosopher, Michel de Montaigne. Although he did not recognize "beasts" as our fellow creatures, his humane attitude is a welcome exception in an age of cruelty.*]

Those natures that are sanguinary toward beasts discover a natural propension to cruelty. After they had accustomed themselves at Rome to spectacles of the slaughter of animals, they proceeded to those of the slaughter of men, to the gladiators. Nature has, herself, I fear, imprinted in man a kind of instinct to inhumanity; nobody takes pleasure in seeing beasts play with and caress one another, but every one is delighted with seeing them dismember, and tear one another to pieces. And that I may not be laughed at for the sympathy I have with them, theology itself enjoins us some favor in their behalf; and considering that one and the same master has lodged us together in this palace for his service, and that they, as well as we, are of his family, it has reason to enjoin us some affection and regard to them. Pythagoras borrowed the metempsychosis from the Egyptians; but it has since been received by several nations, and particularly by our Druids. . . . The religion of our ancient Gauls maintained that souls, being eternal, never ceased to remove and shift their places from one body to another; mixing moreover with this fancy some consideration of divine justice; for according to the deportments of the soul, while it had been in Alexander, they said that God assigned it another body to inhabit, more or less painful, and proper for its condition. If it had been valiant, he lodged it in the body of a lion; if voluptuous, in that of a hog; if timorous, in that of a hart or hare; if malicious, in that of a fox, and so of the rest, till having purified it by this chastisement, it again entered the body of some other man.

As to the relationship between us and beasts, I do not much admit of it; nor of that which several nations, and those among the most ancient and most noble, have practiced, who have not only received brutes into their society and companionship, but have given them a rank infinitely above themselves, esteeming them one while familiars and favorites of the gods, and having them in more than human reverence and respect; others acknowledged no other god or divinity than they.

And the very interpretation that Plutarch gives to this error, which is very well conceived, is advantageous to them: for he says that it was not the cat or the ox, for example, that the Egyptians adored: but that they, in those beasts, adored some image of the divine faculties: in this, patience and utility; in that vivacity, or, as with our neighbors the Burgundians and all the Germans, impatience to see themselves shut up; by which they represented liberty, which they loved and adored above all other godlike attributes, and so of the rest. But when, among the more moderate opinions, I meet with arguments that endeavor to demonstrate the near resemblance between us and animals, how large a share they have in our greatest priviliges, and with how much probability they compare us together, truly I abate a great deal of our presumption, and willingly resign that imaginary sovereignty that is attributed to us over other creatures.

But supposing all this were not true, there is, nevertheless, a certain respect, a general duty of humanity, not only to beasts that have life and sense, but even to trees and plants. We owe justice to men, and graciousness and benignity to other creatures that are capable of it; there is a certain commerce and mutual obligation between them and us. Nor shall I be afraid to confess the tenderness of my nature so childish, that I cannot well refuse to play with my dog, when he the most unseasonably importunes me so to do. The Turks have alms and hospitals for beasts. The Romans had public care to the nourishment of geese, by whose vigilance their capitol had been preserved. The Athenians made a decree that the mules and moyls which had served at the building of the temple called Hecatompedon should be free and suffered to pasture at their own choice, without hindrance. The Agrigentines had a common use solemnly to inter the beasts they had a kindness for, as horses of some rare quality, dogs, and useful birds, and even those that had only been kept to divert their children; and the magnificence that was ordinary with them in all other things, also particularly appeared in the sumptuosity and numbers of monuments erected to this end, and which remained in their beauty several ages after. The Egyptians buried wolves, bears, crocodiles, dogs and cats in sacred places, embalmed their bodies, and put on mourning at their death. Cimon gave an honorable sepulture to the mares with which he had three times gained the prize of the course at the Olympic Games. The ancient Xantippus caused his dog to be interred on an eminence near the sea, which has ever since retained the name, and Plutarch says, that he had a scruple about selling for a small profit to the slaughterer an ox that had been long in his service.

MICHEL DE MONTAIGNE
[*Essays* (1580)]

Fellow Creature or Machine

[In the 17th and even the 18th century, there were French experimenters who *submitted animals to torture in the name of science. They had on their side the enormous prestige of the philosopher-scientist, René Descartes, whose disciples maintained that only man was conscious and all other creatures mere machines which only seemed to feel either pleasure or pain. In a contemporary account, La Fontaine describes the cruel and heartless experiments performed which demonstrated, it was said, how animals seemed to suffer although it was certain they did not.*]

They administered beatings to dogs with perfect indifference and made fun of those who pitied the creatures as if they had felt pain. They said that the animals were clocks; that the cries they emitted when struck, were only the noise of a little spring which had been touched, but that the whole body was without feeling. They nailed poor animals up on boards by their four paws to vivisect them and see the circulation of the blood which was a great subject of conversation.

JEAN DE LA FONTAINE
[Quoted by Loren Eisley in *The Firmament of Time* (1960)]

"Nature's Children All Divide Her Care"

[John Ray helped to found in England what we call the science of biology. He also joined certain philosophers at Cambridge University in issuing the first bold challenge to the orthodox opinion that the world and everything in it had been, as Thomas Aquinas insisted, created to serve man. The study of nature, said Ray, was the study of that wisdom, power, and goodness by which God created and sustained, not man alone, but all living creatures. His treatise was read in many editions for more than a century and was the first popular book in our language to argue that all living things have, like man, their natural rights.]

🐾

Let us then consider the works of God, and observe the operations of His hands: let us take notice of, and admire His infinite wisdom and goodness in the formation of them: no creature in this sublunary world, is capable of so doing, beside man; and yet we are deficient herein: we content ourselves with the knowledge of the tongues, and a little skill in philology, or history perhaps, and antiquity, and neglect that which to me seems more material, I mean natural history, and the works of the Creation: I do not discommend, or derogate from those other studies: I should betray mine own ignorance and weakness should I do so; I only wish that they might not altogether jostle out, and exclude this. I wish that this might be brought in fashion among us; I wish men would be so equal and civil, as not to disparage, deride, and vilify those studies which themselves skill not of, or are not conversant in; no knowledge can be more pleasant than this, none that doth so satisfy and feed the soul; in comparison whereto that of words and phrases seems to me insipid and jejune. That learning (saith a wise and observant prelate) which consists only in the form and pedagogy of arts, or the critical notions upon words and phrases, hath in it this intrinsical imperfection, that it is only so far to be esteemed, as it conduceth to the knowledge of things, being in itself but a kind of pedantry, apt to infect a man with such odd humors of pride, and affectation, and curiosity, as will render him unfit for any great employment. Words being but the images of matter, to be wholly given up to the study of these, what is it but Pygmalion's frenzy, to fall in love with a picture or image. As for *oratory,* which is the best skill about words, that hath by some wise men been esteemed, but a voluntary art, like to cookery, which spoils wholesome meats, and helps unwholesome, by the variety of sauces, serving more to the pleasure of taste, than the health of the body.

It may be (for ought I know, and as some divines have thought) part of our business and employment in eternity, to contemplate the works of God, and give Him the glory of His wisdom, power, and goodness manifested in the creation of them. I am sure it is part of the business of a Sabbath-day, and the Sabbath is a type of that eternal rest; for the Sabbath seems to have been first instituted for a commemoration of the works of the creation, from which God is said to have rested upon the seventh day.

It is not likely that eternal life shall be a torpid and unactive state, or that it shall consist only in an uninterrupted and endless act of love; the other faculties shall be employed as well as the will, in actions suitable to, and perfective of their natures; especially the understanding, the supreme faculty of the soul, which chiefly differenceth us from brute beasts, and makes us capable of virtue and vice, of rewards and punishments, shall be busied and employed in contemplating the words of God, and observing the Divine art and wisdom manifested in the structure and composition of them; and reflecting upon their great architect and praise and glory due to Him. Then shall we clearly see to our great satisfaction and admiration, the ends and uses of these things, which here were either too subtle for us to penetrate and discover, or too remote and unaccessible for us to come to any distinct view of, *viz.* the planets, and fixed stars; those illustrious bodies, whose contents and inhabitants, whose stores and furniture we have here so longing a desire to know, as also their mutual subserviency to each other. Now the mind of man being not capable at once to advert to more than one thing, a particular view and examination of such an innumerable number of vast bodies, and the great multitude of *species,* both animate and inanimate beings, which each of them contains, will afford matter enough to exercise and employ our minds, I do not say, to all eternity, but to many ages, should we do nothing else.

Let it not suffice us to be book-learned, to read what others have written, and to take upon trust more falsehood than truth: but let us ourselves examine things as we have opportunity, and converse with nature as well as books. Let us endeavor to promote and increase this knowledge, and make new discoveries, not so much distrusting our own parts, or despairing of our own abilities, as to think that our industry can add nothing to the inventions of our ancestors, or correct any of their mistakes. Let us not think that the bounds of science are fixed like *Hercules'* pillars, and inscribed with a *ne plus ultra.* Let us not think we have done, when we have learnt what they have delivered to us. The treasures of nature are inexhaustible. Here is employment enough for the vastest parts, the most indefatigable industries, the happiest opportunities, the most prolix and undisturbed vacancies. Much might be done, would we but endeavor, and nothing is insuperable to pains and patience. I know that a new study at first, seems very vast, intricate, and difficult; but after a little resolution and progress, after a man becomes a little acquainted, as I may so say, with it, his understanding is wonderfully cleared up and enlarged, the difficulties vanish, and the thing grows easy and familiar. And for our encouragement in this study, observe what the Psalmist saith, *Psal. III. 2. The Works of the Lord are great, sought out of all them that have pleasure therein.* Which though it be principally spoken of the works of providence, yet may as well be veried of the works of creation. I am sorry to see so little account made of real experimental philosophy in this university; and that those ingenious sciences of the mathematics are so much neglected by us: and therefore do earnestly exhort those that are young, especially gentlemen, to set upon these studies, and take some pains in them. They may possibly invent something of eminent use and advantage to the world; and one such discovery would abundantly compensate the expense and travel of one man's whole life. However, it is enough to maintain and continue what is already invented: neither do I see what more ingenious and manly employment they can pursue, tending more to the satisfaction of their own minds, and the illustration of the glory of God. For He is wonderful in all His works.

But I would not have any man cross his natural genius or inclinations, or undertake such methods of study, as his parts are not fitted to, or not serve those ends to which his friends upon mature deliberation have designed him; but those who do abound with leisure, or who have a natural propension and genius inclining them thereto, or those who by reason of the strength and greatness of their parts, are able to compass and comprehend the whole latitude of learning.

Neither yet need those who are designed to divinity itself, fear to look into these studies, or think they will engross their whole time, and that no considerable progress can be made therein, unless men lay aside and neglect their ordinary callings, and necessary employments. No such matter: our life is long enough, and we might well find time enough, did we husband it well: *vitam non acceptimus brevem sed secimus, nec inopes ejus, sed prodigi sumus,* as Seneca saith, *We have not received a short life, but have made it so; neither do we want time, but are prodigal of it.* And did but young men fill up that time with these studies, which lies upon their hands, which they are incumbered with, and troubled how to pass away, much might be done even so. I do not see, but the study of true physiology, may be justly accounted a proper προπαιδεία, or preparative to divinity. But to leave that, it is a generally received opinion, that all this visible world was created for man; that man is the end of the creation, as if there were no other end of any creature, but some way or other to be serviceable to man. This opinion is as old as Tully; for, saith he, in his Second Book, *De Nat. Deorum. Principio ipse mundus deorum hominumque causa factus est; quaeque in eo sunt omnia ea parata ad fructum hominum inventa sunt.* But though this be vulgarly received, yet wise men nowadays think otherwise. Dr. More affirms, *That creatures are made to enjoy themselves, as well as to serve us; and that it's a gross piece of ignorance and rusticity to think otherwise.* And in another place: *This comes only out of pride and ignorance, or a haughty presumption, because we are encouraged to believe, that in some sense, all things are made for man, therefore to think that they are not at all made for themselves. But he that pronounceth this, is ignorant of the nature of man, and the knowledge of things: for if a good man be merciful to his beast, then surely, a good God is bountiful and benign, and takes pleasure that all his creatures enjoy themselves, that have life and sense, and are capable of enjoyment.*

Those philosophers indeed, who hold man to be the only creature in this sublunary world, endowed with sense and perception, and that all other animals are mere machines or puppets, have some reason to think, that all things here below were made for man. But this opinion seems to me too mean, and unworthy the majesty, wisdom, and power of God; nor can it well consist with his veracity, instead of a multitude of noble creatures, endowed with life and sense, and spontaneous motion, as all mankind till of late years believed, and none ever doubted of (so that it seems we are naturally made to think so) to have stocked the earth with divers sets of *automata*, without all sense and perception, being wholly acted upon from without, by the impulse of external objects.

But be this so, there are infinite other creatures without this earth, which no considerate man can think, were made only for man, and have no other use. For my part, I cannot believe, that all the things in the world were so made for man, that they have no other use.

For it seems to me highly absurd and unreasonable, to think that bodies of such vast magnitude as the fixed stars, were only made to twinkle to us; nay, a multitude of them there are, that do not so much as twinkle, being either by reason of their distance or of their smallness, altogether invisible to the naked eye, and only discoverable by a telescope, and it is likely perfecter telescopes than we yet have, may bring to light many more; and who knows, how many lie out of the ken of the best telescope that can possibly be made. And I believe there are many species in nature, even in this sublunary world, which were never yet taken notice of by man, and consequently of no use to him, which yet we are not to think were created in vain; but may be found out by, and of use to those who shall live after us in future ages. But though in this sense it be not true, that all things were made for man; yet thus far it is, that all the creatures in the world may be some way or other useful to us, at least to exercise our wits and understandings, in considering and contemplating of them, and so afford us subject of admiring and glorifying their and our Maker. Seeing then, we do believe, and assert, that all things were in some sense made for us, we are thereby obliged to make use of them for those purposes for which they serve us, else we frustrate this end of their creation. Now some of them serve only to exercise our minds: many others there be, which might probably serve us to good purpose, whose uses are not discovered, nor are they ever like to be, without pains and industry. True it is, many of the greatest inventions have been accidentally stumbled upon, but not by men supine and careless, but busy and inquisitive. Some reproach methinks it is to learned men, that there should be so many animals still in the world, whose outward shape is not yet taken notice of, or described, much less their way of generation, food, manners, uses, observed.

The Scripture *Psalm 148* calls upon *the Sun, Moon, and Stars; Fire and Hail, Snow and Vapour; stormy Winds and Tempests, Mountains and all Hills; fruitful Trees, and all Cedars; Beasts and all Cattle; creeping Things and flying Fowl, etc. to praise the Lord.* How can that be? Can senseless and inanimate things praise God? Such as are the sun and moon and stars. And although beasts be advanced higher to some degree of sense and perception; yet being void of reason and understanding, they know nothing of the causes of things, or of the author and maker of themselves, and other creatures. All that they are capable of doing, in reference to the praising of God, is (as I said before) by affording matter or subject of praising him, to rational and intelligent beings. So the Psalmist, *Psal. 19. 1: The Heavens declare the Glory of God, and the Firmament sheweth his handy-work.* And therefore the *Psalmist* when he calls upon sun, and moon, and stars, to praise God, doth in effect call upon men and angels, and other rational beings, to consider those great effects of the divine power.

JOHN RAY

[*The Wisdom of God Manifest in the Works of His Creation* (1691)]

An Eighteenth-Century Humanitarian

[*Alexander Pope put into the epigrammatic couplets of his "Essay on Man" many of the ideas which Ray had expressed in prose. (See Introduction, page 23.) He also contributed to a series of periodical essays edited by Joseph Addison and Richard Steele a polite plea for the humane treatment of animals. It was one of the first of many eighteenth-century treatments of the theme.*]

I cannot think it extravagant to imagine, that mankind are no less in proportion accountable for the ill use of their dominion over creatures of the lower rank of beings, than for the exercise of tyranny over their own species. The more entirely the inferior creation is submitted to our power, the more answerable we should seem for our mismanagement of it; and the rather, as the very condition of nature renders these creatures incapable of receiving any recompence in another life for their ill treatment in this.

It is observable of those noxious animals, which have qualities most powerful to injure us, that they naturally avoid mankind, and never hurt us unless provoked or necessitated by hunger. Man, on the other hand, seeks out and pursues even the most inoffensive animals, on purpose to persecute and destroy them.

Montaigne thinks it some reflection upon human nature itself, that few people take delight in seeing beasts caress or play together, but almost everyone is pleased to see them lacerate and worry one another. I am sorry this temper is become almost a distinguishing character of our own nation, from the observation which is made by foreigners of our beloved pastimes, bear-baiting, cock-fighting, and the like. We should find it hard to vindicate the destroying of any thing that has life, merely out of wantonness; yet in this principle our children are bred up, and one of the first pleasures we allow them is the license of inflicting pain upon poor animals; almost as soon as we are sensible what life is ourselves, we make it our sport to take it from other creatures. I cannot but believe a very good use might be made of the fancy which children have for birds and insects. Mr. Locke takes notice of a mother who permitted them to her children, but rewarded or punished them as they treated them well or ill. This was no other than entering them betimes into a daily exercise of humanity, and improving their very diversion to a virtue.

I fancy too, some advantage might be taken of the common notion, that it is ominous or unlucky to destroy some sorts of birds, as swallows or martins; this opinion might possibly arise from the confidence these birds seem to put in us by building under our roofs, so that it is a kind of violation of the laws of hospitality, to murder them. As for robin redbreasts in particular, it is not improbable they owe their security to the old ballad of the Children in the Wood. However it be, I do not know, I say, why this prejudice, well improved and carried as far as it would go, might not be made to conduce to the preservation of many innocent creatures, which are now exposed to all wantonness of an ignorant barbarity.

There are other animals that have the misfortune, for no manner of reason, to be treated as common enemies wherever found. The conceit that a cat has nine lives, has cost at least nine lives in ten of the whole race of them. Scarce a boy in the streets but has in this point outdone Hercules himself, who was famous for killing a monster that had but three lives. Whether the unaccountable animosity against this useful domestic may be any cause of the general persecution of owls (who are a sort of feathered cats), or whether it be only to an unreasonable pique the moderns have taken to a serious countenance, I shall not determine. Though I am inclined to believe the former; since I observe the sole reason alleged for the destruction of frogs, is because they are like toads. Yet amidst all the misfortunes of these unfriended creatures, it is some happiness that we have not yet taken a fancy to eat them: for should our countrymen refine upon the French never so little, it is not to be conceived to what unheard of torments, owls, cats, and frogs may be yet reserved.

When we grow up to men, we have another succession of sanguinary sports; in particular hunting. I dare not attack a diversion which has such authority and custom to support it; but must have leave to be of opinion, that the agitation of that exercise, with the example and number of the chasers, not a little contribute to resist those checks, which compassion would naturally suggest in behalf of the animal pursued. Nor shall I say with Monsieur Fleury, that this sport is a remain of the Gothic barbarity. But I must animadvert upon a certain custom yet in use with us, and barbarous enough to be derived from the Goths, or even the Scythians; I mean that savage compliment our huntsmen pass upon ladies of quality, who are present at the death of a stag, when they put the knife in their hands to cut the throat of a helpless, trembling and weeping creature.

ALEXANDER POPE
[*The Guardian* (1713)]

Merry England

[*In the spacious days of Great Elizabeth there were no humane societies to interfere with the pleasures of cruelty. The Queen herself is said to have attended a bull or bear baiting every Sunday afternoon, and one of the events of the famous nineteen days' entertainment offered to her at Kenilworth in*

1575 was the simultaneous baiting by dogs of thirteen bears. Many of her loyal subjects preferred similar entertainments at the bear "gardens" to the plays of Shakespeare being performed next door, and continental travelers occasionally comment that the English seem peculiarly addicted to such amusements. That they were still available more than a century later is evident from the following announcements.]

≈

At the *Bear Garden in Hockley in the Hole,* 1710. This is to give notice to all Gentlemen, Gamsters, and Others, That on this present *Monday* is a Match to be fought by two Dogs, one from *Newgate* Market, against one of *Honey Lane* Market, at a Bull, for a Guinea to be spent. Five Let goes out off Hand, which goes fairest and farthest in Wins all; like wise a *Green Bull* to be baited, which was never baited before, and a Bull to be turned lose with Fire works all over him; also a Mad Ass to be baited; With variety of Bull baiting and Bear baiting; and a Dog to be drawn up with Fire works.

HARLEIAN MANUSCRIPTS
[Preserved among the items in the Harleian Library at Oxford University]

≈

A mad bull, dressed up with fireworks, is to be turned loose in the same place; likewise a dog dressed up with fireworks; also a bear to be turned loose. N.B.—a cat to be tied to the bull's tail.

WEEKLY JOURNAL (1730)
[Quoted in "The Love of Animals" by Dix Harwood]

Cruel Curiosity

[It will perhaps surprise some to find Dr. Samuel Johnson among the first antivivisectionists.]

≈

The *Idlers* that sport only with inanimate nature may claim some indulgence; if they are useless, they are still innocent: but there are others, whom I know not how to mention without more emotion than my love of quiet willingly admits. Among the inferiour professors of medical knowledge, is a race of wretches, whose lives are only varied by varieties of cruelty; whose favourite amusement is to nail dogs to tables and open them alive; to try how long life may be continued in various degrees of mutilation, or with the excision or laceration of the vital parts; to examine whether burning irons are felt more acutely by the bone or tendon; and whether the more lasting agonies are produced by poison forced into the mouth, or injected into the veins.

It is not without reluctance that I offend the sensibility of the tender mind with images like these. If such cruelties were not practised, it were to be desired that they should not be conceived; but, since they are published every day with ostentation, let me be allowed once to mention them, since I mention them with abhorrence.

Mead has invidiously remarked of *Woodward*, that he gathered shells and stones, and would pass for a philosopher. With pretensions much less reasonable, the anatomical novice tears out the living bowels of an animal, and styles himself physician, prepares himself by familiar cruelty for that profession which he is to exercise upon the tender and the helpless, upon feeble bodies and broken minds, and by which he has opportunities to extend his arts of torture, and continue those experiments upon infancy and age, which he has hitherto tried upon cats and dogs.

What is alleged in defence of these hateful practices, every one knows; but the truth is, that by knives, fire, and poison, knowledge is not always sought, and is very seldom attained. The experiments that have been tried, are tried again; he that burned an animal with irons yesterday, will be willing to amuse himself with burning another to-morrow. I know not, that by living dissections any discovery has been made by which a single malady is more easily cured. And if the knowledge of physiology has been somewhat increased, he surely buys knowledge dear, who learns the use of the lacteals at the expense of his humanity.

SAMUEL JOHNSON
[*The Idler* (1758)]

Two Poets

[Although the eighteenth century was in many ways "The Age of Reason," an astonishing number of its men of letters either ended in madness or were at least, as Samuel Johnson said of himself, "Never quite sane." Two were notable lovers of all animal creation: the gentle William Cowper, whose letters are sprinkled with anecdotes not wholly unlike those which make up The Natural History of Selborne; and the rhapsodical Christopher Smart, a sort of lesser Blake, whose barely coherent praises of God and nature led ultimately to his confinement in a madhouse despite Dr. Johnson's sage protest: "His infirmities were not noxious to society. He insisted on people praying with him; and I'd as lief pray with Kit Smart as anyone else. Another charge was that he did not love clean linen; and I have no passion for it."]

I must tell you a feat of my dog Beau. Walking by the river side, I observed some water-lilies floating at a little distance from the bank. They are a large white flower, with an orange coloured eye, very beautiful. I had a desire to gather one, and, having your long cane in my hand, by the help of it endeavoured to bring one of them within my reach. But the attempt proved vain, and I walked forward. Beau had all the while observed me attentively. Returning soon after toward the same place, I observed him plunge into the river, while I was about forty yards distance from him; and, when I had nearly reached the spot, he swam to land with a lily in his mouth, which he came and laid at my foot. . . .

. . . I have two goldfinches, which in the summer occupy the greenhouse. A few days since, being employed in cleaning out their cages, I placed that which I had in hand upon the table, while the other hung against the wall: the windows and the doors stood wide open. I went to fill the fountain at the pump, and on my return was not a little surprised to find a goldfinch sitting on the top of the cage I had been cleaning, and singing to and kissing the goldfinch within. I approached him, and he discovered no fear; still nearer, and he discovered none. I advanced my hand towards him, and he took no notice of it. I seized him, and supposed I had caught a new bird, but casting my eye upon the other cage perceived my mistake. Its inhabitant, during my absence, had contrived to find an opening, where the wire had been a little bent, and made no other use of the escape it afforded him, than to salute his friend, and to converse with him more intimately than he had done before. I returned him to his proper mansion, but in vain. In less than a minute he had thrust his little person through the aperture again, and again perched upon his neighbour's cage, kissing him, as at the first, and singing, as if transported with the fortunate adventure. I could not but respect such friendship, as for the sake of its gratification had twice declined an opportunity to be free, and, consenting to their union, resolved that for the future one cage should hold them both. I am glad of such incidents; for at a pinch, and when I need entertainment, the versification of them serves to divert me.

WILLIAM COWPER
[From letters written in 1783]

For I will consider my Cat Jeoffry.

For he is the servant of the Living God, duly and daily serving him.

For at the first glance of the glory of God in the East he worships in his way.

For is this done by wreathing his body seven times round with elegant quickness.

For then he leaps up to catch the musk, which is the blessing of God upon his prayer.

For he rolls upon prank to work it in.

For having done duty and received blessing he begins to consider himself.

For this he performs in ten degrees.

For this he looks upon his fore-paws to see if they are clean.

For secondly he kicks up behind to clear away there.

For thirdly he works it upon stretch with the fore-paws extended.

For fourthly he sharpens his paws by wood.

For fifthly he washes himself.

For sixthly he rolls upon wash.

For Seventhly he fleas himself, that he may not be interrupted upon the beat.

For Eighthly he rubs himself against a post.

For Ninthly he looks up for his instructions.

For Tenthly he goes in quest of food.

For having consider'd God and himself he will consider his neighbour.

For if he meets another cat he will kiss her in kindness.

For when he takes his prey he plays with it to give it chance.

For one mouse in seven escapes by his dallying.

For when his day's work is done his business more properly begins.

For keeps the Lord's watch in the night against the adversary.

For he counteracts the powers of darkness by his electrical skin & glaring eyes.

For he counteracts the Devil, who is death, by brisking about the life.

For in his morning orisons he loves the sun and the sun loves him.

For he is of the tribe of Tiger.

For the Cherub Cat is a term of the Angel Tiger.

For he has the subtlety and hissing of a serpent, which in goodness he suppresses.

For he will not do destruction, if he is well-fed, neither will he spit without provocation.

For he purrs in thankfulness, when God tells him he's a good Cat.

For he is an instrument for the children to learn benevolence upon.

For every house is incompleat without him & a blessing is lacking in the spirit.

For the Lord commanded Moses concerning the cats at the departure of the Children of Israel from Egypt.

For every family had one cat at least in the bag.

For the English Cats are the best in Europe.

For he is the cleanest in the use of his fore-paws of any quadrupede.

For the dexterity of his defence is an instance of the love of God to him exceedingly.

For he is the quickest to his mark of any creature.

For he is tenacious of his point.

For he is a mixture of gravity and waggery.

For he knows that God is his Saviour.

For there is nothing sweeter than his peace when at rest.

For there is nothing brisker than his life when in motion.

For he is of the Lord's poor and so indeed is he called by benevolence perpetually—Poor Jeoffry! poor Jeoffry! the rat has bit thy throat.

For I bless the name of the Lord Jesus that Jeoffry is better.

For the divine spirit comes about his body to sustain it in compleat cat.

For his tongue is exceeeing pure so that it has in purity what it wants in musick.

For he is docile and can learn certain things.

For he can set up with gravity which is patience upon approbation.

For he can fetch and carry, which is patience in employment.

For he can jump over a stick which is patience upon proof positive.

For he can spraggle upon waggle at the word of command.

For he can jump from an eminence into his master's bosom.

For he can catch the cork and toss it again.

For he is hated by the hypocrite and miser.

For the former is affraid of detection.

For the latter refuses the charge.

For he camels his back to bear the first notion of business.

For he is good to think on, if a man would express himself neatly.

For he made a great figure in Egypt for his signal services.

For he killed the Icneumon-rat very pernicious by land.

For his ears are so acute that they sting again.

For from this proceeds the passing quickness of his attention.

For by stroaking of him I have found out electricity.

For I perceived God's light about him both wax and fire.

For the Electrical fire is the spiritual substance, which God sends from heaven to sustain the bodies both of man and beast.

For God has blessed him in the variety of his movements.

For, tho he cannot fly, he is an excellent clamberer.

For his motions upon the face of the earth are more than any other quadrupede.

For he can tread to all the measures upon the musick.

For he can swim for life.

For he can creep.

CHRISTOPHER SMART
[Jubilate Agno (unpublished until the 20th century)]

FIRST STAGE OF CRUELTY.

While various Scenes of sportive Woe
   The Infant Race employ.
And tortur'd Victims bleeding shew
   The Tyrant in the Boy.

Behold! a Youth of gentler Heart,
   To spare the Creature's pain
O take, he cries—take all my Tart,
   But Tears and Tart are vain.

Learn from this fair Example—You
   Whom savage Sports delight,
How Cruelty disgusts the view
   While Pity charms the sight.

Published according to Act of Parliament Feb. 1. 1751.

Sentimental Journey

[The influence of Cartesianism has lasted in attenuated form even into our century when behaviorism calls "sentimental" and "anthropomorphic" the assumption that animals think when they seem to be thinking, and experience emotion when they seem to be moved. But common sense tended to reject it even in its heyday. "I would have you say a word or two to the Cardinal de Retz," wrote Madame de Sévigné to her daughter, "about your machines; your machines that love, your machines that have the power of election; your machines that are jealous; and your machines that have fears: Go, Go! Descartes never could pretend to make us believe all this!"

By the late eighteenth century "the man of feeling" had become a familiar hero of fiction and nowhere more self-consciously delineated than by Laurence Sterne.]

'Tis true, said I, correcting the proposition—the Bastile is not an evil to be despised—But strip it of its towers—fill up the fossé—unbarricade the doors—call it simply a confinement, and suppose 'tis some tyrant of a distemper—and not of a man, which holds you in it—the evil vanishes, and you bear the other half without complaint.

I was interrupted in the heyday of this soliloquy, with a voice which I took to be of a child, which complained "it could not get out."— I look'd up and down the passage, and seeing neither man, woman, nor child, I went out without further attention.

In my return back through the passage, I heard the same words repeated twice over; and looking up, I saw it was a starling hung in a little cage—"I can't get out—I can't get out," said the starling.

I stood looking at the bird: and to every person who came through the passage it ran fluttering to the side towards which they approach'd it, with the same lamentation of its captivity—"I can't get out," said the starling—God help thee! said I—but I'll let thee out, cost what it will; so I turned about the cage to get to the door; it was twisted and double twisted so fast with wire, there was no getting it open without pulling the cage to pieces—I took both hands to it.

The bird flew to the place where I was attempting his deliverance, and thrusting his head through the trellis, pressed his breast against it, as if impatient—I fear, poor creature! said I, I cannot set thee at liberty—"No," said the starling—"I can't get out—I can't get out," said the starling.

I vow I never had my affections more tenderly awakened; or do I remember an incident in my life, where the dissipated spirits, to which my reason had been a bubble, were so suddenly call'd home. Mechanical as the notes were, yet so true in tune to nature were they chanted, that in one moment they overthrew all my systematic reasonings upon the Bastile; and I heavily walk'd upstairs, unsaying every word I had said in going down them.

Disguise thyself as thou wilt, still, Slavery! said I—still thou art a bitter draught! and though thousands in all ages have been made to drink of thee, thou art no less bitter on that account. —'Tis thou, thrice sweet and gracious goddess, addressing myself to LIBERTY, whom all in public or in private worship, whose taste is grateful, and ever will be so, till NATURE herself shall change—no *tint* of words can spot thy snowy mantle, or chymic power turn thy scepter into iron—with thee to smile upon him as he eats his crust, the swain is happier than his monarch, from whose court thou art exiled—Gracious heaven! cried I, kneeling down upon the last step but one in my ascent, grant me but health, thou great Bestower of it, and give me but this fair goddess as my companion—and shower down thy miters, if it seems good unto thy divine providence, upon those heads which are aching for them.

The bird in his cage pursued me into my room; I sat down close to my table, and leaning my head upon my hand, I began to figure to myself the miseries of confinement. I was in a right frame for it, and so I gave full scope to my imagination.

I was going to begin with the millions of my fellow-creatures, born to no inheritance but slavery: but finding, however affecting the picture was, that I could not bring it near me, and that the multitude of sad groups in it did but distract me—

—I took a single captive, and having first shut him up in his dungeon, I then look'd through the twilight of his grated door to take his picture.

I beheld his body half wasted away with long expectation and confinement, and felt what kind of sickness of the heart it was which arises from hope deferr'd. Upon looking nearer I saw him pale and feverish: in thirty years the western breeze had not once fann'd his blood—he had seen no sun, no moon, in all that time—nor had the voice of friend or kinsman breathed through his lattice:—his children—

But here my heart began to bleed—and I was forced to go on with another part of the portrait.

He was sitting upon the ground upon a little straw, in the furthest corner of his dungeon, which was alternately his chair and bed: a little calendar of small sticks were laid at the head, notch'd all over with the dismal days and nights he had passed there—he had one of these little sticks in his hand, and with a rusty nail he was etching another day of misery to add to the heap. As I darkened the little light he had, he lifted up a hopeless eye towards the door, then cast it down—shook his head, and went on with his work of affliction. I heard his chains upon his legs, as he turned his body to lay his little stick upon the bundle. —He gave a deep sigh—I saw the iron enter into his soul—I burst into tears—I could not sustain the picture of confinement which my fancy had drawn—I started up from my chair, and called La Fleur—I bid him bespeak me a *remise,* and have it ready at the door of the hotel by nine in the morning.

—I'll go directly, said I, myself to Monsieur le Duc de Choiseul.

La Fleur would have put me to bed; but not willing he should see anything upon my cheek which would cost the honest fellow a heartache—I told him I would go to bed by myself—and bid him go do the same.

I got into my *remise* the hour I promised: La Fleur got up behind, and I bid the coachman make the best of his way to Versailles.

As there was nothing in this road, or rather nothing which I look for in traveling, I cannot fill up the blank better than with a short history of the self-same bird, which became the subject of the last chapter.

Whilst the Honorable Mr. **** was waiting for a wind at Dover, it had been caught upon the cliffs before it could well fly, by an English lad who was his groom; who not caring to destroy it, had taken it in his breast into the packet—and by course of feeding it, and taking it once under his protection, in a day or two grew fond of it, and got it safe along with him to Paris.

At Paris the lad had laid out a livre in a little cage for the starling, and as he had little to do better the five months his master stayed there, he taught it in his mother's tongue the four simple words— (and no more)—to which I own'd myself so much its debtor.

Upon his master's going on for Italy—the lad had given it to the master of the hotel—But his little song for liberty being in an *unknown* language at Paris, the bird had little or no store set by him —so La Fleur bought both him and his cage for me for a bottle of Burgundy.

In my return from Italy I brought him with me to the country in whose language he had learn'd his notes—and telling the story of him to Lord A—, Lord A begg'd the bird of me—in a week Lord A gave him to Lord B—; Lord B made a present of him to Lord C—; and Lord C's gentleman sold him to Lord D's for a shilling—Lord D gave him to Lord E—, and so on—half round the alphabet— From that rank he pass'd into the lower house, and pass'd the hands of as many commoners— But as all these wanted to *get in*—and my bird wanted to *get out*—he had almost as little store set by him in London as in Paris.

It is impossible but many of my readers must have heard of him; and if any by mere chance have ever seen him,—I beg leave to inform them, that that bird was my bird—or some vile copy set up to represent him.

LAURENCE STERNE
[*A Sentimental Journey Through France and Italy* (1768)]

The Bullfight Lingers On

[By the early nineteenth century the more outrageous forms of cruelty had been outlawed in England and bullfighting survived only in those Latin countries which, in some circles, it is still fashionable to visit for the sake of pleasures forbidden at home. Nevertheless, an English traveler of the last century was shocked to find that South Americans enthusiastically applauded spectacles reminiscent of those enjoyed by Shakespeare's contemporaries and undisguised by the artistic refinements so much insisted upon in Spain.]

✦

Being desirous of ascertaining, by every means, the real state of popular feeling, which generally developes itself at public meetings, I went to one of the bull-fights, given in honour of the new Viceroy's installation. It took place in an immense wooden amphitheatre, capable of holding, it was said, twenty thousand people. As we had been disappointed at Valparaiso by a sham bull-fight, we hoped here to witness an exhibition worthy of the mother country. But the resemblance was not less faulty, though in the opposite extreme; for the bulls were here put to death with so many unusual circumstances of cruelty, as not only to make it unlike the proper bull-fights, but to take away all pleasure in the spectacle from persons not habituated to the sight. These exhibitions have been described by so many travellers, that it is needless here to do more than advert to some circumstances peculiar to those of Lima.

After the bull had been repeatedly speared, and tormented by darts and fire-works, and was all streaming with blood, the matador, on a signal from the Viceroy, proceeded to despatch him. Not being, however, sufficiently expert, he merely sheathed his sword in the animal's neck without effect. The bull instantly took his revenge, by tossing the matador to a great height in the air, and he fell apparently dead in the arena. The audience applauded the bull, while the attendants carried off the matador. The bull next attacked a horseman, dismounted him, ripped up the horse's belly, and bore him to the ground; where he was not suffered to die in peace, but was raised on his legs, and urged, by whipping and goading, to move round the ring in a state too horrible to be described, but which afforded the spectators the greatest delight. The noble bull had thus succeeded in baffling his tormentors as long as fair means were used, when a cruel device was thought of to subdue him. A large curved instrument called a Luna was thrown at him, in such a way as to divide the hamstring of the hind legs: such, however, were his strength and spirit, that he did not fall, but actually travelled along at a tolerable pace on his stumps—a most horrible sight! This was not all; for a man armed with a dagger now mounted the bull's back, and rode about for some minutes to the infinite delight of the spectators; who were thrown into ecstasies, and laughed and clapped their hands at every stab given to the miserable animal, not to kill him, but to stimulate him to accelerate his pace; at length, the poor beast, exhausted by loss of blood, fell down and died.

The greater number of the company, although females, seemed enchanted with the brutal scene passing under their eyes, and I looked round, in vain, for a single face that looked grave: every individual seeming quite delighted; and it was melancholy to observe a great proportion of children amongst the spectators; from one of whom, a little girl, only eight years old, I learned that she had already seen three bull-fights; the details of which she gave with great animation and pleasure, dwelling especially on those horrid circumstances I have described. It would shock and disgust to no purpose to give a minute account of other instances of wanton cruelty, which, however, appeared to be the principal recommendation of these exhibitions. But it was impossible to help feeling, in spite of our muchtalked-of neutrality, that any change which would put a stop to such proceedings was greatly to be wished. In every instance in South America, where the cause of independence has succeeded, two measures have been invariably adopted: one the abolition of the slavetrade, and as far as possible of slavery; the other, the relinquishment of bull-fights. With respect to the slave question, most people think alike; but many hesitate as to the propriety of doing away the bullfights, especially they who have witnessed them in Spain only, or who have never witnessed them at all; but it is rare to hear any one condemn their abolition after he has once been present at those of Lima.

I heard a Chilian gentleman offer a curious theory on this subject. He declared, that the Spaniards had systematically sought, by these cruel shows, and other similar means, to degrade the taste of the Colonies, and thereby more easily to tyrannize over the inhabitants. The people, he said, first rendered utterly insensible to the feelings of others, by a constant familiarity with cruelty and injustice, soon became indifferent to the wrongs of their country, and lost, in the end, all motive to generous exertion in themselves.

CAPTAIN BASIL HALL
[Extracts from a Journal Written on the Coasts of Chile, Peru and Mexico (1824)]

Walden Neighbors

[*If Gilbert White was the grandfather of "nature writing" in English, Thoreau was certainly its immediate begetter. Perhaps others before him had felt an equally complete empathy with bird and beast, but no one before had ever succeeded in communicating it so completely.*]

I cannot but see still in my mind's eye those little striped breams poised in Walden's glaucous water. They balance all the rest of the world in my estimation at present, for this is the bream that I have just found, and for the time I neglect all its brethren and am ready to kill the fatted calf on its account. For more than two centuries have men fished here, and have not distinguished this permanent settler of the township. It is not like a new bird, a transient visitor that may not be seen again for years, but there it dwells and has dwelt permanently, who can tell how long? When my eyes first rested on Walden the striped bream was poised in it, though I did not see it; and when Tahatawan paddled his canoe there. How wild it makes the pond and the township, to find a new fish in it! America renews her youth here. But in my account of this bream I cannot go a hair's breadth beyond the mere statement that it exists—the miracle of its existence, my contemporary and neighbor, yet so different from me! I can only poise my thought there by its side and try to think like a bream for a moment. I can only think of precious jewels, of music, poetry, beauty, and the mystery of life. I only see the bream in its orbit, as I see a star, but I care not to measure its distance or weight. The bream, appreciated, floats in the pond as the center of the system, another image of God. Its life no man can explain more than he can his own. I want you to perceive the mystery of the bream. I have a contemporary in Walden. It has fins where I have legs and arms. I have a friend among the fishes, at least a new acquaintance. Its character will interest me, I trust, not its clothes and anatomy. I do not want it to eat. Acquaintance with it is to make my life more rich and eventful. It is as if a poet or an anchorite had moved into the town, whom I can see from time to time and think of yet oftener. Perhaps there are a thousand of these striped bream which no one had thought of in that pond—not their mere impressions in stone, but in the full tide of the bream life.

Though science may sometimes compare herself to a child picking up pebbles on the seashore, that is a rare mood with her; ordinarily her practical belief is that it is only a few pebbles which are *not* known, weighed and measured. A new species of fish signifies hardly more than a new name. See what is contributed in the scientific reports. One counts the fin rays; another measures the intestines; a third daguerreotypes a scale, etc., etc.; otherwise there's nothing to be said. As if all but this were done, and these were very rich and generous contributions to science. Her votaries may be seen wandering along the shore of the ocean of truth, with their backs to that ocean, ready to seize on the shells which are cast up. You would say that the scientific bodies were terribly put to it for objects and subjects. A dead specimen of an animal, if it is only well preserved in alcohol, is just as good for science as a living one preserved in its native element.

What is the amount of my discovery to me? It is not that I have got one in a bottle, that it has got a name in a book, but I have a little fishy friend in the pond. How was it when the youth first discovered fishes? Was it the number of their fin rays or their arrangement, or the place of the fish in some system that made the boy dream of them? Is it these things that interest mankind in the fish, the inhabitant of the water? No, but a faint recognition of a living contemporary, a provoking mystery. One boy thinks of fishes and goes a-fishing from the same motive that his brother searches the poets for rare lines. It is the poetry of fishes which is their chief use; their flesh is their lowest use. The beauty of the fish, that is what it is best worth the while to measure. Its place in our systems is of comparatively little importance. Generally the boy loses some of his perception and his interest in the fish; he degenerates into a fisherman or an ichthyologist.

Shad are still taken in the basin of Concord River, at Lowell, where they are said to be a month earlier than the Merrimack shad, on account of the warmth of the water. Still patiently, almost pathetically, with instinct not to be discouraged, not to be *reasoned* with, revisiting their old haunts, as if their stern fates would relent, and still met by the Corporation with its dam. Poor shad! where is thy redress? When Nature gave thee instinct, gave she thee the heart to bear thy fate? Still wandering the sea in thy scaly armor to inquire humbly at the mouths of rivers if man has perchance left them free for thee to enter. By countless shoals loitering uncertain meanwhile, merely stemming the tide there, in danger from sea foes in spite of thy bright armor, awaiting new instructions, until the sands, until the water itself, tell thee if it be so or not. Thus by whole migrating nations, full of instinct, which is thy faith, in this backward spring, turned adrift; and perchance knowest not where men do *not* dwell, where there are *not* factories, in these days. Armed with no sword, no electric shock, but mere shad, armed only with innocence and a just cause, with tender dumb mouth only forward, and scales easy to be detached.—I for one am with thee, and who knows what may avail a crowbar against that Billerica dam?—Not despairing when whole myriads have gone to feed those sea-monsters during thy suspense, but still brave, indifferent, on easy fin there, like shad reserved for higher destinies. Willing to be decimated for man's behoof after the spawning season. Away with the superficial and selfish phil-*anthropy* of men— who knows what admirable virtue of fishes may be below low-water mark, bearing up against a hard destiny, not admired by that fellow creature who alone can appreciate it! Who hears the fishes when they cry? It will not be forgotten by some memory that we were contemporaries. Thou shalt ere long have thy way up the rivers, up all the rivers of the globe, if I am not mistaken. Yea, even thy dull watery dream shall be more than realized. If it were not so, but thou wert to be overlooked at first and at last, then would not I take their heaven. Yes. I say so, who think I know better than thou canst. Keep a stiff fin, then, and stem all the tides thou mayst meet.

Why do precisely these objects which we behold make a world? Why has man just these species of animals for his neighbors; as if nothing but a mouse could have filled this crevice? I suspect that Pilpay & Co. have put animals to their best use, for they are all beasts of burden, in a sense, made to carry some portion of our thoughts.

The mice which haunted my house were not the common ones, which are said to have been introduced into the country, but a wild native kind not found in the village. I sent one to a distinguished naturalist, and it interested him much. When I was building, one of these had its nest underneath the house, and before I had laid the second floor, and swept out the shavings, would come out regularly at lunch time and pick up the crumbs at my feet. It probably had never seen a man before; and it soon became quite familiar, and would run over my shoes and up my clothes. It could readily ascend the sides of the room by short impulses, like a squirrel, which it resembled in its motions. At length, as I leaned with my elbow on the bench one day, it ran up my clothes, and along my sleeve, and round and round the paper which held my dinner, while I kept the latter close, and dodged and played at bopeep with it; and when at last I held still a piece of cheese between my thumb and finger, it came and nibbled it, sitting in my hand, and afterward cleaned its face and paws, like a fly, and walked away.

A phœbe soon built in my shed, and a robin for protection in a pine which grew against the house. In June the partridge (*Tetrao umbellus*), which is so shy a bird, led her brood past my windows, from the woods in the rear to the front of my house, clucking and calling to them like a hen, and in all her behavior proving herself the hen of the woods. The young suddenly disperse on your approach, at a signal from the mother, as if a whirlwind had swept them away, and they so exactly resemble the dried leaves and twigs that many a traveller has placed his foot in the midst of a brood, and heard the whir of the old bird as she flew off, and her anxious calls and mewing, or seen her trail her wings to attract his attention, without suspecting their neighborhood. The parent will sometimes roll and spin round before you in such a dishabille, that you cannot, for a few moments, detect what kind of creature it is. The young squat still and flat, often running their heads under a leaf, and mind only their mother's directions given from a distance, nor will your approach make them run again and betray themselves. You may even tread on them, or have your eyes on them for a minute, without discovering them. I have held them in my open hand at such a time, and still their only care, obedient to their mother and their instinct, was to squat there without fear or trembling. So perfect is this instinct, that once when I had laid them on the leaves again, and one accidentally fell on its side, it was found with the rest in exactly the same position ten minutes afterward. They are not callow like the young of most birds, but more perfectly developed and precocious even than chickens. The remarkably adult yet innocent expression of their open and serene eyes is very memorable. All intelligence seems reflected in them. They suggest not merely the purity of infancy, but a wisdom clarified by experience. Such an eye was not born when the bird was, but is coeval with the sky it reflects. The woods do not yield another such a gem. The traveller does not often look into such a limpid well. The ignorant or reckless sportsman often shoots the parent at such a time, and leaves these innocents to fall a prey to some prowling beast or bird, or gradually mingle with the decaying leaves which they so much resemble. It is said that when hatched by a hen they will directly disperse on some alarm, and so are lost, for they never hear the mother's call which gathers them again. These were my hens and chickens.

It is remarkable how many creatures live wild and free though secret in the woods, and still sustain themselves in the neighborhood of towns, suspected by hunters only. How retired the otter manages to live here! He grows to be four feet long, as big as a small boy, perhaps without any human being getting a glimpse of him. I formerly saw the raccoon in the woods behind where my house is built, and probably still heard their whinnering at night. Commonly I rested an hour or two in the shade at noon, after planting, and ate my lunch, and read a little by a spring which was the source of a swamp and of a brook, oozing from under Brister's Hill, half a mile from my field. The approach to this was through a succession of descending grassy hollows, full of young pitch pines, into a larger wood about the swamp. There, in a very secluded and shaded spot, under a spreading white pine, there was yet a clean, firm sward to sit on. I had dug out the spring and made a well of clear gray water, where I could dip up a pailful without roiling it, and thither I went for this purpose almost every day in midsummer, when the pond was warmest. Thither, too, the woodcock led her brood, to probe the mud for worms, flying but a foot above them down the bank, while they ran in a troop beneath; but at last, spying me, she would leave her young and circle round and round me, nearer and nearer till within four or five feet, pretending broken wings and legs, to attract my attention, and get off her young, who would already have taken up their march, with faint, wiry peep, single file through the swamp, as she directed. Or I heard the peep of the young when I could not see the parent bird. There too the turtle doves sat over the spring, or fluttered from bough to bough of the soft white pines over my head; or the red squirrel, coursing down the nearest bough, was particularly familiar and inquisitive. You only need sit still long enough in some attractive spot in the woods that all its inhabitants may exhibit themselves to you by turns.

HENRY DAVID THOREAU
[*Walden* (1854)]

Lighter Side of a Philosopher

[Jeremy Bentham was the inventor of Utilitarianism and first propounder of the criterion "Greatest good of the greatest number." He was reasonable to the point of eccentricity but somewhat unexpectedly devoted to both cats and mice, despite his own realization that this involved a divided loyalty.]

Bentham was very fond of animals, particularly *"pussies,"* as he called them, "when they had domestic virtues"; but he had no particular affection for the common race of *cats*. He had one, however, of which he used to boast that he had "made a man of him," and whom he was wont to invite to eat maccaroni at his own table. This puss got knighted, and rejoiced in the name of Sir John Langborn. In his early days he was a frisky, inconsiderate, and, to say the truth, somewhat profligate gentleman; and had, according to the report of his patron, the habit of seducing light and giddy young ladies, of his own race, into the garden of Queen's Square Place: but tired at last, like Solomon, of pleasures and vanities, he became sedate and thoughtful —took to the church, laid down his knightly title, and was installed as the Reverend John Langborn. He gradually obtained a great reputation for sanctity and learning, and a Doctor's degree was conferred upon him. When I knew him, in his declining days, he bore no other name than the Reverend Doctor John Langborn; and he was alike conspicuous for his gravity and philosophy. Great respect was invariably shown his reverence: and it was supposed he was not far off from a mitre, when old age interfered with his hopes and honours. He departed amidst the regrets of his many friends, and was gathered to his fathers, and to eternal rest, in a cemetery in Milton's garden.

"I had a cat," he said, "at Hendon, which used to follow me

about even in the street. George Wilson was very fond of animals too. I remember a cat following him as far as Staines. There was a beautiful pig at Hendon, which I used to rub with my stick. He loved to come and lie down to be rubbed, and took to following me like a dog. I had a remarkably intellectual cat, who never failed to attend one of us when we went round the garden. He grew quite a tyrant, insisting on being fed, and on being noticed. He interrupted my labours: once he came with a most hideous yell, insisting on the door being opened. He tormented Jack (Colls) so much, that Jack threw him out of window. He was so clamorous that it could not be borne, and means were found to send him to another world. His moral qualities were most despotic—his intellectual extraordinary: but he was a universal nuisance."

The mice were encouraged by Bentham to play about in his work-shop. I remember, when one got among his papers, that he exclaimed, "Ho! ho! here's a mouse at work; why won't he come into my lap?—but then I should be stroking him when I ought to be writing legislation, and that would not do."

"I have been catching fish," he said one day; "I have caught a carp, I shall hang him up—feed him with bread and milk. He shall be my tame puss, and shall play about on the floor. But I have a new tame puss. I will make Roebuck my puss for his article on Canada; and many a mouse shall he catch."

One day while we were at dinner, mice had got, as they frequently did, into the drawers of the dinner-table, and were making no small noise. "O you rascals," exclaimed Bentham, "there's an uproar among you. I'll tell puss of you"; and then added: "I became once very intimate with a colony of mice. They used to run up my legs, and eat crumbs from my lap. I love everything that has four legs; so did George Wilson. We were fond of mice, and fond of cats; but it was difficult to reconcile the two affections.

"From my youth I was fond of cats—as I still am. I was once playing with one in my grandmother's room. I had heard the story of cats having nine lives, and being sure of falling on their legs; and I threw the cat out of the window on the grass-plot. When it fell, it turned towards me, looked in my face and mewed. 'Poor thing!' I said, 'thou art reproaching me with my unkindness.' I have a distinct recollection of all these things.

"Cowper's story of his hares, had the highest interest for me when young; for I always enjoyed the society of tame animals. Wilson had the same taste—so had Romilly, who kept a noble puss before he came into great business. I never failed to pay it my respects. I remember accusing Romilly of violating the commandment in the matter of cats. My fondness for animals exposed me to many jokes. An acquaintance of Wilson's came to dine with me, and I gave him a bed in my chambers. He had seen two beautiful asses. One of them had the name of Miss Jenny. At Ford Abbey, there was a young ass of great symmetry and beauty, to which I was much attached, and which grew much attached to me—each fondling the other."

JOHN BOWRING
[Memoirs of Jeremy Bentham (1893)]

"The Grass-Lark"

[*Thoreau hankered after "the nobler animals" which had disappeared from New England, but he had also a strong conviction that little things could be as meaningful as great. He would not have found ridiculous either the Japanese love of crickets or Lafcadio Hearn's distress when a servant's carelessness cost him the song of his "Grass-Lark."*]

His cage is exactly two Japanese inches high and one inch and a half wide: its tiny wooden door, turning upon a pivot, will scarcely admit the tip of my little finger. But he has plenty of room in that cage—room to walk and jump and fly; for he is so small that you must look very carefully through the brown-gauze sides of it in order to catch a glimpse of him. I have always to turn the cage round and round, several times, in a good light, before I can discover his whereabouts; and then I usually find him resting in one of the upper corners—clinging, upsidedown, to his ceiling of gauze.

Imagine a cricket about the size of an ordinary mosquito—with a pair of antennae much longer than his own body and so fine that you can distinguish them only against the light. *Kusa-Hibari,* or "Grass-Lark," is the Japanese name of him; and he is worth in the market exactly twelve cents: that is to say, very much more than his weight in gold. Twelve cents for such a gnat-like thing! . . .

By day he sleeps or meditates, except while occupied with the slice of fresh egg-plant or cucumber which must be poked into his cage every morning. . . . To keep him clean and well fed is somewhat troublesome: could you see him, you would think it absurd to take any pains for the sake of a creature so ridiculously small.

But always at sunset the infinitesimal soul of him awakens: then the room begins to fill with a delicate and ghostly music of indescribable sweetness—a thin, thin silvery rippling and trilling as of tiniest electric bells. As the darkness deepens, the sound becomes sweeter—sometimes swelling till the whole house seems to vibrate with the elfish resonance—sometimes thinning down into the faintest imaginable thread of a voice. But loud or low, it keeps a penetrating quality that is weird . . . All night the atomy thus sings: he ceases only when the temple bell proclaims the hour of dawn.

Now this tiny song is a song of love—vague love of the unseen and unknown. It is quite impossible that he should ever have seen or known, in this present existence of his. Not even his ancestors, for many generations back, could have known anything of the night-life of the fields or the amorous value of song. They were born of eggs hatched in a jar of clay, in the shop of some insect-merchant; and they dwelt thereafter only in cages. But he sings the song of his race as it was sung a myriad years ago, and as faultlessly as if he understood the exact significance of every note. Of course he did not learn the song. It is a song of organic memory, deep, dim memory of other quintillions of lives, when the ghost of him shrilled at night from the dewy grasses of the hills. Then that song brought him love—and death. He has forgotten all about death; but he remembers the love. And therefore he sings now—for the bride that will never come.

So that his longing is unconsciously retrospective: he cries to the dust of the past—he calls to the silence and the gods for the return of time. . . . Human lovers do very much the same thing without knowing it. They call their illusion an Ideal; and their Ideal is, after all, a mere shadowing of race-experience, a phantom of organic memory. The living present has very little to do with it. . . . Perhaps this atomy also has an ideal, or at least the rudiment of an ideal; but, in any event, the tiny desire must utter its plaint in vain.

The fault is not altogether mine. I had been warned that if the creature were mated, he would cease to sing and would speedily die. But, night after night, the plaintive, sweet, unanswered trilling touched me like a reproach—became at last an obsession, an affliction, a torment of conscience; and I tried to buy a female. It was too late in the season; there were no more *kusa-bibari* for sale—either males or females. The insect-merchant laughed and said, "He ought to have died about the twentieth day of the ninth month." (It was already the second day of the tenth month.) But the insect-merchant did not know that I have a good stove in my study and keep the temperature at above 75 degrees F. Wherefore my grass-lark still sings at the close of the eleventh month and I hope to keep him alive until the Period of Greatest Cold. However, the rest of his generation are probably dead: neither for love nor money could I now find him a mate. And were I to set him free in order that he might make the search for himself, he could not possibly live through a single night, even if fortunate enough to escape by day the multitude of his natural enemies in the garden—ants, centipedes and ghastly earth spiders.

Last evening—the twenty-ninth of the eleventh month—an odd feeling came to me as I sat at my desk: a sense of emptiness in the room. Then I became aware that my grass-lark was silent, contrary to his wont. I went to the silent cage and found him lying dead beside a dried-up lump of egg-plant as gray and hard as a stone. Evidently he had not been fed for three or four days; but only the night before his death he had been singing wonderfully—so that I foolishly imagined him to be more than usually contented. My student, Aki, who loves insects, used to feed him; but Aki had gone into the country for a week's holiday and the duty of caring for the grass-lark had devolved upon Hana, the housemaid. She is not sympathetic. Hana the housemaid. She says that she did not forget the mite—but there was no more egg-plant. And she had never thought of substituting a slice of onion or of cucumber! . . . I spoke words of reproof to Hana the housemaid, and she dutifully expressed contrition. But the fairy-music has stopped; and the stillness reproaches; and the room is cold in spite of the stove.

Absurd! . . . I have made a good girl unhappy because of an insect half the size of a barley grain! The quenching of that infinitesimal life troubles me more than I could have believed possible . . . Of course, the mere habit of thinking about a creature's wants—even the wants of a cricket—may create, by insensible degrees, an imaginative interest, an attachment of which one becomes conscious only when the relation is broken. Besides, I had felt so much, in the hush of the night, the charm of the delicate voice—telling of one minute existence dependent upon my will and selfish pleasure, as upon the favor of a god—telling me also that the atom of ghost in the tiny cage, and the atom of ghost within myself, were forever but one and the same in the deeps of the Vast of being . . . And then to think of the little creature hungering and thirsting, night after night, and day after day, while the thoughts of his guardian deity were turned to the weaving of dreams! . . . How bravely, nevertheless, he sang on to the very end—an atrocious end, for he had eaten his own legs! . . . May the gods forgive us all—especially Hana the housemaid!

Yet, after all, to devour one's own legs for hunger is not the worst that can happen to a being cursed with the gift of song. There are human crickets who must eat their own hearts in order to sing.

LAFCADIO HEARN
[*Kotto* (1902)]

Jungle Pet

[*The zoologist Marston Bates has remarked that the more "scientific" any biologist wants to be the less tolerant he is of any emotional involvement with the subjects of his study. It is all right, Bates adds, to "love nature" so long as you don't admit it. But there are exceptions, as this confession by William Beebe will illustrate.*]

🐾

To write of pets is as bad taste as to write in diary form, and, besides, I had made up my mind to have no pets on this expedition. They were a great deal of trouble and a source of distraction from work while they were alive; and one's heart was wrung and one's concentration disturbed at their death. But Kib came one day, brought by a tiny copper-bronze Indian. He looked at me, touched me tentatively with a mobile little paw, and my firm resolution melted away. A young coati-mundi cannot sit man-fashion like a bear-cub, nor is he as fuzzy as a kitten or as helpless as a puppy, but he has ways of winning to the human heart, past all obstacles.

The small Indian thought that three shillings would be a fair exchange; but I knew the par value of such stock, and Kib changed hands for three bits. A week later a thousand shillings would have seemed cheap to his new master. A coati-mundi is a tropical, arboreal raccoon of sorts, with a long, ever-wriggling snout, sharp teeth, eyes that twinkle with humor, and clawed paws which are more skilful than many a fingered hand. By the scientists of the world he is addressed as *Nasua nasua nasua*—which lays itself open to the twin ambiguity of stuttering Latin, or the echoes of a Princetonian football yell. The natural histories call him coati-mundi, while the Indian has by far the best of it, with the ringing, climactic syllables, *Kibihée!* And so, in the case of a being who has received much more than his share of vitality, it was altogether fitting to shorten this to Kib—Dunsany's giver of life upon the earth.

My heart's desire is to run on and tell many paragraphs of Kib; but that, as I have said, would be bad taste, which is one form of immorality. For in such things sentiment runs too closely parallel to sentimentality,—moderation becomes maudlinism,—and one enters the caste of those who tell anecdotes of children, and the latest symptoms of their physical ills. And the deeper one feels the joys of friendship with individual small folk of the jungle, the more difficult it is to convey them to others. And so it is not of the tropical mammal coati-mundi, nor even of the humorous Kib that I think, but of the soul of him galloping up and down his slanting log, of his little inner ego, which changed from a wild thing to one who would hurl himself from any height or distance into a lap, confident that we would save his neck, welcome him, and waste good time playing the game which he invented, of seeing whether we could touch his little cold snout before he hid it beneath his curved arms.

So, in spite of my resolves, our bamboo groves became the homes of numerous little souls of wild folk, whose individuality shone out and dominated the less important incidental casement, whether it happened to be feathers, or fur, or scales. It is interesting to observe how the Adam in one comes to the surface in the matter of names for pets. I know exactly the uncomfortable feeling which must have perturbed the heart of that pioneer of nomenclaturists, to be plumped down in the midst of "the greatest aggregation of animals ever assembled" before the time of Noah, and to be able to speak of them only as *this* or *that, he* or *she.* So we felt when inundated by a host of pets. It is easy to speak of the species by the lawful Latin or Greek name; we mention the specimen on our laboratory table by its common natural-history appellation. But the individual who touches our pity, or concern, or affection, demands a special title—usually absurdly inapt.

Soon, in the bamboo glade about our bungalow, ten little jungle friends came to live; and to us they will always be Kib and Gawain, George and Gregory, Robert and Grandmother, Raoul and Pansy, Jennie and Jellicoe.

Gawain was not a double personality—he was an intermittent reincarnation, vibrating between the inorganic and the essence of vitality. In a reasonable scheme of earthly things he filled the niche of a giant green tree-frog, and one of us seemed to remember that the Knight Gawain was enamored of green, and so we dubbed him. For the hours of daylight Gawain preferred the rôle of a hunched-up pebble of malachite; or if he could find a leaf, he drew eighteen purple vacuum toes beneath him, veiled his eyes with opalescent lids, and slipped from the mineral to the vegetable kingdom, flattened by masterly shading which filled the hollows and leveled the bumps; and the leaf became more of a leaf than it had been before Gawain was merged with it.

Night, or hunger, or the merciless tearing of sleep from his soul wrought magic and transformed him into a glowing, jeweled specter. He sprouted toes and long legs; he rose and inflated his sleek emerald frog-form; his sides blazed forth a mother-of-pearl waist-coat —a myriad mosaics of pink and blue and salmon and mauve; and from nowhere if not from the very depths of his throat, there slowly rose twin globes,—great eyes,—which stood above the flatness of his head, as mosques above an oriental city. Gone were the neutralizing lids, and in their place, strange upright pupils surrounded with vermilion lines and curves and dots, like characters of ancient illuminated Persian script. And with these appalling eyes Gawain looked at us, with these unreal, crimson-flecked globes staring absurdly from an expressionless emerald mask, he contemplated roaches and small grass hoppers, and correctly estimated their distance and activity. We never thought of demanding friendship, or a hint of his voice, or common froggish activities from Gawain. We were content to visit him now and then, to arouse him, and then leave him to disincarnate his vertebral outward phase into cholorophyll or lifeless stone. To muse upon his courtship or emotions was impossible. His life had a feeling of sphinx-like duration—Gawain as a tadpole was unthinkable. He seemed ageless, unreal, wonderfully beautiful, and wholly inexplicable.

WILLIAM BEEBE
[*Edge of the Jungle* (1921)]

A Short Life but a Full One

[*"Physiological experiment on animals," wrote Charles Darwin, "is justifiable for real investigation but not for mere damnable and detestable curiosity." The line is not always easy to draw and it may be partly because he is so acutely aware of this fact that no one has ever written more compassionately about animal pets than Gustav Eckstein, Professor of Physiology in the School of Medicine at the University of Cincinnati.*]

I had got to be a doctor, a man of science, and took a tiny creature, a thing so small it sat with comfort in the palm of my hand, and cut into its skull and removed a tip of its brain. Science has not got much by that, but possibly a few rats have, for he taught me, that little white rat, and I have changed my mind about many things.

The little white rat survived my cunning. There was no mutilation of any function that is commonly said to lodge in the brain. His thought was clear, his spirit brave, he could guide his body, and his length of life seemed even increased, for he reached what in our terms is a hundred years.

The moon tonight is full and flooding through the window. He runs from his chamber—a box that I have set at one end of my roll-top desk—to his granary, a drawer on the other side and below. Back and forth, back and forth. He has been running that way for a month of nights. In the day he sleeps, only with the darkening opens his amber nervous eyes, casts about him, wonders what he missed while away, then yawns, a mighty yawn, and scratches like a mountebank by the side of his ear, and scrubs his face. Scrubs rather his head, the whole of it, uses both hands and the lengths of his arm. And now he cleans his tail, cleans that particularly, knowing that never a healthy rat but has a clean one. Then back and forth, and back and forth, and back and forth again. Suddenly he stops, just in the middle of the top of the desk, and one would say he was porcelain did he not sway and lean far out. It is the moon. He is bathed in the moon's flood. He is struck. He is queer.

She I bring him is a tiny thing. In the half-dark she trembles like a patch of that very moonlight. She rushes, in these first hours, explores all this new, is pleased, is pleased, but vouchsafes him no solitary glance. He is gone to his corner. He watches steadily from there.

I had always said he might have the top of the desk and the upper of the three drawers, and he had always kept to that, but she now lives everywhere, bites through the back of the upper drawer, lets herself hang and drop, and by that strategy coming thus from the rear, is in possession of all, immediately bringing her belongings, really his belongings and my belongings—one leap from the top to where I drive my distracted pen, another leap to the drawer, and thereafter subterranean grumblings and thuds and perturbations.

He cannot understand it—this fine slender woman, that she should be so material. What can she think of doing with it all? What does she dream?

I cannot understand either—his bedding, his food, my pencil, my pens, the cork of my ink bottle, the eraser with the chewable rubber at one end and the chewable tuft of brush at the other. Hour after hour diagonally across my work she goes, head held high to keep what she carries above her flying feet. In human distances it must be twenty miles. Certainly more than the tiny burnings of that tiny body drive that machine. Only late does she cease. She looks where he huddles uncovered in his chamber. She seems to think him over. She comes to a conclusion. She waddles toward him, settles into him, drops her head, is ostensibly asleep. He cannot sleep. He does not even close his eyes, squats there motionless, almost breathless, is afraid he may disturb her. I pick up the few gnawed bits of my belongings, turn out the lights.

Three weeks ago was the wedding. So soon as I arrived this morning she made me comprehend it was newspaper she wanted. I brought her a newspaper. She put her foot on it, as if to establish possession, then looked at me hard.

"A single newspaper?"

I brought her an armful.

All day she stuck to the job, did not eat, did not drink. I placed food and drink before her. She ran round them. When I persisted she ran through them, trailed them. The paper she tore into strips, leaped with the strips to the drawer, there continued the tearing, each strip into squares. By noon an inch of squares bedded the bottom of the drawer. By evening, three inches. By midnight five. And now, shortly after, she is ready to rest. Still she has not eaten. I ask her again. She only turns her head.

Poor husband now and then has tried to tear a little paper too, but it was not in his character, a big bulging character. This new young wife has made great changes in our ways, his and mine. A hush lies over the establishment. I sit before my desk, but do not work. She sits by my side. She is thinking her thoughts. And so is he. And so am I.

Next morning the mother and father are moving about. Mother is thin. They are thirteen, if I count them right, and they wiggle and worm and topple and tumble. She will not eat even now, and he does not find it easy, either. He is bewildered. How can anything like that have happened? I try to explain to him, but I do not rightly understand, myself, and he climbs heavily out of the drawer, and on my arm, and in my pocket hides his confused head. By evening, however, he has talked it over with her, and she has told him something I could not, and in consequence he is licking her, and she is licking them, and he is so interested in what he is doing that he steps all over them, and they squeak and step over one another, the smallest the most stepped on. No one in the heap seems able to take in the whole of the heap. That is somehow sad.

Three out of the litter I intended to leave little mother, but she would have a big family or none. At least she was indifferent to three. Two I found when I came on the fourth morning, dead. The third I never found, though, fearing it might have got into difficulty, I looked under every square of paper. I regret they are gone. They had the color and somewhat the form of the fingers of the newborn baby. The little pink legs were so weak that they dragged, and the little pink tails dragged symmetrically between them. Boneless they seemed, and sightless they were, and they kept up an aimless motion.

Mother appears unconcerned about what has happened, but I am not sure, for mother is hidden deep under her white hair, and perhaps is hidden deeper even than that. At any rate, father, who knows her better than I, is more solicitous today than usual. He picks her vermin with a more insistent care. She lies there very flat, spreads the maximum of surface to the smooth cool table below, and the maximum of surface to great father above. The exertion makes him pant. As to his feelings about the babies, I believe they were mixed. Thirteen was many, and though they were lovely, it must be admitted they were restless.

Both are asleep. I reach into the chamber to pet the back of mother's heaving neck. She starts. She bites me. It is not much of a bite and she is grieved. She probably thought that I was coming for one of the brood. She glances nervously about, finds it hard to recollect.

Toward ten every evening the two take turns to bathe. I have fitted a board across the basin under the tap where the water drips one drop at a time. To be wet all over makes them very weak and very unhappy, but to catch one drop, and wash vigorously with that, and then catch another, that is different. I myself also look forward to it—to see the way they rise from the board, put out those marvelous hands, and wait for the drop.

Father this morning is lying on his side, his two hands folded just under his nose, as if he had fallen asleep in prayer. Father's sleep is pictured with dreams. I can tell by the way he waves the tip of his tail, and when the dream gets too vivid he turns, settles on his belly, sidles over to where mother is sleeping on her belly. Then he scratches his head. A little later he scratches his head again. This time he wakes sufficiently to realize that though he is scratching his head he feels nothing. Promptly he scratches again, and still feels nothing. It is a condition so peculiar that it breaks through his sleep. He opens one eye, not far, but far enough to make out what has happened, for he is scratching not his head but hers, she having pushed hers under his neck and brought it out just inside his right hand. The discovery does not anger him. It does not even surprise him. Gently he puts her head aside, and scratches his own.

Father grows older and older. Then one evening he leaves drawers and desk top. He goes to be an eagle. At least he goes to be an eagle if it is true that yearning has its way. His gaze was always at the edges of his universe.

I am filled with the pain of the shortness of everything. That is a common pain. But it is freshened by the shortness of this little life. His great events were a thirtieth the length of my great events, yet they make mine seem not long, but brief. When I saw his death coming, how truly frightful was the feeling that nothing could stop it. And that also is a common feeling. But this life lay right there in my hand and made my helplessness seem so much more helpless. Good care and good food and warmth would save him an uneasy week, perhaps, and were I able to add all the cunning in the world it would save him another week perhaps. How then must I know with a new strong draft of conviction that gentleness and gaiety are the best of life.

He knew that. He knew how to be affectionate to his friends. To mother he yielded not only what she needed but what she wanted, and what she did not want, what the sweet and lavish extravagance of her youth and sex made her wish only to cast to the winds, cast off the precipice into the dark empty spaces of the universe.

Every night the last months he and I used to play a game. He had too heavy a body, and his legs were too short, and where he walked he rubbed the earth, so it was difficult to pretend to flee ahead of my hand, then abruptly in the midst of that flight to rear on his hind legs, give the length of his body an exaggerated shiver, as in some barbaric dance, and then continue to flee. Yet that was the game.

I think of that now. I think as one does of everything, of the night he made it plain he needed a wife, and how she nevertheless confounded him when she came, and of the litters that passed one by one, and the signs of maturity, how they passed, and the signs of age, and all in my hand, he learning every day to be less a rat, excellent though that is, learning to be more and more thoughtful, and then the final sharpness, how he mastered even that, grew gentler and gentler, and one night went to be an eagle.

Poor little mother! Babies gone and father gone. I describe how it is with father this morning, how he is off to the Peruvian mountains, and how, a short distance below the highest peak, where there is a good shelter against the blasts of the south, under great wings, nudging his brothers and sisters, he is beginning again, is waiting, though perhaps he knows it not, for little mother.

I put my hand into the dark of the drawer, and she pretends my fingers are the whilom family. She scrubs them roughly one by one. She crawls under them, crawls over them, goes round the nails and up into the crotches. She scrubs them roughly, and when each is done bites it, bumps it aside. I talk to her. She answers out of the dark. Father never would use his voice. Hers is a kind of cluck, and after she has spoken she is quiet. And I am quiet. Each of us has it in mind to wait on what the other will do. But she never can wait, must at least turn round, shove her little self through a quarter of a circle, then fix me with one great glowing eye. What she sees of me with that eye I have no notion. Nor have I any notion of what she makes of what she sees, more than that it is an embodiment with which in her loneliness she finds it possible to commune.

GUSTAV ECKSTEIN
[*Lives* (1932)]

The Friendly Wolf

[When Lois and Herbert Crisler spent eighteen months in Alaska's far north photographing for a Disney film, they fell in love with the much maligned wolf. Here is an account of two pets which they took as cubs.]

🐾

Daily he took the wolves for a walk on leashes, wearing little harnesses, which betrayed his pride in his wolves. Surprisingly, they were the first pets we had ever had. Living in wilderness as we had done ever since our marriage, we could neither take a pet along when backpacking in the mountains, nor have a neighbor feed it while we were gone. There was no neighbor; we had always lived miles from other humans. Moreover, any pet would have either killed, or been killed by, wild animals. Yet Cris, I knew, still felt wistful over Tim, a cougar dog he had once had.

One afternoon when the wolves were leading as usual, like rocks or rebels, Cris suddenly said, "I'm going to turn them loose and let them follow us home."

"Oh, no! They can outrun us and we'll never see them again."

Cris knelt and stripped off the pretty harnesses. "It's a calculated risk." It was the first of a long series of bold gestures of friendship to the wolves.

As I feared, the wolves sped away. Then came a revelation—our first real nugget of wolf knowledge. Lady whirled and ran back toward Cris and as she came she demonstrated what is surely one of the prettiest, most endearing gestures in the world, the wolf "smile." We had not known it existed.

She smiled with her whole body. She humped her back like an inverted smile. She sleeked her ears into her fur and tossed her big forepaws gaily to either side as well as back and forth, as if they were on universal joints. Nearing Cris, she produced the most bewitching part of the smile: she tilted her head aside and lifted her opposite forepaw high, as if entreating friendliness. She looked up at Cris with an expression of pure joy, such as we had never seen on her keen little black face before. Cris's eyes too were wreathed in happiness.

For the first time we realized the beauty of a wolf's eyes. The whole wolf face is considered by Dr. Rudolph Schenkel to be one of the most expressive of animal faces, and much of the expression resides in the quick-changing eyes. You can never do justice to them until you are close to the wolf; from even a little distance black lines of fur and socket prolong them into slant slits. But when you see them a few feet away they are level and large and as clear as pure water, gray or gold or green according to mood and individual wolf. The changeable black pupils, enlarging readily with emotion, may be radiant or lighted by the fierce spark of anxiety or anger.

The rest of the wolf's face changes with feeling too. Eyelids knot or smooth, ears point alertly or snug flat in friendliness. Also—and this, says the animal artist, William Berry, makes a wolf's face very hard to draw—there are changes in the slight but very complex musculature of the muzzle.

The smile goes on naturally into the "full wolf greeting." When the wolf tilts head aside, bowing his neck, he may proceed to lay his neck clear down on the ground and unroll his eel-supple spine to follow—a dancer's maneuver no dog could perform. A wolf can perform it without falling over only because he takes a remarkably wide base with hind paws. And he does it all in one fluent gesture, accompanied with the dazzling sweetness of the eyes.

Much has been made of the first part of the full wolf greeting, that is, "presenting the neck to the enemy." But the wolf is presenting his neck to the ground, preparatory to laying himself at your feet and it doesn't matter to him which way he turns his neck to do it. If he tilts his head away from you, "offering" his vulnerable neck, it is because he has an impulse to raise his paw toward you—lay it over your own neck if that has a low enough elevation at the moment, or lay himself at your feet.

From this day on, the smile was a constant feature of our lives. And always it warmed our hearts, made us smile too. We soon found that out on the tundra the most reassuring gesture we could make to the little wolves, doubtfully watching as we approached, was to do a wolf smile ourselves. We crouched, elbows to sides, and flipped forearms sidewise. A wolf reads the lowering of your elevation as friendliness. Whether they figured out that our idea was that we were smiling I don't know. But they took the crouch and paw flip as our regular recognition sign. They smiled and tossed their own paws sidewise and ran to us.

We thought nothing about it, but in the first instance of many we had imitated the wolf in order to control him.

And did the wolves follow us home on this day when Cris gave them liberty and received the smile? By no means. But they did glance back occasionally to see if we were coming! We did not have the ghost of an understanding of it yet, but we were part of their pack. The social wolves wanted us along, though personally they were so elusive they frustrated all attempts at cuddling them.

At last that day they were in the pen and fed, and you never saw such relaxed, contented little animals. Cris, passing as I got supper, whispered in my ear, half for fun, half shyly, "I like my little wolves."

From now on they ran free on our daily walks.

We had the brave indispensable "starting ignorance" that afterward one marvels at. We could not dream the turbulence ahead as we would try to live in a degree of freedom with animals not human-oriented.

We were motivated superficially by the desire to photograph the wolves. For us this was premised, of course, on friendship. And we wanted to photograph them in their natural habitat because of the outlook dominating our thinking and even our way of life: we believed that the last frail wonderful webs of wilderness now vanishing from Earth are of some infinite value, a value only sensed and very deep—and liable to perish and be lost in this day. Wilderness without its animals is dead—dead scenery. Animals without wilderness are a closed book.

So the harnesses were put away forever and I was horrified to see that harness marks remained on the wolves' fur, dimly pale even on Lady's luscious black coat. Incredulously I wondered if harness had touched fur at some critical point in fur maturation. I did not know that "harness marks" are the wolf pattern!

Now the wolves introduced us to the tundra as never before. First they showed us each wee anonymous clot of bone and feathers— birds that had died here this past spring. Sick, old, tired, or perhaps caught in a late storm, they had made the long flight to the great tundra where they first saw light and heard song, and here had died.

Lady made her first kill, a mouse, and bore it to Cris when he praised her. She danced clear around him, brilliant and smiling with pride.

Next the wolves introduced us to that authentic mark of wild nature, the Grimm's fairytale effect!

We were taking them by a new route one day and I glanced back to see why Lady wasn't coming. The black wolf stood by her first patch of newly opened dark-pink daisies, acquainting herself with them. She brushed her nose across them, raised her paw and touched them. Long afterward we were to glimpse other young wolves acquaint themselves in this way with newly opened flower patches.

A wolf's curiosity is impersonal. It goes beyond food and fear.

Lady patted her first puffball, sprang back and sneezed, then patted it again. She ran curiously to where I sat picking and eating the first sour blueberries. I mashed a few, she licked them, watched attentively while I picked and gave her more. Then she picked and ate a few berries for herself. Wolves have to learn.

But those incidents had connection with food. Pure impersonal fascination with the unknown showed on the morning she first met ice. She stood examining the ice in her water pan, touching it with her paw. Even after I poured water over it, she reached her paw through the water and stroked that novel satin underneath.

There was a dark, puzzling side to the wolves' nature. Cris thought he would please them one day by taking them to a caribou carcass he had found. Instead of being pleased, the wolves acted dark and troubled. Then little Lady undertook a huge task her parents no doubt would normally have performed: she began to cache the meat.

She tore off a chunk, took it away and holding it in her jaws busily dug a hole. She laid the meat in the hole, covered it, not with her paws but with her slender nose, brushing duff over it, then hurried back for more. The wolf did not put all her eggs in one basket. Each piece was cached in a different spot.

And Trigger? He ate!

Was this a sex difference or a personality difference between him and Lady? Long afterward we watched Lady work like a dog in hot sun for two hours, caching a kill piecemeal, while Master Trigger relaxed nearby in the shade of willow bushes. But also we were to see him work even harder than Lady, carrying very heavy pieces a long distance to cache them; and when he did, it was invariably under stimulus of competition from strangers liable to get his meat. Lady's feeling seemed to be more generalized: you cached meat; that was what you did.

The two wolves were very different. Lady was wild; she was totally independent. She was fearless and gay and she always led, never at a loss for where to go or what to do. Trigger had a combination of traits that baffled me: he was lordly yet shy, perhaps a natural combination at that. He was mixed; Lady was single. Always she seemed to be "going someplace," as if to meet destiny. Trifles along the way were a matter of indifference to her.

Not to Trigger. He was luxury-loving. As a matter of course on hot days he took the one cool spot in the pen, a denlike hollow. Lady indifferently slept where she could, in the sun. When Cris dug a shady hollow for her too, she was distrustful of it for two days. Wildness.

Yet Trigger depended on Lady emotionally. There was no gate to the pen. We laid back the top band of wire at one point and stepped over the lower. Trigger lost his head one evening. We had lifted Lady into the pen unobserved. In fact Cris had carried her part way home. Trigger thought she was gone. He ran back to look for her and when he did come to the pen and she bowed and smiled, inviting play, along the inside of the fence, he was so distraught he would not let us catch him to put him in.

But once inside, the poor wolfie for once cared nothing for comfort. He wanted only to be close to Lady. Even the next day he deserted his shady hollow to lie beside her in the hot sun, one big bony leg across her tuffy baby fur.

LOIS CRISLER
[*Arctic Wild* (1958)]

LEGENDS,
FANTASIES,
AND FICTIONS

When the peacock sees his feet, he screams wildly, thinking that they are not in keeping with the rest of his body.

SAINT EPIPHANIUS

When a turtle-dove is widowed by the loss of her spouse, she takes a dread against the marriage bed. . . . Know then, O Woman, how much widowhood is esteemed when it is shown forth even in birds.

Twelfth-Century Bestiary

. . . the toad, ugly and venomous,
Bears yet a precious jewel in his head.

SHAKESPEARE
As You Like It

If you were to make little fishes talk, they would talk like whales.

OLIVER GOLDSMITH to SAMUEL JOHNSON

Chasser la Nature

[*The wisdom of the East is often more prudential and worldly than that of Europe, and the difference is clear even in the early fables, as witness this ancedote from the Sanskrit collection called* The Panchatantra. *It exists in various ancient versions, and its date, though early, is uncertain.*]

The billows of the Ganges were dotted with pearly foam born of the leaping of fishes frightened at hearing the roar of the waters that broke on the rugged, rocky shore. On the bank was a hermitage crowded with holy men devoting their time to the performance of sacred rites—chanting, self-denial, self-torture, study, fasting, and sacrifice. They would take purified water only, and that in measured sips. Their bodies wasted under a diet of bulbs, roots, fruits, and moss. A loin-cloth made of bark formed their scanty raiment.

The father of the hermitage was named Yajnavalkya. After he had bathed in the sacred stream and had begun to rinse his mouth, a little female mouse dropped from a hawk's beak and fell into his hand. When he saw what she was, he laid her on a banyan leaf, repeated his bath and mouth-rinsing, and performed a ceremony of purification. Then through the magic power of his holiness, he changed her into a girl, and took her with him to his hermitage.

As his wife was childless, he said to her: "Take her, my dear wife. She has come into life as your daughter, and you must rear her carefully." So the wife reared her and spoiled her with petting. As soon as the girl reached the age of twelve, the mother saw that she was ready for marriage, and said to her husband: "My dear husband, how can you fail to see that the time is passing when your daughter should marry?"

And he replied: "You are quite right, my dear. . . .

"So, if she is willing, I will summon the blessèd sun, and give her to him." "I see no harm in that," said his wife. "Let it be done."

The holy man therefore summoned the sun, who appeared without delay, and said: "Holy sir, why am I summoned?" The father said: "Here is a daughter of mine. Be kind enough to marry her." Then, turning to his daughter, he said: "Little girl, how do you like him, this blessèd lamp of the three worlds?" "No, father," said the girl. "He is too burning hot. I could not like him. Please summon another one, more excellent than he is."

Upon hearing this, the holy man said to the sun: "Blessèd one, is there any superior to you?" And the sun replied: "Yes, the cloud is superior even to me. When he covers me, I disappear."

So the holy man summoned the cloud next, and said to the maiden: "Little girl, I will give you to him." "No," said she. "This one is black and frigid. Give me to someone finer than he."

Then the holy man asked: "O cloud, is there anyone superior to you?" And the cloud replied: "The wind is superior even to me."

So he summoned the wind, and said: "Little girl, I give you to him." "Father," said she, "this one is too fidgety. Please invite somebody superior even to him." So the holy man said: "O wind, is there anyone superior even to you?" "Yes," said the wind. "The mountain is superior to me."

So he summoned the mountain and said to the maiden: "Little girl, I give you to him." "Oh, father," said she. "He is rough all over, and stiff. Please give me to somebody else."

So the holy man asked: "O kingly mountain, is there anyone superior even to you?" "Yes," said the mountain. "Mice are superior to me."

Then the holy man summoned a mouse, and presented him to the girl, saying: "Little girl, do you like this mouse?"

The moment she saw him, she felt: "My own kind, my own kind," and her body thrilled and quivered, and she said: "Father dear, turn me into a mouse, and give me to him. Then I can keep house as my kind of people ought to do."

And her father, through the magic power of his holiness, turned her into a mouse, and gave her to him.

"And that is why I say:

Though mountain, sun, and cloud and wind
    Were suitors at her feet,

The Mouse-maid turned to mouse again—
Nature is hard to beat.

THE PANCHATANTRA
[Translated by Arthur W. Ryder (1925)]

The Scandalous Behavior of Zeus

[Greeks of the Golden Age were compelled to refer with a straight face to ancient tales of the amorous Zeus, who assumed the form of various animals when the fancy struck him to seduce or to rape some attractive maiden, either human or semi-divine. By the second century A.D., however, their sophisticated descendants found these tales more spicy than awe-inspiring, and the satirist Lucian found them good material for his flippant dialogues.]

ZEPHYRUS. You have seen Agenor, the Sidonian?

NOTUS. The father of Europa? I have. What then?

ZEPHYRUS. I am just going to tell you what then.

NOTUS. Meaning no doubt, that Jupiter has been a great while in love with the young woman. I knew that before, without your telling me.

ZEPHYRUS. You might know, I dare say, of his being in love; but the sequel of the story you are now to learn from me. Europa had gone down to the sea-shore, accompanied by some play-fellows of her own age; when Jupiter, having assumed the form of a most beautiful Bull, made his appearance amongst them, as fond of play as any one of them: he was all over milk-white, his horns were elegantly turned, and his looks were gentle. He so wantoned on the beach, and bellowed so charmingly, that Europa was induced to venture herself upon his back. Which she had no sooner done, than away he ran with her, as fast as his heels could carry him, to the sea, into which he immediately jumped, and betook himself to swimming. The young woman, most terribly frightened, laid hold of one of his horns with her left hand, to save herself from falling; while, with the other, she had enough to do to keep her clothes from being discomposed by the wind.

NOTUS. On my word, you have been most notably entertained. Jupiter in the sea, with his fair one on his back! A gallant spectacle!

ZEPHYRUS. The best part of it is to come. The sea, Notus, was no longer ruffled with waves, but perfectly calm, smooth, and serene. We winds had nothing in the world to do, nothing more than to attend, and observe what was going forward. Little Cupids fluttering on the surface of the water, in which now and then they wetted their toes, carried lighted torches, and joined in the bridal song. Nereids, half naked, were to be seen riding on Dolphins, all clapping their hands. The family of Tritons, and every inhabitant of the waves, that was not an absolute fright, came dancing about the maid. Neptune attended his chariot, and, with Amphitrite by his side, merrily went before, clearing the way as he saw his brother out of his element. Last of all came Venus, borne aloft on a shell by a couple of Tritons, and scattering flowers on Europa. Thus it was all the way from Phoenicia to Crete. Where, when once he had set foot on the island, our bull was a bull no longer. Jupiter was himself again, and led by the hand to the Dictaean grove the blushing maid, whose down-cast eyes and blushing cheeks sufficiently declared her apprehension. Our business was to tumble about the waves, and riffle the sea.

NOTUS. You have been very fortunate indeed! while I had nothing better to look at than griffins, elephants and Negroes.

LUCIAN
[*Dialogues of the Gods* (2nd century A.D.)]

The Golden Ass

[When Shakespeare had Bottom, the weaver, turned into a donkey, he was undoubtedly recalling what is probably the most entertaining work of prose fiction before Don Quixote. Not much is known about its author, Lucius Apuleius, beyond the fact that he was an African-born Roman who called his work Metamorphoses though it was long ago rechristened The Golden Ass. Among its many episodes is the story of Cupid and Psyche, but the main narrative is concerned with the adventures, often amorous, of the hero whom a sorceress promises to turn into a bird but who finds himself transformed into an ass instead.]

". . . But one thing I had almost forgot to inquire: what must I say or do, in order to get rid of my wings, and return to my own form as Lucius?"

"Be in no anxiety," she said, "about all that matter; for my mistress has made me acquainted with every thing that can again change such forms into the human shape. But do not suppose that this was done through any kind feeling towards me, but in order that I might assist her with the requisite remedies when she returns home. Only think with what simple and trifling herbs such a mighty result is brought about: for instance, a little anise, with some leaves of laurel infused in spring water, and used as a lotion and a draught."

Having assured me of this over and over again, she stole into her mistress's chamber with the greatest trepidation, and took a little box out of the casket. Having first hugged and kissed it, and offered up a prayer that it would favour me with a prosperous flight, I hastily divested myself of all my garments, then greedily dipping my fingers into the box, and taking thence a considerable quantity of the ointment, I rubbed it all over my body and limbs. And now, flapping my arms up and down, I anxiously awaited my change into a bird. But no down, no shooting wings appeared, but my hairs evidently became thickened into bristles, and my tender skin was hardened into a hide; my hands and feet, too, no longer furnished with distinct fingers and toes, formed as many massive hoofs, and a long tail projected from the extremity of my spine. My face was now enormous, my mouth wide, my nostrils gaping, and my lips hanging down. In like manner my ears grew hairy, and of immoderate length, and I found in every respect I had become enlarged. Thus, hopelessly surveying all parts of my body, I beheld myself changed not into a bird, but an ass.

I wished to upbraid Fotis for the deed she had done; but, now deprived both of the gesture and voice of man, I could only expostulate with her silently with my under-lip hanging down, and looking sideways at her with tearful eyes. As for her, as soon as she beheld me thus changed, she beat her face with her hands, and cried aloud, "Wretch that I am, I am undone! In my haste and flurry I mistook one box for the other, deceived by their similarity. It is fortunate, how-ever, that a remedy for this transformation is easily to be obtained; for, by only chewing roses, you will put off the form of an ass, and in an instant will become my Lucius once again. I only wish that I had prepared as usual some garlands of roses for us last evening; for then you would not have had to suffer the delay even of a single night. But, at the break of dawn, the remedy shall be provided for you."

Thus did she lament; and as for me, though I was a perfect ass, and instead of Lucius, a beast of burden, I still retained human sense: long and deeply, in fact, did I consider with myself, whether I ought not to bite and kick that most wicked woman to death. How-ever, better thoughts recalled me from such rash designs, lest, by in-flicting on Fotis the punishment of death, I should at once put an end to all chances of efficient assistance. So, bending my head low, shak-ing my ears, I silently swallowed my wrongs for a time, and submit-ting to my most dreadful misfortune, I betook myself to the stable to the good horse which had carried me so well, and there I found an-other ass also, which belonged to my former host Milo. Now it oc-curred to me that, if there are in dumb animals any silent and natural ties of sympathy, this horse of mine, being influenced by a certain feeling of recognition and compassion, would afford me room for a lodging, and the rights of hospitality. But, O Jupiter Hospitalis, and all you the guardian divinities of Faith! this very excellent nag of mine, and the ass, put their heads together, and immediately plotted schemes for my destruction; and as soon as they beheld me approach-ing the manger, laying back their ears and quite frantic with rage, they furiously attacked me with their heels, fearing I had design upon their food; consequently I was driven away into the farthest corner from that very barley, which the evening before I had placed, with my own hands, before that most grateful servant of mine.

Thus harshly treated and sent into banishment, I betook my-self to a corner of the stable. And while I reflected on the insolence of my companions, and formed plans of vengeance against the perfidious steed, for the next day, when I should have become Lucius once more by the aid of the roses, I beheld against the central square pillar which supported the beams of the stable, a statue of the goddess Hippona, standing within a shrine, and nicely adorned with garlands of roses, and those, too, recently gathered. Inspired with hope, the moment I espied the salutary remedy, I boldly mounted as far as ever my fore legs could stretch; and then with neck at full length, and extending my lips as much as I possibly could, I endeavoured to catch hold of the garlands. But by a most unlucky chance, just as I was endeavouring to accomplish this, my servant lad, who had the constant charge of my horse, suddenly espied me, sprang to his feet in a great rage, and exclaimed, "How long are we to put up with this vile hack, which, but a few moments ago, was for making an attack upon the food of the cattle, and is now doing the same even to the statues of the Gods? But if I don't this very instant cause this sacrilegious beast to be both sore and crippled"—and searching for something with which to strike me, he stumbled upon a bundle of sticks that lay there, and, picking out a knotted cudgel, the largest he could find among them all, he did not cease to belabour my poor sides, until a loud thumping and banging at the outer gates, and an uproar of the neighbours shouting thieves! struck him with terror, and he took to his heels.

The next moment the doors were burst open, an armed band of robbers rushed in, and surrounded the house on all sides; people ran from all quarters to help the defence, but the robbers beat them off. Being all furnished with swords and torches, they illuminated the darkness of the night; and their swords gleamed like the rays of the rising sun. Then with their strong axes they broke open the stout bars and fastenings of a strong room in the middle of the house, which was filled with Milo's treasures, and having completely ransacked it, they hastily divided the booty, and tied it up in separate packages. Now the number of packages exceeded that of the men who were to carry them. Hence, being brought to extraordinary shifts, through a superabundance of wealth, they led forth us, the two asses, and my horse, from the stable, loaded us with the heaviest burdens they possibly could, and drove us before them from the empty house, flourishing their sticks over us. Leaving one of their companions behind as a spy, to bring them word as to any proceedings taken in consequence of the robbery, they hurried us along through the bye-paths of the mountains, beating us every now and then, so that through the weight of my load, the steepness of the mountain, and the interminable length of the way, I was no better than a dead donkey. At last I very seriously thought of resorting to the aid of the civil power, and liberating myself from so many miseries, by invoking the august name of the Emperor.

Accordingly, when, in broad daylight, we were passing through a certain populous village, which was thronged with people celebrating a fair, I strove, in the midst of that crowd of Greeks, to utter the august name of Cæsar, in the native language, and I cried out O distinctly and sonorously; but that was all, for the name of Cæsar I **was** not able to pronounce. The robbers abominating my discordant clamour, thumped and gored my miserable hide, and left it hardly fit for a corn sieve. But at last, that *good* Jupiter bestowed on me an unexpected chance of deliverance. For after we had passed by many small farms and fine country houses, I espied a delightful little garden, in which, besides other sweet flowers, there were virgin roses, dripping with the morning dew. With longing desire, and overjoyed by the hope of safety, I moved towards them. But while, with quivering lips, I was preparing to seize them, this very important reflection came across me: if I divested myself of the asinine form, and again became Lucius, while in the hands of the robbers, they would surely kill me, either as a supposed magician, or for fear that I should inform against them. For the present, therefore, as a matter of necessity, I abstained from roses, and putting up with my present misfortune, was fain to champ my bridle under the guise of an ass.

LUCIUS APULEIUS
[*The Golden Ass* (2nd century A.D.)]

Preacher's Vade Mecum

[*Modern after-dinner speakers have frequent recourse to books compiled for the express purpose of supplying them with anecdotes which can be used to point a moral. A certain medieval book once served popular preachers in much the same way. Its stories were drawn from an amazing variety of sources, and the "application" of each was indicated. Chaucer, Shakespeare, and Spenser also drew upon it for allusions and plots.*]

✒

In the reign of a certain king there lived a proud and oppressive seneschal. Now near the royal palace was a forest well stocked with game; and by the direction of this person various pits were dug there, and covered with leaves, for the purpose of entrapping the beasts. It happened that the seneschal himself went into this forest, and with much exaltation of heart exclaimed internally, "Lives there a being in the empire more powerful than I am?" This braggart thought was scarcely formed, ere he rode upon one of his own pit-falls, and immediately disappeared. The same day had been taken a lion, a monkey, and a serpent. Terrified at the situation into which fate had thrown him, he cried out lustily, and his noise awoke a poor man called Guido, who had come with his ass into that forest to procure firewood, by the sale of which he got his bread. Hastening to the mouth of the pit, and ascertaining the occasion of the clamour, he was promised great wealth if he would extricate the seneschal from his perilous situation. "My friend," answered Guido, "I have no means of obtaining a livelihood except by the faggots which I collect: if I neglect this for a single day, I shall be thrown into the greatest difficulties." The seneschal re-iterated his promises of enriching him; and Guido went back to the city, and returned with a long cord, which he let down into the pit, and bade the seneschal bind it round his waist. But before he could apply it to the intended purpose, the lion leaped forward, and seizing upon the cord, was drawn up in his stead. Immediately, exhibiting great signs of pleasure, the beast ran off into the wood. The rope again descended, and the monkey having noticed the success of the lion, vaulted above the man's head, and shaking the cord, was in like manner set at liberty. Without staying to return thanks he hurried off to his haunts. A third time the cord was let down, and the serpent twining around it, was drawn up and escaped. "O my good friend," said the seneschal, "the beasts are gone, now draw me up quickly, I pray you." Guido complied, and afterwards succeeded in drawing up his horse, which the seneschal instantly mounted and rode back to the palace. Guido returned home; and his wife observing that he had come without wood, was very dejected, and inquired the cause. He related what had occurred, and the riches he was to receive for his service. The wife's countenance brightened, and early in the morning she posted off her husband to the palace. But the seneschal denied all knowledge of him, and ordered him to be whipped for his presumption. The porter executed the directions, and beat him so severely that he left him half dead. As soon as Guido's wife understood this, she saddled their ass, and brought him home in a very infirm state. The sickness which ensued, consumed the whole of their little property; but as soon as he had recovered he returned to his usual occupation in the wood. Whilst he was thus employed, he beheld afar off ten asses laden with packs, and a lion by the latter one, pursuing the path which led towards Guido. On looking narrowly at this beast, he remembered that it was the same which he had freed from its imprisonment in the pit. The lion signified with his foot, that he should take the loaded asses, and go home. This Guido did, and the lion followed. On arriving at his own door, the noble beast fawned upon him, and wagging his tail as if in triumph, ran back to the woods. Guido caused proclamation to be made in different churches, that if any asses had been lost, the owners should come to him; but no one appearing to demand them, he opened the packages, and to his great joy, discovered them full of money. On the second day Guido returned to the forest, but forgot an iron instrument to cleave the wood. He looked up, and beheld the monkey whose liberation he had effected; and the animal, by help of teeth and nails, accomplished his desires. Guido then loaded his asses and went home. The next day he renewed his visit to the forest; and sitting down to prepare his instrument, discerned the serpent, whose escape he had aided, carrying a stone in its mouth of three colours; the one white, another black, and the third red. It opened its mouth and let the stone fall into Guido's lap. Having done this, it departed. Guido took the stone to a skilful lapidary, who had no sooner inspected it than he knew its virtues, and would willingly have paid him an hundred florins for it. But Guido refused; and by means of that singular stone, obtained great wealth, and was promoted to a military command. The emperor having heard of the extraordinary qualities which it possessed, desired to see it. Guido went accordingly; and the emperor was so struck with its uncommon beauty, that he wished to purchase it at any rate; and threatened, if Guido refused compliance, to banish him the kingdom. "My lord," answered he, "I will sell the stone; but let me say one thing if the price be not given, it shall be presently restored to me." He demanded three hundred florins, and then taking it from a small coffer, put it into the emperor's hands. Full of admiration, he exclaimed, "Tell me where you procured this most beautiful stone." This he did, and narrated from the beginning the seneschal's accident, and subsequent ingratitude. He told how severely he had been injured by his command; and the benefits he had received from the lion, the monkey, and serpent. Much moved at the recital, the emperor sent for the seneschal and said, "What is this I hear of thee?" He was unable to reply. "O wretch!" continued the emperor, "monster of ingratitude! Guido liberated thee from the most imminent danger, and for this thou hast nearly destroyed him. Dost thou see how even irrational things have rendered him good for the service he performed? But thou hast returned evil for good. Therefore I deprive thee of thy dignity, which I will bestow upon Guido, and I further adjudge you to be suspended on a cross." This decree infinitely rejoiced the noblemen of the empire: and Guido, full of honours and years, ended his day in peace.

APPLICATION

My beloved, the emperor is God; the pauper, man. The forest is the world, which is full of pits. The lion is the Son of God, who assumed humanity, the monkey is conscience; and the serpent is a prelate or confessor; the cord is Christ's passion. The loaded asses are the divine precepts.

ANONYMOUS
[Gesta Romanorum (13th century)]

The Magpie Who Talked Too Much

[*The humor in the moralized tales of the Middle Ages is usually unconscious —but not always.*]

I woll tell you an ensaumple of a woman that ete the good morsell in the absence of her husbonde.

Ther was a woman that had a pie in a cage, that spake and wolde tell talys that she saw do. And so it happed that her husbonde made kepe a gret ele in a litell ponde in his gardin, to that entent to yeue it sum of his frendes that wolde come to see hym; but the wyff, whanne her husbond was oute, saide to her maide, "late us ete the gret ele, and y will saie to my husbond that the otour hathe eten hym"; and so it was done. And whan the good man was come, the pye began to tell hym how her maistresse had eten the ele. And he yode to the ponde, and fonde not the ele. And he asked his wiff wher the ele was become. And she wende to have excused her, but he saide her, "excuse you not, for y wote well ye have eten yt, for the pye hathe told me." And so ther was gret noyse betwene the man and hys wiff for etinge of the ele. But whanne the good man was gone, the maistresse and the maide come to the pie, and plucked of all the fedres on the pyes hede, saieng, "thou hast discovered us of the ele"; and thus was the pore pye plucked. But ever after, whanne the pie sawe a balled or a pilled man, or a woman with an high forhede, the pie saide to hem, "ye spake of the ele." And therfor here is an en-saumple that no woman shulde ete no lycorous morcelles in the absens and withoute weting of her husbond, but yef it so were that it be with folk of worshipp, to make hem chere; for this woman was afterward mocked for the pye and the ele.

THE KNIGHT DE LA TOUR LANDRY
(15th century A.D.)

Unnatural History

[Unnatural history, as it is sometimes called, must be at least as voluminous as the natural, and it is certainly a great deal older. It ranges all the way from prehistoric myth, through the moralized tales of the bestiaries, down to the conscious fiction of today. It includes the often excusable mistakes of the early naturalists who were trying to tell the truth as well as folk beliefs which have persisted, little changed, for thousands of years—in part, perhaps, just because they are so picturesque and so interesting.

Two of the oldest and most persistent tales are the pleasant story of the Grateful Beast and the varied but far from pleasant legend of the werewolf. Here are two versions of the first tale, and one of the second.]

As to gratitude (for it seems to me, we had need bring this word into a little greater repute) this one example, which Apion reports himself to have been an eyewitness of, shall suffice. "One day," says he, "that at Rome they entertained the people with the fighting of several strange beasts, and principally of lions of an unusual size. There was one among the rest who, by his furious deportment, by the strength and largeness of his limbs, and by his loud and dreadful roaring, attracted the eyes of all the spectators. Among the other slaves, that were presented to the people in this combat of beasts, there was one Androclus, of Dacia belonging to a Roman lord of consular dignity. This lion, having seen him at a distance, first made a sudden stop, as it were, in a wondering posture; and then softly approached nearer in a gentle and peaceable manner, as if it were to enter into acquaintance with him; this being done, and being now assured of what he sought, he began to wag his tail, as dogs do when they flatter their masters, and to kiss and lick the hands and thighs of the poor wretch, who was beside himself and almost dead with fear. Androclus having, by this kindness of the lion, a little come to himself, and having taken so much heart as to consider and recognize him, it was a singular pleasure to see the joy and caresses that passed between them. At which the people breaking into loud acclamations of joy, the emperor caused the slave to be called, to know from him the cause of so strange an event. He thereupon told him a new and a very wonderful story: 'My master, said he, being proconsul in Africa, I was constrained by his severity and cruel usage, being daily beaten, to steal from him and to run away. And to hide myself securely from a person of so great authority in the province, I thought it my best way to fly to the solitudes, sands, and uninhabitable parts of that country, resolved, in case the means of supporting life should fail me, to make some shift or other to kill myself. The sun being excessively hot at noon, and the heat intolerable, I found a retired and almost inaccessible cave, and went into it. Soon after there came in to me this lion with one foot wounded and bloody, complaining and groaning with the pain he endured: at his coming I was exceedingly afraid, but he having espied me hid in a corner of his den, came gently to me, holding out and showing me his wounded foot, as if he demanded my assistance in his distress. I then drew out a great splinter he had got there, and growing a little more familiar with him, squeezing the wound, thrust out the dirt and gravel that he had got into it, wiped and cleansed it as well as I could. He, finding himself something better and much eased of his pain, lay down to repose, and presently fell asleep with his foot in my hand. From that time forward, he and I lived together in this cave three whole years, upon the same diet; for of the beasts that he killed in hunting he always brought me the best pieces, which I roasted in the sun for want of fire, and so ate them. At last growing weary of this wild and brutish life, the lion being one day gone abroad to hunt for our ordinary provision, I escaped from thence, and the third day after was taken by the soldiers, who brought me from Africa to this city to my master, who presently condemned me to die, and to be exposed to the wild beasts. Now, by what I see, this lion was also taken soon after, who would now recompense me for the benefit and cure that he had received at my hands.' This is the story that Androclus told the emperor, which he also conveyed from hand to hand to the people: wherefore at the universal request, he was absolved from his sentence and set at liberty; and the lion was, by order of the people, presented to him. "We afterward saw," says Apion, "Androclus leading this lion, in nothing but a small leash, from tavern to tavern at Rome, and receiving what money everybody would give him, the lion being so gentle, as to suffer himself to be covered with the flowers that the people threw upon him; every one that met him saying: 'There goes the lion that entertained the man; there goes the man that cured the lion.' "

MICHEL DE MONTAIGNE
[*Essays* (1580)]

Lycanthropia, which *Avicenna* calls *Cucubuth,* others *Lupinam insaniam,* or Wolf-madness, when men run howling about graves and fields in the night, and will not be persuaded but that they are wolves, or some such beasts. *Aëtius* and *Paulus* call it a kind of *Melancholy;* but I should rather refer it to *Madness,* as most do. Some make a doubt of it whether there be any such disease. *Donat. ab Altomari* saith, that he saw two of them in his time: *Wierus* tells a story of such a one at *Padua,* 1541, that would not believe to the contrary, but that he was a wolf. He hath another instance of a *Spaniard,* who thought himself a bear: *Forestus* confirms as much by many examples; one amongst the rest of which he was an eye-witness, at *Alkmaar* in *Holland,* a poor husbandman that still hunted about graves, & kept in churchyards, of a pale, black, ugly, & fearful look. Such belike, or little better, were *King Prœtus'* daughters that thought themselves kine. And *Nebuchadnezzar* in *Daniel,* as some interpreters hold, was only troubled with this kind of madness. This disease perhaps gave occasion to that bold assertion of *Pliny, some men were turned into wolves in his time, and from wolves to men again:* and to that fable of *Pausanias,* of a man that was ten years a wolf, and afterwards turned to his former shape: to *Ovid's* tale of *Lycaon, &c.* He that is desirous to hear of this Disease, or more examples, let him read *Austin* in his 18th Book *De Civitate Dei, cap.* 5; *Mizaldus, cent.* 5.77; *Sckenkius, lib.* 1; *Hildesheim, spicil.* 2. *de Mania; Forestus, lib.* 10. *de morbis cerebri; Olaus Magnus; Vincentius Bellavicensis, spec. met. lib.* 31. *c.* 122; *Picrius, Bodine, Zuinger, Zeilger, Peucer, Wierus, Spranger, &c. This malady,* saith *Avicenna,* troubleth men most in February, and is now-a-days frequent in *Bohemia* and *Hungary,* according to *Heurnius. Schernitzius* will have it common in *Livonia.* They lie hid most part all day, and go abroad in the night, barking, howling, at graves and deserts; *they have usually hollow eyes, scabbed legs and thighs, very dry and pale,* saith *Altomarus;* he gives a reason there of all the symptoms, and sets down a brief cure of them.

ROBERT BURTON
[*The Anatomy of Melancholy* (1621)]

It happened one day as he was sitting in his cell, a hyæna came to him, her whelp was in her mouth; she set it down beside the door, she knocked on the door with her head. The old man heard her knock, he came out thinking that a brother had come to him. When he opened the door he saw the hyæna, he was astounded, saying, "What does she want here?" She filled her mouth with her whelp, she held it out to the old man, weeping. The old man took the whelp in his hands, steady in simplicity, he turned it this way and that, looking in its body for what ailed it. When he had considered the whelp, behold, it was blind in its two eyes. He took it, he groaned, he spat on its face, he signed it on the eyes with his finger: straightway the whelp saw, it went to its mother's dug, it sucked, it followed her, they went away to that river . . . and into the marsh they made their way. The sheep of the Lybians, they bring them once each year into the marsh of Scete to eat the *shoushet,* and the herdsmen that live in the villages over against Pernouj, they also bring their oxen into the marsh of Scete to eat the green herbage, once a year.

The hyæna left a day behind her. The next day she came to the old man, she had a sheepskin in her mouth, thick with wool, freshly killed, she had it over her; she struck the door with her head. The old man was sitting in the enclosure. When he heard the knock at the door, he got up, he opened it: he found the hyæna, the sheepskin over her. He said to the hyæna, "Where hast thou been? Where hast thou found this, if thou hast not eaten a sheep? As that which thou hast brought me comes of violence, I will not take it."

The hyæna struck her head upon the ground, she bent her paws, and on her knees she prayed him, as if she had been a man, to take it. He said to her, "I have but now told thee that I will not take it, unless thou makest me this promise: I *will not vex the poor by eating their sheep.*" She made many movements of her head, up and down, as if she were promising him. Again he repeated it to her, saying, "Unless thou dost promise me, saying, *I will not kill a creature alive;* from to-day thou wilt eat thy prey when it is dead. If thou art distressed, seeking and finding none, come hither, and I will give thee bread. From this hour, do hurt to no creature." And the hyæna bowed her head to the ground, and dropped on her knees, bending her paws, moving her head up and down, looking at his face as if she were promising him. And the old man perceived in his heart that it was the purpose of God Who gives understanding to beasts for a reproach unto ourselves, and he gave glory to God Who gives understanding to the beasts, he sang in the Egyptian tongue God, Who liveth for ever, for the soul hath honour: he said, "I give glory to Thee O God, Who wast with Daniel in the lion's den, Who didst give understanding unto beasts: also Thou hast given understanding to this hyæna and Thou hast not forgotten me: but Thou hast made me perceive that it is Thy ordering." And the old man took the skin from the hyæna, and she went away. From time to time she would come to seek the old man; if she had not been able to find food, she would come to him and he would throw her a loaf. She did this many a time. And the old man slept on the skin until he died. And I have seen it with my own eyes.

HELEN WADDELL
[*Beasts and Saints* (1934)]

A Witch's Familiar

[The last witch to be executed in the British Isles was burned in Scotland in 1727. Yet the law lingered so far behind educated opinion that more than a decade before that Joseph Addison was making fun of the whole superstition and especially of the broomstick and the "familiar." Mr. Spectator gives this report of a visit of inspection on which he was conducted by his country friend Sir Roger de Coverley.]

I begged my friend Sir Roger to go with me into her hovel which stood in a solitary corner under the side of a wood. Upon our first entering, Sir Roger winked at me and pointed at something that stood behind the door which, upon looking that way, I found to be an old broom-staff. At the same time he whispered to me in the ear to take notice of a tabby cat that sat in the chimney corner, which, as the knight told me, lay under as bad a report as Moll White herself; for besides that Moll is said often to accompany her in the same shape, the cat is reported to have spoke twice or thrice in her life, and to have played several parts above the capacity of an ordinary cat.

JOSEPH ADDISON
[*The Spectator* (1711-1712)]

What Is a Long Life?

[The eighteenth century was especially fond of pseudo-Oriental tales carrying a moral. For a change, Benjamin Franklin chose a bit of natural history to illustrate the relativity of time.]

You may remember, my dear friend, that when we lately spent that happy day in the delightful garden and sweet society of the Moulin Joly, I stopt a little in one of our walks, and staid some time behind the company. We had been shown numberless skeletons of a kind of little fly, called an ephemera, whose successive generations, we were told, were bred and expired within the day. I happened to see a living company of them on a leaf, who appeared to be engaged in conversation. You know I understand all the inferior animal tongues: my too

great application to the study of them is the best excuse I can give for the little progress I have made in your charming language. I listened through curiosity to the discourse of these little creatures; but as they, in their national vivacity, spoke three or four together, I could make but little of their conversation. I found, however, by some broken expressions that I heard now and then, they were disputing warmly on the merit of two foreign musicians, one a *cousin,* the other a *moscheto;* in which dispute they spent their time, seemingly as regardless of the shortness of life as if they had been sure of living a month. Happy people! thought I, you live certainly under a wise, just, and mild government, since you have no public grievances to complain of, nor any subject of contention but the perfections and imperfections of foreign music. I turned my head from them to an old grey-headed one, who was single on another leaf, and talking to himself. Being amused with his soliloquy, I put it down in writing, in hopes it will likewise amuse her to whom I am so much indebted for the most pleasing of all amusements, her delicious company and heavenly harmony.

"It was," said he, "the opinion of learned philosophers of our race, who lived and flourished long before my time, that this vast world, the Moulin Joly, could not itself subsist more than eighteen hours; and I think there was some foundation for that opinion, since, by the apparent motion of the great luminary that gives life to all nature, and which in my time has evidently declined considerably towards the ocean at the end of our earth, it must then finish its course, be extinguished in the waters that surround us, and leave the world in cold and darkness, necessarily producing universal death and destruction. I have lived seven of those hours, a great age, being no less than four hundred and twenty minutes of time. How very few of us continue so long! I have seen generations born, flourish, and expire. My present friends are the children and grandchildren of the friends of my youth, who are now, alas, no more! And I must soon follow them; for, by the course of nature, though still in health, I cannot expect to live above seven or eight minutes longer. What now avails all my toil and labor, in amassing honey-dew on this leaf, which I cannot live to enjoy! What the political struggles I have been engaged in, for the good of my compatriot inhabitants of this bush, or my philosophical studies for the benefit of our race in general! for, in politics, what can laws do without morals? Our present race of ephemeræ will in a course of minutes become corrupt, like those of other and older bushes, and consequently as wretched. And in philosophy how small our progress! Alas! art is long, and life is short! My friends would comfort me with the idea of a name, they say, I shall leave behind me; and they tell me I have lived long enough to nature and to glory. But what will fame be to an ephemera who no longer exists? And what will become of all history in the eighteenth hour, when the world itself, even the whole Moulin Joly, shall come to its end, and be buried in universal ruin?"

To me, after all my eager pursuits, no solid pleasures now remain, but the reflection of a long life spent in meaning well, the sensible conversation of a few good lady ephemeræ, and now and then a kind smile and a tune from the ever amiable *Brillante*.

BENJAMIN FRANKLIN
[*Bagatelles* (1778)]

Does a Cat Lay Eggs?

[*Many odd people called upon Samuel Johnson to ask advice concerning their even odder problems. It was perhaps Hodge, the most famous of his several cats, who was the cause of the explosion provoked by one of Dr. Johnson's odd visitors.*]

"Another strange thing he told me once which there was no danger of forgetting: how a young gentleman called on him one morning, and told him that his father having, just before his death, dropped suddenly into the enjoyment of an ample fortune, he, the son, was willing to qualify himself for genteel society by adding some literature to his other endowments, and wished to be put in an easy way of obtaining it. Johnson recommended the university: 'for you read Latin, Sir, with *facility*, I read it a little to be sure, Sir. 'But do you read it *with facility*, I say?' Upon my word, Sir, I do not very well know, but I rather believe not. Mr. Johnson now began to recommend other branches of science, when he found languages at such an immeasurable distance, and advising him to study natural history, there arose some talk about animals, and their divisions into oviparous and viviparous; And the cat here, Sir, said the youth who wished for instruction, pray in which class is she? Our doctor's patience and desire of doing good began now to give way to the natural roughness of his temper. 'You would do well (said he) to look for some person to be always about you, Sir, who is capable of explaining such matters, and not come to us (there were some literary friends present as I recollect) to know whether the cat lays eggs or not: get a discreet man to keep you company, there are so many who would be glad of your table and fifty pounds a year.' The young gentleman retired, and in less than a week informed his friends that he had fixed on a preceptor to whom no objections could be made."

HESTER LYNCH PIOZZI
[*Anecdotes of the Late Dr. Samuel Johnson* (1786)]

Dangerous Woman

[*The most famous of all modern vampire stories is, of course, Dracula, but the best is probably Gautier's tale of the young priest who solved, almost too late, the mystery of the beautiful woman who had seduced him into a secret life. "Sometimes I fancied myself a priest who dreamed every night he was a nobleman; sometimes I fancied I was a nobleman who dreamed he was a priest." Here is the climax of the tale.*]

For some time past Clarimonda's health had been failing. Her complexion was becoming paler and paler every day. The doctors, when called in, failed to understand her disease and knew not how to treat it. They prescribed insignificant remedies, and did not return. Meanwhile she became plainly paler, and colder and colder. She was almost as white and as dead as on that famous night in the unknown château. I was bitterly grieved to see her thus slowly pining away. She, touched by my sorrow, smiled gently and sadly at me with the smile of one who knows she is dying.

One morning I was seated by her bed breakfasting at a small table, in order not to leave her a minute. As I pared a fruit I happened to cut my finger rather deeply. The blood immediately flowed in a purple stream, and a few drops fell upon Clarimonda. Her eyes lighted up, her face assumed an expression of fierce and savage joy which I had never before beheld. She sprang from her bed with the agility of an animal, of a monkey or of a cat, and sprang at my wound, which she began to suck with an air of inexpressible delight. She sipped the blood slowly and carefully like a gourmand who enjoys a glass of sherry or Syracuse wine; she winked her eyes, the green pupils of which had become oblong instead of round. From time to time she broke off to kiss my hand, then she again pressed the wound with her lips so as to draw out a few more red drops. When she saw that the blood had ceased to flow, she rose up, rosier than a May morn, her face full, her eyes moist and shining, her hand soft and warm; in a word, more beautiful than ever and in a perfect state of health.

"I shall not die! I shall not die!" she said, half mad with joy, as she hung around my neck. "I shall be able to love you a long time yet. My life is in yours, and all that I am comes from you. A few drops of your rich, noble blood, more precious and more efficacious than all the elixirs in the world, have restored my life."

The scene preoccupied me a long time and filled me with strange doubts concerning Clarimonda. That very evening, when sleep took me back to the presbytery, I saw Father Serapion, graver and more care-worn than ever. He looked at me attentively, and said to me: "Not satisfied with losing your soul, you want to lose your body also. Unfortunate youth, what a trap you have fallen into!" The tone in which he said these few words struck me greatly, but in spite of its vivacity, the impression was soon dispelled and numerous other thoughts effaced it from my mind. However, one evening I saw in my mirror, the perfidious position of which she had not taken into account, Clarimonda pouring a powder into the cup of spiced wine she was accustomed to prepare for me after the meal. I took the cup, feigned to carry it to my lips, and put it away as if to finish it later at leisure, but I profited by a moment when my beauty had turned her back, to throw the contents under the table, after which I withdrew to my room and went to bed, thoroughly determined not to sleep, and to see what she would do. I had not long to wait. Clarimonda entered in her night-dress, and having thrown it off, stretched herself in the bed by me. When she was quite certain that I was asleep, she bared my arm, drew a golden pin from her hair, and whispered, "One drop, nothing but a little red drop, a ruby at the end of my needle! Since you still love me, I must not die. Oh, my dear love! I shall drink your beautiful, brilliant, purple blood. Sleep, my sole treasure, my god and my child. I shall not hurt you, I shall only take as much of your life as I need not to lose my own. If I did not love you so much, I might make up my mind to have other lovers whose veins I would drain; but since I have known you, I have a horror of every one else. Oh, what a lovely arm! how round and white it is! I shall never dare to prick that pretty blue vein." And as she spoke, she wept, and I felt her tears upon my arm which she held in her hands. At last she made up her mind, pricked me with the needle, and began to suck the blood that flowed. Though she had scarcely imbibed a few drops, she feared to exhaust me. She tied my arm with a narrow band, after having rubbed my wound with an unguent which healed it immediately.

I could no longer doubt; Father Serapion was right. However, in spite of the certainty, I could not help loving Clarimonda, and I would willingly have given her all the blood she needed in order to support her factitious existence. Besides, I was not much afraid, for the woman guarded me against the vampire; what I had heard and seen completely reassured me. At that time I had full-blooded veins which would not be very speedily exhausted, and I did not care whether my life went drop by drop. I would have opened my arm myself and said to her, "Drink, and let my life enter your body with my blood." I avoided alluding in the least to the narcotic which she had poured out for me and the scene of the pin, and we lived in the most perfect harmony.

Yet my priestly scruples tormented me more than ever, and I knew not what new penance to invent to tame and mortify my flesh. Although all these visions were involuntary and I in no wise took part in them, I dared not touch the crucifix with hands so impure and a mind so soiled by such debauch, whether real or imaginary. After falling into these fatiguing hallucinations, I tried to keep from sleeping. I kept my eyes open with my fingers, and remained standing by the wall struggling against slumber with all my strength; but soon it would force itself into my eyes, and seeing that the struggle was useless, I let fall my arms with discouragement and weariness, while the current carried me again to the perfidious shores. Serapion exhorted me most vehemently, and harshly reproached me with weakness and lack of fervour. One day, when he had been more agitated than usual, he said to me:—

"There is but one way of ridding you of this obsession, and although it is extreme, we must make use of it. Great evils require great remedies. I know where Clarimonda is buried. We must dig her up, and you shall see in what a pitiful condition is the object of your love. You will no longer be tempted to lose your soul for a loathsome body devoured by worms and about to fall into dust. It will assuredly bring you back to your senses."

For myself, I was so wearied of my double life that I accepted, wishing to know once for all whether it was the priest or the nobleman who was the dupe of an illusion. I was determined to kill, for the benefit of the one or the other, one of the two men who were in me, or to kill them both, for such a life as I had been leading was unendurable. Father Serapion provided a pick, a crowbar, and a lantern, and at midnight we repaired to the cemetery of ——, the place of which he knew accurately, as well as the disposition of the graves. Having cast the light of our lantern upon the inscriptions on several tombs, we at last reached a stone half hidden by tall grass and covered with moss and parasitical plants, on which we made out this partial inscription: "Here lies Clarimonda, who in her lifetime was the most beautiful woman in the world. . . ."

"This is the spot," said Serapion, and putting down the lantern, he introduced the crowbar in the joints of the stone and began to raise it. The stone yielded, and he set to work with the pick. I watched him, darker and more silent than the night itself. As for him, bending over this funereal work, he perspired heavily and his quick breath sounded like the rattle in a dying man's throat. It was a strange spectacle, and any one who might have seen us would have taken us rather for men profaning the tomb and robbing the shrouds than for priests of God. Serapion's zeal had something harsh and savage which made him resemble a demon rather than an apostle or an angel, and his face, with its austere features sharply brought out by the light of the lantern, was in no wise reassuring. I felt an icy sweat break out on my limbs, my hair rose upon my head. Within myself I considered the action of the severe Serapion an abominable sacrilege, and I wished that from the sombre clouds that passed heavily over our heads might flash a bolt that would reduce him to powder. The owls, perched on the cypresses, troubled by the light of the lantern, struck the glass with their dusty wings and uttered plaintive cries. The foxes yelped in the distance, and innumerable sinister noises rose in the silence.

At last Serapion's pick struck the coffin, which gave out the dull, sonorous sound which nothingness gives out when it is touched. He pulled off the cover, and I saw Clarimonda, pale as marble, her hands clasped, her white shroud forming but one line from her head to her feet. A little red drop shone like a rose at the corner of her discoloured lips. Serapion at the sight of it became furious.

"Ah! there you are, you demon, you shameless courtesan! You who drink blood and gold!" and he cast on the body and the coffin quantities of holy water, tracing with the sprinkler a cross upon the coffin. The holy dew no sooner touched poor Clarimonda than her lovely body fell into dust and became only a hideous mass of ashes and half-calcined bones. "There is your mistress, my lord Romualdo," said the inexorable priest, as he pointed to the remains. "Are you now still tempted to go to the Lido and Fusino with your beauty?"

I bowed my head. Something had been shattered within me. I returned to my presbytery, and lord Romualdo, the lover of Clarimonda, left the poor priest with whom he had so long kept such strange company. Only the next night I saw Clarimonda. She said to me, as the first time under the porch of the church, "Unfortunate man! unfortunate man! What have you done? Why did you listen to that foolish priest? Were you not happy? What have I done to you, that you should go and violate my poor tomb and lay bare the wretchedness of my nothingness? All communion between our souls and bodies is henceforth broken. Farewell; you will regret me."

She vanished in air like a vapour, and I never saw her again. Alas! she spoke the truth. I have regretted her more than once, and I still regret her. I purchased the peace of my soul very dearly. The love of God was not too much to replace her love.

Such, brother, is the story of my youth. Never look upon a woman, and walk always with your eyes cast on the ground, for chaste and calm though you may be, a single minute may make you lose eternity.

THÉOPHILE GAUTIER
[*The Vampire* (1836)]

Unhappy Ending

[*One of the simplest, saddest and best of all animal stories comes from Alphonse Daudet's Letters from My Mill.*]

You will always be the same, my poor Gringoire!

What! a place is offered to you as reporter on one of the best Parisian newspapers, and you have the coolness to refuse it? Look at yourself, you luckless fellow! look at your shabby jacket, those dilapidated breeches, and that thin face that cries out hunger. It is to this that your passion for noble verse has brought you! This is what your loyal ten years' service as page to Sire Apollo has won! On the whole, are you not ashamed of it?

Come, make yourself a reporter, imbecile; make yourself a reporter. You will earn good crownpieces, and have your knife and fork at Brébant's, and you can exhibit yourself on all first nights with a new feather in your cap.

No? What, you won't? You insist on living free and as you please to the end of the chapter? Well, then! listen to the history of M. Seguin's goat. You will see what is gained by wishing to live at liberty.

M. Seguin never had luck with his goats. He lost them in all kinds of ways. One fine morning they broke their tether and wandered away to the mountain, where a wolf ate them. Neither the caresses of their master nor fear of the wolf, nothing could restrain them. They were, it appeared, independent goats, wanting at any cost free air and liberty.

The worthy M. Seguin, who did not understand the nature of his animals, was shocked. He said:

"That's enough; goats are bored by living with me; I won't keep another."

However, after losing six in that way, he was not discouraged, and he bought a seventh; but this time he was careful to get her quite young, so young that she might the better get accustomed to live with him.

Ah! Gringoire, she was pretty, that little goat of M. Seguin's, so pretty with her soft eyes, her little tuft of beard like a sub-officer, her black and shiny hoofs, her ribbed horns, and her long, white hair which wrapped her like a mantle! She was almost as charming as that kid of Esmeralda's—you remember, Gringoire?—and then, so docile, so coaxing, letting herself be milked without budging, and never putting her foot in the bowl! A love of a little goat!

Behind M. Seguin's house was a field hedged round with hawthorn. It was there that he put his new boarder. He fastened her to a stake, at the very best part of the meadow, taking care to give her plenty of rope; and from time to time he went to see if she was satisfied. The goat seemed very happy, and cropped the grass with such heartiness that M. Seguin was delighted.

"At last," thought the poor man, "here's one at least that isn't bored by living with me!"

M. Seguin deceived himself; the goat was bored.

One day she said to herself, looking at the mountain:—

"How nice it must be up there! What a pleasure to skip in the heather, without this cursed rope, which rubs my neck! It is all very well for asses and cattle to browse in a field, but goats! why, *they* want the open."

From that moment the grass of the meadow seemed to her insipid. Ennui seized her. She grew thin, her milk was scanty. It was really piteous to see her, straining at the tether all day, her head turned to the mountain, her nostril flaming, and she saying "Ma-ë" so sadly.

M. Seguin saw that something was the matter with his goat, but he did not know what. One morning, after he had milked her, the goat turned round and said to him in her patois:—

"Listen, M. Seguin; I am so weary here with you; let me go on the mountain."

"Ah! *mon Dieu!* She, too!" cried poor M. Seguin, stupefied, and he let fall the bowl; then, sitting down on the grass at the side of his goat he said:—

"Oh! Blanchette, would you leave me?"

And Blanchette answered:—

"Yes, M. Seguin."

"Isn't there grass enough here to please you?"

"Oh! plenty, M. Seguin."

"Do I tie you too short? shall I lengthen the rope?"

"It isn't worth while, M. Seguin."

"Then what is the matter? what do you want?"

"I want to go on the mountain, M. Seguin."

"But, you unhappy little thing, don't you know there are wolves on the mountain? What would you do if a wolf attacked you?"

"I'd butt him with my horns."

"A wolf wouldn't care for your horns. He has eaten up goats of mine with much bigger horns than yours. Don't you remember that poor old Renaude who was here last year? Strong and spiteful as a ram. She fought all night with the wolf, but, in the morning, the wolf ate her."

"*Pecaïre!* Poor Renaude! But that does not matter, M. Seguin; let me go to the mountain."

"Merciful powers!" exclaimed M. Seguin, "what *is* the matter with my goats? Another one for the wolf to eat! Well, no, I shall save you in spite of yourself, you slut! and for fear you should break your rope I shall put you in the stable, and there you will stay."

Whereupon M. Seguin led the goat into his brand-new stable, and double-locked the door. Unfortunately, he forgot the window, and hardly had he turned his back before the little one was out and away.

You laugh, Gringoire? *Parbleu!* I suppose so; you take the side of the goats against that good M. Seguin. We'll see if you laugh presently.

When the white goat reached the mountain there was general delight. Never had the old fir-trees seen anything so pretty. They received her like a little princess. The chestnut-trees bent to the ground to kiss her with the tips of their branches. The golden gorse opened wide to let her pass, and smelt just as sweet as it could. In fact, the whole mountain welcomed her.

You can imagine, Gringoire, how happy she was! No more rope, no stake, nothing to prevent her from skipping and browsing as she pleased. My dear fellow, the grass was above her horns! and such grass!—luscious, delicate, toothsome, made of all sorts of plants. Quite another thing from that grass in the meadow. And the flowers, oh!

Great blue campanulas and crimson foxgloves with their long calyxes, a perfect forest of wild-flowers giving out an intoxicating sweetness.

The white goat, a little tipsy, wallowed in the thick of them with her legs in the air, and rolled down the banks pell-mell with the falling leaves and the chestnuts. Then, suddenly, she sprang to her feet with a bound, and hop! away she went, head foremost, through thicket and bushes, now on a rock, now in a gully, up there, down there, everywhere. You would have said that ten of M. Seguin's goats were on the mountain.

The fact is, Blanchette was afraid of nothing.

She sprang with a bound over torrents that spattered her as she passed with a dust of damp spray. Then, all dripping, she would stretch herself out on a nice flat rock and dry in the sun. Once, coming to the edge of a slope with a bit of laurel between her teeth, she saw below, far below on the plain, the house of M. Seguin with the meadow behind it; and she laughed till she cried.

"How small it is!" she said; "how could I ever have lived there?"

Poor little thing! being perched so high she fancied she was tall as the world.

Well! it was a good day for M. Seguin's goat. About noon, running from right to left, she fell in with a herd of chamois munching a wild vine with all their teeth. Among them our little white-gowned rover made quite a sensation. They gave her the choicest place at the vine, and all those gentlemen were very gallant. In fact, it appears—but this is between ourselves, Gringoire—that a young chamois with a black coat had the great good fortune to please Blanchette. The pair wandered off in the woods for an hour or so, and if you want to know what they said to each other, go ask those chattering brooks that are running invisible through the mosses.

Suddenly the wind freshened. The mountain grew violent; it was dusk.

"Already!" said the little goat; and she stopped, quite surprised.

Below, the fields were drowned in mist. M. Seguin's meadow disappeared in the fog, and nothing could be seen of the house but the roof and a trifle of smoke. She heard the little bells of a flock that was on its way home, and her soul grew sad. A falcon, making for his nest, swept her with his wings as he passed. She shuddered. Then came a howl on the mountain:

"Hoo! hoo!"

She thought of the wolf; all day that silly young thing had never once thought of it. At the same moment a horn sounded far, far down the valley. It was that good M. Seguin, making a last effort.

"Hoo! hoo!" howled the wolf.

"Come back! come back!" cried the horn.

Blanchette felt a wish to return, but remembering the stake, the rope, the hedge of the field, she thought that she never could endure that life again and 't was better to remain where she was.

The horn ceased to sound.

The goat heard behind her the rustling of leaves. She turned and saw in the shadow two short ears, erect, and two eyes shining. It was the wolf.

Enormous, motionless, seated on his tail, he was looking at the little white goat and smacking his lips in advance. As he knew very well he should eat her up, the wolf was not in a hurry; but when she turned round and saw him he began to laugh wickedly: "Ha! ha! M. Seguin's little goat!—" and he licked his great red tongue round his wily chops.

Blanchette felt she was lost. For an instant, remembering the story of old Renaude, who had fought all night only to be eaten in the morning, she said to herself that 't was better, perhaps, to be eaten at once; but then, thinking otherwise, she put herself on guard, head low, horns forward, like the brave little goat that she was. Not that she had any hope of killing the wolf,—goats can't kill wolves,—but only to see if she, too, could hold out as long as old Renaude.

Then the monster advanced, and the pretty little horns began the dance.

Ah! the brave goatling! with what heart she went at it! More than ten times—I'm not exaggerating, Gringoire—more than ten times she forced the wolf back to get breath. During each of these momentary truces the dainty little thing nibbled one more blade of her dearly loved grass; then, with her mouth full, she returned to the combat. It lasted all through the night. From time to time M. Seguin's goat looked up at the stars as they danced on the cloudless sky and said to herself:—

"Oh! if I can only hold out till dawn."

One after another, the stars went out. Blanchette redoubled the blows of her horns, and the wolf the snap of his teeth. A pale gleam showed on the horizon. The hoarse crowing of a cock rose from a barnyard.

"At last!" said the poor little goat, who had only awaited the dawn to die; and she stretched herself out on the ground in her pretty white fur all spotted with gore.

Then the wolf fell upon her and ate her up.

Adieu, Gringoire!

The story you have now heard is not a tale of my own invention. If ever you come to Provence, our farmers will often tell you of *la cabro de Moussu Seguin, que se battégue touto la neui emé lou loup, e piei lou matin lou loup la mangé.*

You understand me, Gringoire: "And then, in the morning, the wolf ate her up."

ALPHONSE DAUDET
[*Letters from My Mill* (1866)]

Why the Coyote Is So Smart

[Tales explaining why this animal or that happened to be what he is (or looks the way he does) exist in many cultures—Asiatic, European, and North American. Here is one as told by some of the Indians of California.]

❧

A great many hundred snows ago, Kareya, sitting on the Sacred Stool, created the world. First, he made the fishes in the big water, then the animals on the green land, and last of all, The Man. But the animals were all alike yet in power, and it was not yet ordained which should be for food to others, and which should be food for The Man. Then Kareya bade them all assemble together in a certain place, that The Man might give each his power and his rank. So the animals all met together, a great many hundred snows ago, on an evening when the sun was set, that they might wait over night for the coming of The Man on the morrow. Now Kareya commanded The Man to make bows and arrows, as many as there were animals, and to give the longest to the one that should have the most power, and the shortest to the one that should have the least. So he did, and after nine sleeps his work was ended, and the bows and arrows which he made were very many.

Now the animals being gathered together in one place, went to sleep, that they might rise on the morrow and go forth to meet The Man. But the coyote was exceedingly cunning, above all the beasts that were, he was so cunning. So he considered within himself how he might get the longest bow, and so have the greatest power, and have all animals for his meat. He determined to stay awake all night, while the others slept, and so go forth first in the morning and get the longest bow. This he devised within his cunning mind, and then he laughed to himself, and stretched out his snout on his fore-paws, and pretended to sleep, like the others. But about midnight he began to get sleepy, and he had to walk around camp and scratch his eyes a considerable time to keep them open. But still he grew more sleepy, and he had to skip and jump about like a good one to keep awake. He made so much noise this way that he woke up some of the other animals, and he had to think of another plan. About the time the morning star came up, he was so sleepy that he couldn't keep his eyes open any longer. Then he took two little sticks and sharpened them at the ends, and propped open his eyelids, whereupon he thought he was safe, and he concluded he would take just a little nap, with his eyes open, watching the morning star. But in a few minutes he was sound asleep, and the sharp sticks pierced through his eyelids, and pinned them fast together.

So the morning star mounted up very swiftly, and then there came a peep of daybreak, and the birds began to sing, and the animals began to rise and stretch themselves, but still the coyote lay fast asleep. At last it was broad daylight, and then the sun rose, and all the animals went forth to meet The Man. He gave the longest bow to the cougar, so he had the greatest power of all; and the second longest to the bear; and so on, giving the next to the last to the poor frog. But he still had the shortest one left, and he cried out, "What animal have I missed?" Then the animals began to look about, and they soon spied the coyote lying fast asleep, with the sharp sticks pinning his eyelids together. Upon that all the animals set up a great laugh, and they jumped on the coyote and danced upon him. Then they led him to The Man—for he could see nothing because of the sticks— and The Man pulled out the sticks, and gave him the shortest bow of all, which would shoot an arrow hardly more than a foot. And all the animals laughed very much.

But The Man took pity on the coyote, because he was now the weakest of all animals, weaker even than the frog, and he prayed to Kareya for him, and Kareya gave him cunning, ten times more than before, so that he was cunning above all the animals of the wood. So the coyote was a friend to The Man and to his children after him, and helped him, and did many things for him, as we shall see hereafter.

In the legendary lore of the Karok the coyote plays the same conspicuous part that Reynard does in ours, and the sagacious tricks that are accredited to him are endless. When one Karok has killed another, he frequently barks like the coyote in the belief that he will thereby be endued with so much of that animal's cunning that he will be able to elude the punishment due to his crime.

STEPHEN POWERS
[*The Tribes of California* (1873)]

By the Great Grey-Green Greasy Limpopo

[*Some naturalists are almost as much offended by Rudyard Kipling's enthusiastic espousal of what he called The Law of the Jungle as political liberals are by his conception of the White Man's Burden. Be that as it may, he certainly wrote the best of all modern How-the-Something-Got-His-Something animal tales.*]

🐾

In the High and Far-Off Times the Elephant, O Best Beloved, had no trunk. He had only a blackish, bulgy nose, as big as a boot, that he could wriggle about from side to side; but he couldn't pick up things with it. But there was one Elephant—a new Elephant—an Elephant's Child—who was full of 'satiable curtiosity, and that means he asked ever so many questions. *And* he lived in Africa, and he filled all Africa with his 'satiable curtiosities. He asked his tall aunt, the Ostrich, why her tail-feathers grew just so, and his tall aunt, the Ostrich, spanked him with her hard, hard claw. He asked his tall uncle, the Giraffe, what made his skin spotty, and his tall uncle, the Giraffe, spanked him with his hard, hard hoof. And still he was full of 'satiable curtiosity! He asked his broad aunt, the Hippopotamus, why her eyes were red, and his broad aunt, the Hippopotamus, spanked him with her broad, broad hoof; and he asked his hairy uncle, the Baboon, why melons tasted just so, and his hairy uncle, the Baboon, spanked him with his hairy, hairy paw. And *still* he was full of 'satiable curtiosity! He asked questions about everything that he saw, or heard, or felt, or smelt, or touched, and all his uncles and aunts spanked him. And still he was full of 'satiable curtiosity!

One fine morning in the middle of the Precession of the Equinoxes this 'satiable Elephant's Child asked a new fine question that he had never asked before. He asked, "What does the Crocodile have for dinner?" Then everybody said, "Hush!" in a loud and dretful tone, and they spanked him immediately and directly, without stopping, for a long time.

By and by, when that was finished, he came upon Kolokolo Bird sitting in the middle of a wait-a-bit thorn-bush, and he said, "My father has spanked me, and my mother has spanked me; all my aunts and uncles have spanked me for my 'satiable curtiosity; and *still* I want to know what the Crocodile has for dinner!"

Then Kolokolo Bird said, with a mournful cry, "Go to the banks of the great grey-green greasy Limpopo River, all set about with fever trees, and find out."

That very next morning, when there was nothing left of the Equinoxes, because the Precession had preceded according to precedent, this 'satiable Elephant's Child took a hundred pounds of bananas (the little short red kind), and a hundred pounds of sugar-cane (the long purple kind), and seventeen melons (the greeny-crackly kind), and said to all his dear families, "Good-bye. I am going to the great grey-green, greasy Limpopo River, all set about with fever-trees, to find out what the Crocodile has for dinner." And they all spanked him once more for luck, though he asked them most politely to stop.

Then he went away, a little warm, but not at all astonished, eating melons, and throwing the rind about, because he could not pick it up.

He went from Graham's Town to Kimberley, and from Kimberley to Khama's Country, and from Khama's Country he went east by north, eating melons all the time, till at last he came to the banks of the great grey-green, greasy Limpopo River, all set about with fever-trees, precisely as Kolokolo Bird had said.

Now you must know and understand, O Best Beloved, that till that very week, and day, and hour, and minute, this 'satiable Elephant's Child had never seen a Crocodile, and did not know what one was like. It was all his 'satiable curtiosity.

The first thing that he found was a Bi-Coloured-Python-Rock-Snake curled round a rock.

" 'Scuse me," said the Elephant's Child most politely, "but have you seen such a thing as a Crocodile in these promiscuous parts?"

"*Have* I seen a Crocodile?" said the Bi-Coloured-Python-Rock-Snake, in a voice of dretful scorn. "What will you ask me next?"

" 'Scuse me," said the Elephant's Child, "but could you kindly tell me what he has for dinner?"

Then the Bi-Coloured-Python-Rock-Snake uncoiled himself very quickly from the rock, and spanked the Elephant's Child with his scalesome, flailsome tail.

"That is odd," said the Elephant's Child, "because my father and my mother, and my uncle and my aunt, not to mention my other aunt, the Hippopotamus, and my other uncle, the Baboon, have all spanked me for my 'satiable curtiosity—and I suppose this is the same thing."

So he said goodbye very politely to the Bi-Coloured-Python-Rock-Snake, and helped to coil him up on the rock again, and went on, a little warm, but not at all astonished, eating melons, and throwing the rind about, because he could not pick it up, till he trod on what he thought was a log of wood at the very edge of the great grey-green, greasy Limpopo River, all set about with fever-trees.

But it was really the Crocodile, O Best Beloved, and the Crocodile winked one eye—like this!

" 'Scuse me," said the Elephant's Child most politely, "but do you happen to have seen a Crocodile in these promiscuous parts?"

Then the Crocodile winked the other eye, and lifted half his tail out of the mud; and the Elephant's Child stepped back most politely, because he did not wish to be spanked again.

"Come hither, Little One," said the Crocodile. "Why do you ask such things?"

" 'Scuse me," said the Elephant's Child most politely, "but my father has spanked me, my mother has spanked me, not to mention my tall aunt, the Ostrich, and my tall uncle, the Giraffe, who can kick ever so hard, as well as my broad aunt, the Hippopotamus, and my hairy uncle, the Baboon, *and* including the Bi-Coloured-Python-Rock-Snake, with the scalesome, flailsome tail, just up the bank, who spanks harder than any of them; and *so,* if it's quite all the same to you, I don't want to be spanked any more."

"Come hither, Little One," said the Crocodile, "for I am the Crocodile," and he wept crocodile-tears to show it was quite true.

Then the Elephant's Child grew all breathless, and panted, and kneeled down on the bank and said, "You are the very person I have been looking for all these long days. Will you please tell me what you have for dinner?"

"Come hither, Little One," said the Crocodile, "and I'll whisper."

Then the Elephant's Child put his head down close to the Crocodile's musky, tusky mouth, and the Crocodile caught him by his little nose, which up to that very week, day, hour, and minute, had been no bigger than a boot, though much more useful.

"I think," said the Crocodile—and he said it between his teeth, like this—"I think to-day I will begin with Elephant's Child!"

At this, O Best Beloved, the Elephant's Child was much annoyed, and he said, speaking through his nose, like this, "Led go! You are hurtig be!"

Then the Bi-Coloured-Python-Rock-Snake scuffled down from the bank and said, "My young friend, if you do not now, immediately and instantly, pull as hard as ever you can, it is my opinion that your acquaintance in the large-pattern leather ulster" (and by this he meant the Crocodile) "will jerk you into yonder limpid stream before you can say Jack Robinson."

This is the way Bi-Coloured-Python-Rock-Snakes always talk.

Then the Elephant's Child sat back on his little haunches, and pulled, and pulled, and pulled, and his nose began to stretch. And the Crocodile floundered into the water, making it all creamy with great sweeps of his tale, and *he* pulled, and pulled, and pulled.

And the Elephant's Child's nose kept on stretching; and the Elephant's Child spread all his little four legs and pulled, and pulled, and pulled, and his nose kept on stretching; and the Crocodile threshed his tail like an oar, and *he* pulled, and pulled, and pulled, and at each pull the Elephant's Child's nose grew longer and longer —and it hurt him hijjus!

Then the Elephant's Child felt his legs slipping, and he said through his nose, which was now nearly five feet long, "This is too butch for be!"

Then the Bi-Coloured-Python-Rock-Snake came down from the bank, and knotted himself in a double-clove-hitch round the

Elephant's Child's hind legs, and said, "Rash and inexperienced traveller, we will now seriously devote ourselves to a little high tension, because if we do not, it is my impression that yonder self-propelling man-of-war with the armour-plated upper deck" (and by this, O Best Beloved, he meant the Crocodile) "will permanently vitiate your future career."

That is the way all Bi-Coloured-Python-Rock-Snakes always talk.

So he pulled, and the Elephant's Child pulled, and the Crocodile pulled; but the Elephant's Child and the Bi-Coloured-Python-Rock-Snake pulled hardest; and at last the Crocodile let go of the Elephant's Child's nose with a plop that you could hear all up and down the Limpopo.

Then the Elephant's Child sat down most hard and sudden; but first he was careful to say "Thank you" to the Bi-Coloured-Python-Rock-Snake; and next he was kind to his poor pulled nose, and wrapped it all up in cool banana leaves, and hung it in the great grey-green, greasy Limpopo to cool.

"What are you doing that for?" said the Bi-Coloured-Python-Rock-Snake.

" 'Scuse me," said the Elephant's Child, "but my nose is badly out of shape, and I am waiting for it to shrink."

"Then you will have to wait a long time," said the Bi-Coloured-Python-Rock-Snake. "Some people do not know what is good for them."

The Elephant's Child sat there for three days waiting for his nose to shrink. But it never grew any shorter, and, besides, it made him squint. For, O Best Beloved, you will see and understand that the Crocodile had pulled it out into a really truly trunk same as all Elephants have to-day.

At the end of the third day a fly came and stung him on the shoulder, and before he knew what he was doing he lifted up his trunk and hit that fly dead with the end of it.

" 'Vantage number one!" said the Bi-Coloured-Python-Rock-Snake. "You couldn't have done that with a mere-smear nose. Try and eat a little now."

Before he thought what he was doing the Elephant's Child put out his trunk and plucked a large bundle of grass, dusted it clean against his fore legs, and stuffed it into his own mouth.

" 'Vantage number two!" said the Bi-Coloured-Python-Rock-Snake. "You couldn't have done that with a mere-smear nose. Don't you think the sun is very hot here?"

"It is," said the Elephant's Child, and before he thought what he was doing he schlooped up a schloop of mud from the banks of the great grey-green, greasy Limpopo, and slapped it on his head, where it made a cool schloopy-sloshy mud-cap all trickly behind his ears.

" 'Vantage number three!" said the Bi-Coloured-Python-Rock-Snake. "You couldn't have done that with a mere-smear nose. Now how do you feel about being spanked again?"

" 'Scuse me," said the Elephant's Child, "but I should not like it at all."

"How would you like to spank somebody?" said the Bi-Coloured-Python-Rock-Snake.

"I should like it very much indeed," said the Elephant's Child.

"Well," said the Bi-Coloured-Python-Rock-Snake, "you will find that new nose of yours very useful to spank people with."

"Thank you," said the Elephant's Child, "I'll remember that; and now I think I'll go home to all my dear families and try."

So the Elephant's Child went home across Africa frisking and whisking his trunk. When he wanted fruit to eat he pulled fruit down from a tree, instead of waiting for it to fall as he used to do. When he wanted grass he plucked grass up from the ground, instead of going on his knees as he used to do. When the flies bit him he broke off the branch of a tree and used it as a fly-whisk; and he made himself a new, cool, slushy-squshy mud-cap whenever the sun was hot. When he felt lonely walking through Africa he sang to himself down his trunk, and the noise was louder than several brass bands. He went especially out of his way to find a broad Hippopotamus (she was no relation of his), and he spanked her very hard, to make sure that the Bi-Coloured-Python-Rock-Snake had spoken the truth about his new trunk. The rest of the time he picked up the melon rinds that he had dropped on his way to the Limpopo—for he was a Tidy Pachyderm.

One dark evening he came back to all his dear families, and he coiled up his trunk and said, "How do you do?" They were very glad to see him, and immediately said, "Come here and be spanked for your 'satiable curtiosity."

"Pooh," said the Elephant's Child. "I don't think you peoples know anything about spanking; but *I* do, and I'll show you."

Then he uncurled his trunk and knocked two of his dear brothers head over heels.

"O Bananas!" said they, "where did you learn that trick, and what have you done to your nose?"

"I got a new one from the Crocodile on the banks of the great grey-green, greasy Limpopo River," said the Elephant's Child. "I asked him what he had for dinner, and he gave me this to keep."

"It looks very ugly," said his hairy uncle, the Baboon.

"It does," said the Elephant's Child. "But it's very useful," and he picked up his hairy uncle, the Baboon, by one hairy leg, and hove him into a hornet's nest.

Then that bad Elephant's Child spanked all his dear families for a long time, till they were very warm and greatly astonished. He pulled out his tall Ostrich aunt's tail-feathers; and he caught his tall uncle, the Giraffe, by the hind leg, and dragged him through a thorn-bush; and he shouted at his broad aunt, the Hippopotamus, and blew bubbles into her ear when she was sleeping in the water after meals; but he never let any one touch Kolokolo Bird.

At last things grew so exciting that his dear families went off one by one in a hurry to the banks of the great grey-green, greasy Limpopo River, all set about with fever-trees, to borrow new noses from the Crocodile. When they came back nobody spanked anybody any more; and ever since that day, O Best Beloved, all the Elephants you will ever see, besides all those that you won't, have trunks precisely like the trunk of the 'satiable Elephant's Child.

RUDYARD KIPLING
[Just So Stories (1902-1903)]

On Choosing Your Grandfather

[The apes are by no means the handsomest of the animals and they share with the human being some of his least admirable traits—including a love of mischief and destruction for their own sakes. Were we (or evolution) ill-advised to choose them as our ancestors? Clarence Day asked the question and went on to imagine what the world would be like if we had happened to be super-cats, for instance, rather than super-apes.]

✍

Some one is entering. Hush! If I could but describe her! Languorous, slender and passionate. Sleepy eyes that see everything. An indolent purposeful step. An unimaginable grace. If you were *her* lover, my boy, you would learn how fierce love can be, how capricious and sudden, how hostile, how ecstatic, how violent!

Think what the state of the arts would have been in such cities.

They would have had few comedies on their stage; no farces. Cats care little for fun. In the circus, superlative acrobats. No clowns.

In drama and singing they would have surpassed us probably. Even in the stage of arrested development as mere animals, in which we see cats, they wail with a passionate intensity at night in our yards. Imagine how a Caruso descended from such beings would sing.

In literature they would not have begged for happy endings.

They would have been personally more self-assured than we, far freer of cheap imitativeness of each other in manners and art, and hence more original in art; more clearly aware of what they really desired, not cringingly watchful of what was expected of them; less widely observant perhaps, more deeply thoughtful.

Their artists would have produced less however, even though they felt more. A super-cat artist would have valued the pictures he drew for their effects on himself; he wouldn't have cared a rap whether anyone else saw them or not. He would not have bothered, usually, to give any form to his conceptions. Simply to have had the sensation would have for him been enough. But since simians love to be noticed, it does not content them to have a conception; they must wrestle with it until it takes a form in which others can see it. They doom the artistic impulse to toil with its nose to the grindstone, until their idea is expressed in a book or a statue. Are they right? I have doubts. The artistic impulse seems not to wish to produce finished work. It certainly deserts us half-way, after the idea is born; and if we go on, art is labor. With the cats, art is joy.

But the dominant characteristic of this fine race is cunning. And hence I think it would have been through their craftiness, chiefly, that they would have felt the impulse to study, and the wish to advance. Craft is a cat's delight: craft they never can have too much of. So it would have been from one triumph of cunning to another that they would have marched. That would have been the greatest driving force of their civilization.

This would have meant great progress in invention and science

—or in some fields of science, the economic for instance. But it would have retarded them in others. Craft studies the world calculatingly, from without, instead of understandingly from within. Especially would it have cheapened the feline philosophies; for not simply how to know but how to circumvent the universe would have been their desire. Mankind's curiosity is disinterested; it seems purer by contrast. That is to say, made as we are, it seems purer to us. What we call disinterested, however, super-cats might call aimless. (Aimlessness is one of the regular simian traits.)

I don't mean to be prejudiced in favor of the simian side. Curiosity may be as debasing, I grant you, as craft. And craft might turn into artifices of a kind which would be noble and fine. Just as the ignorant and fitful curiosity of some little monkey is hardly to be compared to the astronomer's magnificent search, so the craft and cunning we see in our pussies would bear small relation to the high-minded planning of some ruler of the race we are imagining.

And yet—craft *is* self-defeating in the end. Transmute it into its finest possible form, let it be as subtle and civilized as you please, as yearning and noble, as enlightened, it still sets itself over against the wholeness of things; its rôle is that of the part at war with the whole. Milton's Lucifer had the mind of a fine super-cat.

That craft may defeat itself in the end, however, is not the real point. That doesn't explain why the lions aren't ruling the planet. The trouble is, it would defeat itself in the beginning. It would have too bitterly stressed the struggle for existence. Conflict and struggle make civilizations virile, but they do not by themselves make civilizations. Mutual aid and support are needed for that. There the felines are lacking. They do not co-operate well; they have small group-devotion. Their lordliness, their strong self-regard, and their coolness of heart, have somehow thwarted the chance of their racial progress.

CLARENCE DAY
[*This Simian World* (1941)]

With a Grain of Salt

[When Benvenuto Cellini was a child his father pointed out to him a salamander crawling comfortably in the flames and then gave the boy a sound
box on the ear—rightfully supposing that the incident would never be forgotten and that Benvenuto could always bear witness to a wonder which some
skeptics discounted.

Here are three versions of alleged observations which most naturalists
refuse to accept but which have been repeated for centuries, often by witnesses
who would be quite acceptable in a court of law. None is more remarkable
than the last, though Colette's husband is not by any means the only respectable citizen who claims to have seen the fox get rid of his parasites by
taking a ball of hair (or grass) into his mouth, submerging to the muzzle in
the water, and then, when all the fleas have taken refuge on the hair ball,
letting it drift away downstream.]

"The rector of a parish in Westmorland assured me that he had witnessed this feat. Having lost many eggs belonging to a laying hen, he
was induced to watch to discover the thief. One morning, soon after
the cackling bird had given warning that she had deposited an egg, he
observed two rats come out of a hole in the hen-house and proceed
direct to the nest. One of the rats then laid down on its side, while the
other rat rolled the egg so near it that it could embrace it with its feet.
Having now obtained a secure hold of its egg, its companion dragged
it into the hole by its tail, and disappeared."

HENRY MOSES
[Letter to *The Zoologist* (1865)]

Have you ever heard tell of Pelisson's spider that so passionately loved music? I for one am ready to believe it and also to add, as my slender contribution to the sum of human knowledge, the story of the spider that my mother kept—as my father expressed it—on her ceiling, in that year that ushered in my sixteenth spring. A handsome garden spider she was, her belly like a clove of garlic emblazoned with an ornate cross. In the daytime she slept, or hunted in the web that she had spun across the bedroom ceiling. But during the night, towards three o'clock in the morning, at the moment when her chronic insomnia caused my mother to relight the lamp and open her bedside book, the great spider would also wake, and after a careful survey would lower herself from the ceiling by a thread, directly above the little oil lamp upon which a bowl of chocolate simmered through the night. Slowly she would descend, swinging limply to and fro like a big bead, and grasping the edge of the cup with all her eight legs, she would bend over head foremost and drink to satiety. Then she would draw herself ceilingwards again, heavy with creamy chocolate, her ascent punctuated by the pauses and meditations imposed by an over-loaded stomach, and would resume her post in the centre of her silken rigging.

✑

It was my first husband, too, who saw the fox drowning its fleas one day when he was out shooting. Holding on to a bunch of weeds with its teeth, it lowered itself backward into the water very, very gradually until it was right up to its muzzle.

COLETTE

[*Sido* and *My Mother's House*. Translated by Una Trowbridge and Enid McLeod (1953)]

FROM ARISTOTLE TO DARWIN TO?

We ought not childishly neglect the study of the meaner animals because there is something wonderful in all of nature. . . . We ought to investigate all sorts of animals because all of them will reveal something of nature and something of beauty.

ARISTOTLE
The Parts of Animals

I confess that there are many men so barbarous that they make no account of this kind of learning . . . showing themselves therein more unreasonable and brutish than the irrational beasts. For next unto man are those creatures ranked in dignity, and they were ordained by God to live upon the same earth, and to be fellow-commoners with man.

JOHN ROWLAND
Epistle Dedicatory to Topsell's *History of Four-footed Beasts*

We must however acknowledge, as it seems to me, that man with all his noble qualities . . . still bears in his bodily frame the indelible stamp of his lowly origin.

CHARLES DARWIN
Descent of Man

"The Master of Those Who Know"

[Aristotle was the first (and for many centuries the last) voluminous writer on natural history whose aims and methods are guided by what we call the scientific spirit. Sometimes he led himself astray by indulging that fondness for a priori reasoning to which the Greeks were attracted; more often he perpetuated errors because, like all scientists, he was sometimes obliged to rely on the reports of others. But his intention was to get at the facts and nothing but the facts.

If he believed that eels did not reproduce by a sexual process, it was because no such breeding had ever been observed and it remained a great mystery down to the twentieth century, when the improbable truth was discovered: all these fresh-water creatures (European as well as American) breed in the southeastern Atlantic. From there the very un-eel-like larvae make their way to European or American rivers.]

In some animals the sexes are distinct, in others they are not so, these are said to beget and be with young by a likeness to other creatures. There is neither male nor female in fixed animals, nor in testacea. In the malacia and malacostraca there are male and female individuals, and in all animals with feet, whether they have two or four, which produce either an animal, an egg, or a worm from coition.

In other kinds the sexes are either single or not single; as in all quadrupeds there is the male and female, in the testacea it is not so, for as some vegetables are fertile and others barren, so it is in these. Among insects and fishes there are some that have no differences of this kind, as the eel is neither male nor female, nor is anything produced from them.

But those persons who say that some eels appear to have

creatures like worms, of the size of a hair, attached to them, speak without observation, not having seen how they really are; for none of these creatures are viviparous without being first oviparous, none of them have ever been observed to contain ova; those that are viviparous have the embryo attached to the uterus, and not to the abdomen, for there it would be digested like food. The distinction made between the so-called male and female eel that the male has a larger and longer head, and that the head of the female is smaller, and more rounded, is a generic, and not a sexual distinction.

There are some fish called epitragiæ, and among fresh-water fish the cyprinus and balagrus are of the same nature, which never have ova or semen; those which are firm and fat, and have a small intestine, appear to be the best. There are creatures, such as the testacea, and plants, which beget, and produce young, but have no organ of coition; and so also in fishes the psetus, erythrhinus, and the channa. All these appear to have ova.

In sanguineous animals with feet that are not oviparous, the males are generally larger and longer lived than the females, except the hemionus, but the females of this animal are both larger and longer lived: in oviparous and viviparous animals, as in fish and insects, the females are larger than the males, as the serpent, pha-langium, ascalabotes, and frog; in fish likewise, as in most of the small gregarious selache, and all that inhabit rocks.

It is evident that female fishes have longer lives than males, because females are caught of a greater age than the males; the upper and more forward parts of all animals are larger and stronger, and more firmly built in the male; the hinder and lower parts in the female. This is the case in the human subject, and all viviparous animals with feet: the female is less sinewy, the joints are weaker, and the hairs finer, in those with hair; in those without hair, its analogues are of the same nature; the female has softer flesh and weaker knees than the male, the legs are slighter; the feet of females are more graceful, in all that have these members.

All females, also, have a smaller and more acute voice than the males, but in oxen the females utter a deeper sound than the males; the parts denoting strength, as the teeth, tusks, horns, and spurs, and such other parts, are possessed by the males, but not by the females, as the roe-deer has none, and the hens of some birds with spurs have none; the sow has no tusks: in some animals they exist in both sexes, only stronger and longer in the males, as the horns of bulls are stronger than those of cows.

Eels are not produced from sexual intercourse, nor are they oviparous, nor have they ever been detected with semen or ova, nor when dissected do they appear to possess either seminal or uterine viscera; and this is the only kind of sanguineous animal which does not originate either in sexual intercourse or in ova. It is, however, manifest that this is the case, for, after rain, they have been reproduced in some marshy ponds, from which all the water was drawn and the mud cleaned out; but they are never produced in dry places nor in ponds that are always full, for they live upon and are nourished by rain water. It is plain, therefore, that they are not produced either from sexual intercourse or from ova. Some persons have thought that they were productive, because some eels have parasitical worms, and they thought that these became eels.

This, however, is not the case, but they originate in what are called the entrails of the earth, which are found spontaneously in mud and moist earth. They have been observed making their escape from them, and others have been found in them when cut up and dissected. These originate both in the sea and in rivers wherein putrid matter is abundant; in those places in the sea which are full of fuci, and near the banks of rivers and ponds, for in these places the heat causes much putridity. This is the mode of generation in eels.

The reproductive function is not active in all fish at the same time or the same manner, nor are they pregnant during the same length of time. Before the season of sexual intercourse the males and females begin to assemble, and at the period of intercourse and the production of their ova they pair together. Some of them do not remain pregnant more than thirty days, and others not so long: but all of them remain so for a number of days, which can be distributed into seven. Those which some persons call marini remain pregnant for the longest period. The sargus becomes pregnant in the month of December, and remains so for thirty days. The kind of cestreus which some persons call the chelon and the myxon are pregnant at the same time as the sargus. All these suffer in their pregnancy, wherefore they are driven to the shore at this season; for in the vehemence of their desire they are carried towards the land, and always continue in motion during this period till they have produced their ova. The cestreus is more remarkable for this than any other fish. As soon as they have deposited their ova, they become quiet.

In many fish there is a limit to their reproductive powers, when worms make their appearance in their abdomen. These worms are small living creatures, which expel the reproductive substance. The small fry of the rhyas makes its appearance in the spring, and that of many others about the vernal equinox. Other fish do not produce at this season of the year, but in the summer or near the autumnal equinox.

It is from the following facts that we may more reasonably infer that fishes sleep. Very often it is possible to take a fish off its guard so far as to catch hold of it or to give it a blow unawares; and all the while that you are preparing to catch or strike it, the fish is quite still but for a slight motion of the tail. And it is quite obvious that the animal is sleeping, from its movements if any disturbance be made during its repose; for it moves just as you would expect in a creature suddenly awakened. Further, owing to their being asleep, fish may be captured by torchlight. The watchmen in the tunny-fishery often take advantage of the fish being asleep to envelop them in a circle of nets; and it is quite obvious that they were thus sleeping by their lying still and allowing the glistening under-parts of their bodies to become visible, while the capture is taking place. They sleep in the night-time more than during the day; and so soundly at night that you may cast the net without making them stir. Fish, as a general rule, sleep close to the ground, or to the sand or to a stone at the bottom, or after concealing themselves under a rock or the ground. Flat fish go to sleep in the sand; and they can be distinguished by the outlines of their shapes in the sand, and are caught in this position by being speared with pronged instruments. The basse, the chrysophrys or gilthead, the mullet, and fish of the like sort are often caught in the daytime by the prong owing to their having been surprised when sleeping; for it is scarcely probable that such fish could be pronged while awake. Cartilaginous fish sleep at times so soundly that they may be caught by hand. The dolphin and the whale, and all such as are furnished with a blow-hole, sleep with the blow-hole over the surface of the water, and breathe through the blow-hole while they keep up a quiet flapping of their fins; indeed, some mariners assure us that they have actually heard the dolphin snoring.

ARISTOTLE
[*History of Animals* (4th century B.C.)]

The Credulous Roman

[For nearly fifteen hundred years the chief source of what men knew or were willing to believe about the animal kingdom was not Aristotle but Pliny the Elder, whose vast Natural History, an uncritical compilation of fact, fancy, superstition, and legend, was put together by an industrious man of books who made few if any observations and seemed ready to believe anything he had heard or read. When he described, for instance, Roman methods of agriculture and husbandry, he was often soundly informative; but he loved the marvelous and he seems to have had little more sense of fact than the authors of the bestiaries who often plundered, simplified, and moralized suitable bits of the misinformation with which he supplied them.

The following selections are typical of his reliance upon the tall tales current in his day. But the last is also untypical in one curious respect. It is one of those cases where folk beliefs have been revealed by the most recent investigations to be less far from the truth than a century of sober science had supposed. The dolphin actually is, so it now seems, one of the most intelligent of all the mammals, almost as friendly as the dog with the human species, and remarkably co-operative. One enthusiastic biologist has recently suggested that his intelligence may possibly be very nearly equal to man's.]

Let us now pass on to the other animals, and first of all to the land animals. The elephant is the largest of them all, and in intelligence approaches the nearest to man. It understands the language of its country, it obeys commands, and it remembers all the duties which it has been taught. It is sensible alike of the pleasures of love and glory, and, to a degree that is rare among men even, possesses notions of honesty, prudence, and equity; it has a religious respect also for the stars, and a veneration for the sun and the moon. It is said by some

authors, that, at the first appearance of the new moon, herds of these
animals come down from the forests of Mauritania to a river, the
name of which is Amilo, and that they there purify themselves in
solemn form by sprinkling their bodies with water; after which, having thus saluted the heavenly body, they return to the woods, carrying
before them the young ones which are fatigued. They are supposed to
have a notion, too, of the differences of religion; and when about to
cross the sea, they cannot be prevailed upon to go on board the ship,
until their keeper has promised upon oath that they shall return home
again. They have been seen, too, when worn out by disease (for even
these vast masses are liable to disease), lying on their back, and throwing the grass up into the air, as if deputing the earth to intercede for
them with its prayers. As a proof of their extreme docility, they pay
homage to the king, fall upon their knees, and offer him the crown.
Those of smaller growth, which the Indians call bastards, are employed by them in ploughing.

The first harnessed elephants that were seen at Rome, were in
the triumph of Pompeius Magnus over Africa, when they drew his
chariot; a thing that is said to have been done long before at the triumph of Father Liber on the conquest of India. Procilius says, that
those which were used at the triumph of Pompeius, were unable to go
in harness through the gate of the city. In the exhibition of gladiators
which was given by Germanicus, the elephants performed a sort of
dance with their uncouth and irregular movements. It was a common
thing to see them throw arrows with such strength, that the wind was
unable to turn them from their course, to imitate among themselves
the combats of the gladiators, and to frolic through the steps of the
Pyrrhic dance. After this, too, they walked upon the tight-rope, and
four of them would carry a litter in which lay a fifth, which represented a woman lying-in. They afterwards took their places at table,
reclining upon couches which were filled with people; and so nicely
did they manage their steps, that they did not so much as touch any of
those who were drinking there.

It is a well-known fact, that one of these animals, who was
slower then usual in learning what was taught him, and had been frequently chastised with blows, was found conning over his lesson in the
night-time. It is a most surprising thing also, that the elephant is able
not only to walk up the tight-rope backwards; but to come down it as
well, with the head foremost. Mutianus, who was three times consul,

informs us that one of these animals had been taught to trace the Greek letters, and that he used to write in that language the following words: "I have myself written these words, and have dedicated the Celtic spoils." Mutianus states also, that he himself was witness to the fact, that when some elephants were being landed at Puteoli and were compelled to leave the ship, being terrified at the length of the platform, which extended from the vessel to the shore, they walked backwards, in order to deceive themselves by forming a false estimate of the distance.

These animals are well aware that the only spoil that we are anxious to procure of them is the part which forms their weapon of defence, by Juba, called their horns, but by Herodotus, a much older writer, as well as by general usage and more appropriately, their teeth. Hence it is that, when their tusks have fallen off, either by accident or from old age, they bury them in the earth. These tusks form the only real ivory, and, even in these, the part which is covered by the flesh is merely common bone, and of no value whatever; though, indeed, of late, in consequence of the insufficient supply of ivory, they have begun to cut the bones as well into thin plates. Large teeth, in fact, are now rarely found, except in India, the demands of luxury having exhausted all those in our part of the world. The youthfulness of the animal is ascertained by the whiteness of the teeth. These animals take the greatest care of their teeth; they pay especial attention to the point of one of them, that it may not be found blunt when wanted for combat; the other they employ for various purposes, such as digging up roots and pushing forward heavy weights. When they are surrounded by the hunters, they place those in front which have the smallest teeth, that the enemy may think that the spoil is not worth the combat; and afterwards, when they are weary of resistance, they break off their teeth.

It is the vulgar notion, that the hyæna possesses in itself both sexes, being a male during one year, and a female the next, and that it becomes pregnant without the co-operation of the male; Aristotle, however, denies this. The neck, with the mane, runs continuously into the back-bone, so that the animal cannot bend this part without turning round the whole body. Many other wonderful things are also related of this animal; and strangest of all, that it imitates the human voice among the stalls of the shepherds; and while there, learns the name of some one of them, and then calls him away, and devours him. It is said also, that it can imitate a man vomiting, and that, in this way, it attracts the dogs, and then falls upon them. It is the only animal that digs up graves, in order to obtain the bodies of the dead. The female is rarely caught: its eyes, it is said, are of a thousand various colours and changes of shade. It is said also, that on coming in contact with its shadow, dogs will lose their voice, and that, by certain magical influences, it can render any animal immoveable, round which it has walked three times.

Bears couple in the beginning of winter, and not after the fashion of other quadrupeds; for both animals lie down and embrace each other. The female then retires by herself to a separate den, and there brings forth on the thirtieth day, mostly five young ones. When first born, they are shapeless masses of white flesh, a little larger than mice; their claws alone being prominent. The mother then licks them gradually into proper shape. There is nothing more uncommon than to see a she-bear in the act of parturition. The male remains in his retreat for forty days, the female four months. If they happen to have no den, they construct a retreat with branches and shrubs, which is made impenetrable to the rain and is lined with soft leaves. During the first fourteen days they are overcome by so deep a sleep, that they cannot be aroused by wounds even. They become wonderfully fat, too, while in this lethargic state. This fat is much used in medicine; and it is very useful in preventing the hair from falling off. At the end of these fourteen days they sit up, and find nourishment by sucking their forepaws. They warm their cubs, when cold, by pressing them to the breast, not unlike the way in which birds brood over their eggs. It is a very astonishing thing, but Theophrastus believes it, that if we preserve the flesh of the bear, the animal being killed in its dormant state, it will increase in bulk, even though it may have been cooked. During this period no signs of food are to be found in the stomach of the animal, and only a very slight quantity of liquid; there are a few drops of blood only near the heart, but none whatever in any other part of the body. They leave their retreat in the spring, the males being remarkably fat: of this circumstance, however, we cannot give any satisfactory explanation, for the sleep, during which they increase so much in bulk, lasts, as we have already stated, only fourteen days. When they come out, they eat a certain plant, which is known as aros, in order to relax the bowels, which would otherwise become in a state of constipation; and they sharpen the edges of their teeth against the young shoots of the trees. Their eye-sight is dull, for which reason in especial, they seek the combs of bees, in order that from the bees stinging them in the throat and drawing blood, the oppression in the head may be relieved. The head of the bear is extremely weak, whereas, in the lion, it is remarkable for its strength: on which account it is, that when the bear, impelled by any alarm, is about to precipitate itself from a rock, it covers its head with its paws. In the arena of the Circus they are often to be seen killed by a blow on the head with the fist. The people of Spain have a belief, that there is some kind of magical poison in the brain of the bear, and therefore burn the heads of those that have been killed in their public games; for it is averred, that the brain, when mixed with drink, produces in man the rage of the bear. These animals walk on two feet, and climb down trees backwards. They can overcome the bull, by suspending themselves, by all four legs, from its muzzle and horns, thus wearing out its powers by their weight. In no other animal is stupidity found more adroit in devising mischief. It is recorded in our Annals, that on the fourteenth day before the calends of October, in the consulship of M. Piso and M. Messala, Domitius Ahenobarbus, the curule ædile, brought into the Circus one hundred Numidian bears, and as many Æthiopian hunters. I am surprised to find the word Numidian added, seeing that it is well known that there are no bears produced in Africa.

The dolphin is an animal not only friendly to man but a lover of music as well; he is charmed by melodious concerts, and more especially by the notes of the water-organ. It does not dread man, as though a stranger to him, but comes to meet ships, leaps and bounds to and fro, vies with them in swiftness, and passes them even when in full sail.

In the reign of the late Emperor Augustus, a dolphin which had been carried to the Lucrine Lake conceived a most wonderful affection for the child of a certain poor man, who was in the habit of going that way from Baiæ to Puteoli to school, and who used to stop there in the middle of the day, call him by his name of Simo, and would often entice him to the banks of the lake with pieces of bread which he carried for the purpose. I should really have felt ashamed to mention this, had not the incident been stated in writing in the works of Mæcenas, Fabianus, Flavius Alfius, and many others. At whatever hour of the day he might happen to be called by the boy, and although hidden and out of sight at the bottom of the water, he would instantly fly to the surface, and after feeding from his hand, would present his back for him to mount, taking care to conceal the spiny projection of his fins in their sheath, as it were; and so, sportively taking him up on his back, he would carry him over a wide expanse of sea to the school at Puteoli, and in a similar manner bring him back again. This happened for several years, until at last the boy happened to fall ill of some malady, and died. The dolphin, however, still came to the spot as usual, with a sorrowful air and manifesting every sign of deep affliction, until at last, a thing of which no one felt the slightest doubt, he died purely of sorrow and regret.

Within these few years also, another at Hippo Diarrhytus, on the coast of Africa, in a similar manner used to receive his food from the hands of various persons, present himself for their caresses, sport about among the swimmers, and carry them on his back. On being rubbed with unguents by Flavianus, the then proconsul of Africa, he was lulled to sleep, as it appeared, by the sensation of an odour so new to him, and floated about just as though he had been dead. For some months after this, he carefully avoided all intercourse with man, just as though he had received some affront or other; but at the end of that time he returned, and afforded just the same wonderful scenes as before. At last, the vexations that were caused them by having to entertain so many influential men who came to see this sight, compelled the people of Hippo to put the animal to death.

Before this, there was a similar story told of a child at the city of Iasus, for whom a dolphin was long observed to have conceived a most ardent affection, until at last, as the animal was eagerly following him as he was making for the shore, it was carried by the tide on the sands, and there expired. Alexander the Great appointed this boy high priest of Neptune at Babylon, interpreting this extraordinary attachment as a convincing proof of the favour of that divinity.

Hegesidemus has also informed us, that in the same city of Iasus there was another boy also, Hermias by name, who in a similar manner used to traverse the sea on a dolphin's back, but that on one occasion a tempest suddenly arising, he lost his life, and was brought back dead; upon which, the dolphin, who thus admitted that he had been the cause of his death, would not return to the sea, but lay down upon the dry land, and there expired.

Theophrastus informs us, that the very same thing happened at Naupactus also; nor, in fact is there any limit to similar instances. The Amphilochians and the Tarentines have similar stories also about children and dolphins; and all these give an air of credibility to the one that is told of Arion, the famous performer on the lyre. The mariners being on the point of throwing him into the sea, for the purpose of taking possession of the money he had earned, he prevailed upon them to allow him one more song, accompanied with the music of his lyre. The melody attracted numbers of dolphins around the ship, and, upon throwing himself into the sea, he was taken up by one of them, and borne in safety to the shore of the Promontory of Tænarum.

PLINY THE ELDER

[*Natural History* (1st and 2nd centuries A.D.)]

The Wonders of Instinct

[*Montaigne was neither the first nor the last to remark that (as Alexander Pope was to put it a century and a half later) "Nature's children all divide her care." Cautious as always, and as becomes a skeptic, he stated the fact but advanced no theories either to explain it or to explain it away.*]

As to the rest, what is there in our intelligence that we do not see in the operations of animals? Is there a polity better ordered, the offices better distributed, and more inviolably observed and maintained, than that of bees? Can we imagine that such and so regular a distribution of employments can be carried on without reason and prudence?

The swallows that we see at the return of the spring, searching all the corners of our houses for the most commodious places wherein to build their nests, do they seek without judgment, and among a thousand, choose out the most proper for their purpose, without discretion? In that elegant and admirable contexture of their buildings, can birds rather make choice of a square figure than a round, of an obtuse than of a right angle, without knowing their properties and effects? Do they bring water and then clay without knowing that the hardness of the latter grows softer by being wet? Do they mat their palaces with moss or down, without foreseeing that their tender young will lie more safe and easy? Do they secure themselves from the rainy winds, and place their lodgings toward the east, without knowing the different qualities of those winds, and considering that one is more wholesome than the other? Why does the spider make her web tighter in one place and slacker in another? Why now make one sort of knot and then another, if she has not the deliberation, thought, and conclusion? We sufficiently discover in most of their works how much animals excel us, and how weak our art is to imitate them. We see, nevertheless, in our ruder performances that we there employ all our faculties, and apply the utmost power of our souls; why do we not conclude the same of them? Why should we attribute to I know not what natural and servile inclination the works that surpass all we can do by nature and art? Wherein, before we are aware, we give them a mighty advantage over us, in making nature, with a maternal sweetness, to accompany and lead them, as it were, by the hand, to all the actions and commodities of their life, while she leaves us to chance and fortune, and to seek out, by art, the things that are necessary to our conversation; at the same time denying us the means of being able, by any instruction or contention of understanding to arrive at the natural sufficiency of beasts; so that their brutish stupidity surpasses in all conveniences all that our divine intelligence can do. Really, at this rate, we might with great reason call her an unjust stepmother: but it is nothing so: our polity is not so irregular and deformed.

Nature has been universally kind to all her creatures, and there is not one she has not amply furnished with all means necessary for the conversation of its being; for the common complaints that I hear men make (as the license of their opinions one while lifts them up to the clouds, and then again depresses them to the Antipodes), that we are the only animal abandoned, naked upon the bare earth, tied and bound, not having wherewithal to arm and clothe us, but by the spoil of others; whereas nature has covered all other creatures with shells, husks, bark, hair, wool, prickles, leather, down, feathers, scales, silk, according to the necessities of their being; has armed them with talons, teeth, horns, wherewith to assault and defend, and has herself taught them that which is most proper for them, to swim, to run, to fly, and to sing, whereas man neither knows how to walk, speak, eat, or do anything but weep, without teaching. . . .

Those complaints are false: there is in the polity of the world a greater equality and more uniform relation. Our skins are as sufficient to defend us from the injuries of the weather, as theirs from them: witness several nations that still know not the use of clothes. Our ancient Gauls were but slenderly clad, no more than the Irish, our neighbors, in so cold a climate. But we may better judge of this by ourselves: for all those parts that we are pleased to expose to the wind and the air, the face, the hands, the lips, the shoulders, the head, according to various custom, are found very able to endure it; if there be a tender part about us, and that seems to be in danger of cold, it should be the stomach where the digestion is, and yet our fathers had this always open, and our ladies, tender and delicate as they are, go sometimes half bare as low as the navel. Nor is the binding and swathing of infants any more necessary; and the Lacedæmonian mothers brought up theirs in all liberty of motion of members, without any ligature at all. Our crying is common to us, with most other animals, and there are but few creatures that are not observed to groan and bemoan themselves a long time after they come into the world, forasmuch as it is a behavior suitable to the weakness wherein they find themselves. As to the usage of eating, it is in us, as in them, natural, and without instruction; . . .

Who doubts but an infant, arrived to the strength of feeding himself, may shift to seek his food? and the earth produces and offers him wherewithal to supply his necessity without other culture and art, and if not at all times, no more does she do it to beasts; witness the provision we see ants and other creatures hoard up against the dead seasons of the year. The late discovered nations, so abundantly furnished with meat and natural drink, without trouble or preparation, give us to understand that bread is not our only food, and that without tillage our mother nature has provided us abundantly with all we stand in need of; nay, it would appear, still more fully and plentifully than she does at present, when we have mixed up these with our own industry. . . . The depravity and irregularity of our appetite outstrip all the inventions we can contrive to satisfy it.

As to arms, we have more that are natural than most other animals, more various motions of the limbs, and naturally and without lessons, extract more service from them: those that are trained up to fight naked, are seen to throw themselves upon hazard like our own; if some beasts surpass us in this advantage, we surpass several others. And the industry of fortifying the body and protecting it by acquired means we have by instinct and natural precept; as, for examples: the elephant sharpens and whets the teeth he makes use of in war (for he has particular ones for that service which he spares and never employs at all to any other use); when bulls go to fight, they toss and throw the dust about them; boars whet their tusks; and the ichneumon, when he is about to engage with the crocodile, fortifies his body by covering and encrusting it all over with close-wrought, well-kneaded slime, as with a cuirass: why shall we not say, that it is also natural for us to arm ourselves with wood and iron?

As to speech, it is certain that, if it be not natural, it is not necessary. Nevertheless, I believe that a child who had been brought up in absolute solitude, remote from all society of men (which would be a trial very hard to make) would have some kind of speech to express his meaning: and 'tis not to be supposed that nature would have denied that to us which she has given to several other animals: for what other than speech is the faculty we observe in them of complaining, rejoicing, calling to one another for succor, and the softer murmurings of love, which they perform with the voice? And why should they not speak to one another? they speak very well to us, and we to them; in how many several ways do we speak to our dogs, and they answer us? We converse with them in another sort of language and other appellations than we do with birds, hogs, oxen, and horses; and alter the idiom according to the kind.

MICHEL DE MONTAIGNE
[*Essays* (1580)]

Vulgar Errors

[That ugly modern word debunk (which often stands for a vulgar thing) would certainly have been rejected by Sir Thomas Browne even if it had been as familiar to the seventeenth century as it became in the twentieth. In fact, Sir Thomas chose to write in the most learnedly Latinized style he could devise. But Pseudodoxia Epidemica, or Vulgar Errors, was perhaps the first (and, for a long time, best known) work systematically devoted to questioning an astonishing number of popular opinions about the physical world. It deals especially with the supposed nature and behavior of animals though it also includes a learned discourse on the absurdity of painters who represent Adam and Eve with navels. Less quaint and more remarkable is his anticipa-

tion of a much later science in rejecting the assumption that acquired characteristics can be inherited.]

The first shall be of the Elephant, whereof there generally passeth an
opinion it hath no joints; and this absurdity is seconded with another,
that being unable to lie down, it sleepeth against a Tree; which the
Hunters observing, do saw it almost asunder; whereon the Beast re-
lying, by the fall of the Tree, falls also down it self, and is able to rise
no more. Which conceit is not the daughter of later times, but an old
and gray-headed error, even in the days of *Aristotle,* as he delivereth
in his Book, *De incessu Animalium,* and stands successively related by
several other authors: by *Diodorus Siculus, Strabo, Ambrose, Cas-
siodore, Solinus,* and many more. Now herein methinks men much
forget themselves, not well considering the absurdity of such asser-
tions.

For first, they affirm it hath no joints, and yet concede it walks
and moves about; whereby they conceive there may be a progression
or advancement made in Motion without inflexion of parts. Now all
progression or Animals locomotion being (as *Aristotle* teacheth) performed *tractu et pulsu;* that is, by drawing on, or impelling forward
some part which was before in station, or at quiet; where there are no
joints or flexures, neither can there be these actions. And this is true,
not onely in Quadrupedes, Volatils, and Fishes, which have distinct
and prominent Organs of Motion, Legs, Wings, and Fins; but in such
also as perform their progression by the Trunk, as Serpents, Worms,
and Leeches. Whereof though some want bones, and all extended ar-
ticulations, yet have they arthritical Analogies, and by the motion of
fibrous and musculous parts, are able to make progression. Which to
conceive in bodies inflexible, and without all protrusion of parts, were
to expect a Race from *Hercules* his pillars; or hope to behold the effects of *Orpheus* his Harp, when trees found joints, and danced after
his Musick.

Again, While men conceive they never lie down, and enjoy not
the position of rest, ordained unto all pedestrious Animals, hereby
they imagine (what reason cannot conceive) that an Animal of the
vastest dimension and longest duration, should live in a continual motion, without that alternity and vicissitude of rest whereby all others
continue; and yet must thus much come to pass, if we opinion they lye
not down and enjoy no decumbence at all. For station is properly no
rest, but one kind of motion, relating unto that which Physitians (from

Galen) do name extensive or tonical; that is, an extension of the muscles and organs of motion maintaining the body at length or in its proper figure.

Wherein although it seem to be unmoved, it is not without all Motion; for in this position the muscles are sensibly extended, and labour to support the body; which permitted unto its proper gravity, would suddenly subside and fall unto the earth; as it happeneth in sleep, diseases, and death. From which occult action and invisible motion of the muscles in station (as *Galen* declareth) proceed more offensive lassitudes then from ambulation. And therefore the Tyranny of some have tormented men with long and enforced station, and though *Ixion* and *Sisiphus* which always moved, do seem to have the hardest measure; yet was not *Titius* favoured, that lay extended upon *Caucasus;* and *Tantalus* suffered somewhat more than thirst, that stood perpetually in Hell. Thus *Mercurialis* in his Gymnasticks justly makes standing one kind of exercise; and *Galen* when we lie down, commends unto us middle figures, that is, not to lye directly, or at length, but somewhat inflected, that the muscles may be at rest; for such as he termeth *Hypobolemaioi* or figures, of excess, either shrinking up or stretching out, are wearisome positions, and such as perturb the quiet of those parts. Now various parts do variously discover these indolent and quiet positions, some in right lines, as the wrists: some at right angles, as the cubit: others at oblique angles, as the fingers and the knees: all resting satisfied in postures of moderation, and none enduring the extremity of flexure or extension.

Moreover men herein do strangely forget the obvious relations of history, affirming they have no joints, whereas they dayly read of several actions which are not performable without them. They forget what is delivered by *Xiphilinus,* and also by *Suetonius* in the lives of *Nero* and *Galba,* that Elephants have been instructed to walk on ropes, in publick shews before the people. Which is not easily performed by man, and requireth not only a broad foot, but a pliable flexure of joints, and commandible dispose of all parts of progression. They pass by that memorable place in *Curtius,* concerning the Elephant of King *Porus, Indus qui Elephantem regebat, descendere eum ratus, more solito procumbere jussit in genua cæteri quoque (ita enim instituti erant) demisere corpora in terram.* They remember not the expression of *Osorius,* when he speaks of the Elephant presented to *Leo* the tenth, *Pontificem ter genibus flexis, et demisso corporis habitu venerabundus salutavit.* But above all, they call not to mind that memorable shew of *Germanicus,* wherein twelve Elephants danced unto the sound of Musick, and after laid them down in the *Tricliniums,* or places of festival Recumbency.

They forget the Etymologie of the Knee, approved by some Grammarians. They disturb the position of the young ones in the womb: which upon extension of legs is not easily conceivable; and contrary unto the general contrivance of Nature. Nor do they consider the impossible exclusion thereof, upon extension and rigour of the legs.

Lastly, they forget or consult not experience, whereof not many years past, we have had the advantage in *England,* by an Elephant shewn in many parts thereof, not only in the posture of standing, but kneeling and lying down. Whereby although the opinion at present be well suppressed, yet from some strings of tradition, and fruitful recurrence of errour, it is not improbable it may revive in the next generation again.

That a Man hath one Rib less then a Woman, is a common conceit derived from the History of *Genesis,* wherein it stands delivered, that *Eve* was framed out of a Rib of *Adam;* whence 'tis concluded the sex of man still wants that rib our Father lost in *Eve.* And this is not only passant with the many, but was urged against *Columbus* in an Anatomy of his at *Pisa,* where having prepared the Sceleton of a woman that chanced to have thirteen ribs on one side, there arose a party that cried him down, and even unto oaths affirmed, this was the rib wherein a woman exceeded. Were this true, it would ocularly silence that dispute out of which side *Eve* was framed; it would determine the opinion of *Oleaster,* that she was made out of the ribs of both sides, or such as from the expression of the Text maintain there was a plurality of ribs required; and might indeed decry the parabolical exposition of *Origen, Cajetan,* and such as fearing to concede a monstrosity, or mutilate the integrity of *Adam,* preventively conceive the creation of thirteen ribs.

But this will not consist with reason or inspection. For if we survey the Sceleton of both sexes, and therein the compage of bones, we shall readily discover that men and women have four and twenty ribs, that is, twelve on each side, seven greater annexed unto the Sternon, and five lesser which come short thereof. Wherein if it sometimes happen that either sex exceed, the conformation is irregular, deflecting from the common rate or number, and no more inferrible upon mankind, then the monstrosity of the son of *Rapha,* or the

vitious excess in the number of fingers and toes. And although some difference there be in figure and the female *os inominatum* be somewhat more protuberant, to make a fairer cavity for the Infant; the coccyx sometime more reflected to give the easier delivery, and the ribs themselves seem a little flatter, yet are they equal in number. And therefore while *Aristotle* doubteth the relations made of Nations, which had but seven ribs on a side, and yet delivereth, that men have generally no more than eight; as he rejecteth their history, so can we not accept of his Anatomy.

Again, Although we concede there wanted one rib in the Sceleton of *Adam*, yet were it repugnant unto reason and common observation that his posterity should want the same. For we observe that mutilations are not transmitted from father unto son; the blind begetting such as can see, men with one eye children with two, and cripples mutilate in their own persons do come out perfect in their generations. For the seed conveyeth with it not only the extract and single Idea of every part, whereby it transmits their perfections or infirmities; but double and over again; whereby sometimes it multipliciously delineates the same, as in Twins, in mixed and numerous generations. Parts of the seed do seem to contain the Idea and power of the whole; so parents deprived of hands, beget manual issues, and the defect of those parts is supplied by the Idea of others. So in one grain of corn appearing similary and insufficient for a plural germination, there lyeth dormant the virtuality of many other; and from thence sometimes proceed above an hundred ears. And thus may be made out the cause of multiparous productions; for though the seminal materials disperse and separate in the matrix, the formative operator will not delineate a part, but endeavour the formation of the whole; effecting the same as far as the matter will permit, and from dividing materials attempt entire formations.

That a Salamander is able to live in flames, to endure and put out fire, is an assertion, not only of great antiquity, but confirmed by frequent, and not contemptible testimony. The *Egyptians* have drawn it into their Hieroglyphicks, *Aristotle* seemeth to embrace it; more plainly *Nicander, Sarenus Sammonicus, Ælian* and *Pliny*, who assigns the cause of this effect: An Animal (saith he) so cold that it extinguisheth the fire like Ice. All which notwithstanding, there is on the negative, Authority and Experience; *Sextius* a Physitian, as *Pliny* delivereth, denied this effect; *Dioscorides* affirmed it a point of folly to believe it; *Galen* that it endureth the fire a while, but in continuance is consumed therein. For experimental conviction, *Mathiolus* affirmeth, he saw a Salamander burnt in a very short time; and of the like assertion is *Amatus Lusitanus;* and most plainly *Pierius,* whose words in his Hieroglyphicks are these: *Whereas it is commonly said that a Salamander extinguisheth fire, we have found by experience, that it is so far from quenching hot coals, that it dieth immediately therein.* As for the contrary assertion of *Aristotle,* it is but by hear say, as common opinion believeth, *Hæc enim (ut aiunt) ignem ingrediens, eum extinguit;* and therefore there was no absurdity in *Galen,* when as a Septical medicine he commended the ashes of a Salamander; and *Magicians* in vain from the power of this Tradition, at the burning of Towns or Houses expect a relief from Salamanders.

The ground of this opinion, might be some sensible resistance of fire observed in the Salamander: which being, as *Galen* determineth, cold in the fourth, and moist in the third degree, and having also a mucous humidity above and under the skin, by vertue thereof it may a while endure the flame: which being consumed, it can resist no more. Such an humidity there is observed in Newtes, or Water-Lizards, especially if their skins be perforated or pricked. Thus will Frogs and Snails endure the Flame: thus will whites of Eggs, vitreous or glassie flegm extinguish a coal: thus are unguents made which protect a while from the fire: and thus beside the *Hirpini* there are later stories of men that have passed untoucht through the fire. And therefore some truth we allow in the tradition: truth according unto *Galen,* that it may for a time resist a flame, or as *Scaliger* avers, extinguish or put out a coal: for thus much will many humid bodies perform: but that it perseveres and lives in that destructive element, is a fallacious enlargement. Nor do we reasonably conclude, because for a time it endureth fire, it subdueth and extinguisheth the same, because by a cold and aluminous moisture, it is able a while to resist it: from a peculiarity of Nature it subsisteth and liveth in it.

It hath been much promoted by Stories of incombustible napkins and textures which endure the fire, whose materials are called by the name of Salamanders wool. Which many too literally apprehending, conceive some investing part, or tegument of the Salamander: wherein beside that they mistake the condition of this Animal (which is a kind of Lizard, a quadruped corticated and depilous, that is, without wool, fur, or hair) they observe not the method and general rule of nature; whereby all Quadrupeds oviparous, as Lizards, Frogs, Tortois, Chamelions, Crocodiles, are without hair, and have no covering part or hairy investment at all. And if they conceive that from the skin of the Salamander, these incremable pieces are composed; beside the experiments made upon the living, that of *Brassavolus* will step in, who in the search of this truth, did burn the skin of one dead.

Nor is this Salamanders wooll desumed from any Animal, but a Mineral substance Metaphorically so impostures, there may be veritable Relations of some, who without a miracle, and by peculiarity of temper, have far out fasted *Elias.* Which notwithstanding doth not take off the miracle; for that may be miraculously effected in one, which is naturally causable in another. Some naturally living unto an hundred; unto which age, others notwithstanding could not attain without a miracle.

The common opinion of the *Ostrich, Struthio-camelus* or *Sparrow-Camel* conceives that it digesteth Iron; and this is confirmed by the affirmations of many; beside swarms of others, *Rhodiginus* in his prelections taketh it for granted, *Johannes Langius* in his Epistles pleadeth experiment for it; the common picture also confirmeth it, which usually describeth this Animal with an horseshoe in its mouth. Notwithstanding upon enquiry we find it very questionable, and the negative seems most reasonably entertained; whose verity indeed we do the rather desire, because hereby we shall relieve our ignorance of one occult quality; for in the list thereof it is accounted, and in that notion imperiously obtruded upon us. For my part, although I have had the sight of this Animal, I have not had the opportunity of its experiment, but have received great occasion of doubt, from learned discourses thereon.

For *Aristotle* and *Oppianus* who have particularly treated hereof are silent in this singularity; either omitting it as dubious, or as the Comment saith, rejecting it as fabulous. *Pliny* speaketh generally, affirming only, the digestion is wonderful in this Animal; Ælian delivereth, that it digesteth stones without any mention of Iron; *Leo Africanus,* who lived in those Countries wherein they most abound, speaketh diminutively, and but half way into this assertion: *Surdum ac simplex animal est, quicquid invenit, absque delectu, usque ad ferrum devorat: Fernelius* in his second *De abditis rerum causis,* extenuates it, and *Riolanus* in his Comment thereof positively denies it. Some have experimentally refuted it, as *Albertus Magnus;* and most plainly *Ulysses Aldrovandus,* whose words are these: *Ego ferri frusta devorare, dum Tridenti essem, observavi, sed quæ incocta rursus ex-*

cerneret, that is, at my being at Trent, I observed the *Ostrich* to swallow Iron, but yet to exclude it undigested again.

SIR THOMAS BROWNE
[*Pseudodoxia Epidemica* (1646)]

John Ray and Two Unsolved Problems

[John Ray, whose philosophical position was illustrated by some passages in an earlier section, was a scientist as well as a philosopher and concerned with many scientific questions, of which one (the meaning of instinct) is still in dispute while the other (spontaneous generation) was not completely disposed of to everyone's satisfaction before another century had passed.]

I shall take notice of the various strange instincts of animals; which will necessarily demonstrate, that they are directed to ends unknown to them, by a wise superintendant. As, 1. That all creatures should know how to defend themselves, and offend their enemies; where their natural weapons are situate, and how to make use of them. A calf will so manage his head as though he would push with his horns even before they shoot. A boar knows the use of his tusks; a dog of his teeth; a horse of his hoofs; a cock of his spurs; a bee of her sting; a ram will butt his head, yea though he be brought up tame, and never saw that manner of fighting. Now, why another animal which hath no horns should not make a show of pushing, or no spurs, of striking with his legs, and the like, I know not, but that every kind is providentially directed to the use of its proper and natural weapons. 2. That those animals that are weak, and have neither weapons nor courage to fight, are for the most part created swift of foot or wing, and so being naturally timorous, are both willing and able to save themselves by flight. 3. That poultry, partridge, and other birds, should at the first sight know birds of prey, and make sign of it by a peculiar note of their voice to their young, who presently thereupon hide themselves; that the lamb should acknowledge the wolf its enemy, though it had never seen one before, as is taken for granted by most naturalists, and may for ought I know be true, argues the providence of nature, or more truly the God of nature, who for their preservation hath put such an instinct into them. 4. That young animals, so soon as they have been brought forth, should know their food. As for example: such as are nourished with milk, presently find their way to the paps, and suck at them, whereas none of those that are not designed for that nourishment ever offer to suck, or to seek out any such food. Again, 5. That such creatures as are whole-footed, or fin-toed, *viz.* some birds, and quadrupeds, are naturally directed to go into the water and swim there, as we see ducklings, though hatched and led by a hen, if she brings them to the brink of a river or pond of water, they presently leave her, and in they go, though they never saw any such thing done before; and though the hen clucks and calls, and doth what she can to keep them out: This Pliny takes notice of, *Hist. Nat.* lib. 10. cap. 55., in these words, speaking of hens: *Super omnia est anatum ovis subditis atq; exclusis admiratio, primo no planè agnoscentis foetum: mox incertos incubitus sollicite convocantis: postremo lamenta circa piscinae stagna, mergentibus se pullis naturâ duce.* So that we see every part in animals is fitted to its use, and the knowledge of this use put into them. For neither do any sort of web-footed fowls live constantly upon the land, or fear to enter the water, nor any land-fowl so much as attempt to swim there. 6. Birds of the same kind make their nests of the same materials, laid in the same order, and exactly of the same figure, so that by the sight of the nest one may certainly know what bird it belongs to. And this they do, though living in distant countries, and though they never saw, nor could see any nest made, that is, though taken out of the nest and brought up by hand; neither were any of the same kind ever observed to make a different nest, either for matter or fashion. This, together with the curious and artificial contexture of such nests, and their fitness and convenience for the reception, hatching, and cherishing the eggs and young of their respective builders, (which we have before taken notice of) is a great argument of a superior author of their and others' natures, who hath endowed them with these instincts, whereby they are as it were acted and driven to bring about ends which themselves aim not at, (so far as we can discern) but are directed to; for (as Aristotle observes) *They act not by any art, neither do they enquire, neither do they deliberate about what they do.* And therefore, as Dr. Cudworth saith well, they are not masters of that wisdom according to which they act, but only passive to the instincts and impresses thereof upon them. And indeed to affirm, that brute animals do all these things by a knowledge of their own, and which themselves are masters of, and that without deliberation and consultation, were to make them to be endowed with a most perfect intellect, far transcending that of human reason: whereas it is plain enough, that brutes are not above consultation, but below it; and that these instincts of nature in them, are nothing but a kind of fate upon them.

The migration of birds from a hotter to a colder country, or a colder to a hotter, according to the seasons of the year, as their nature is, I know not how to give an account of, it is so strange and admirable. What moves them to shift their quarters? You will say, the disagreeableness of the temper of the air to the constitution of their bodies, or want of food. But how come they to be directed to the same place yearly, though sometimes but a little island, as the *Soland Goose* to the *Basse* of *Edinburgh Frith,* which they could not possibly see, and so it could have no influence upon them that way? The cold or the heat might possibly drive them in a right line from either, but that they should impel land-birds to venture over a wide ocean, of which they can see no end, is strange and unaccountable: one would think that the sight of so much water, and present fear of drowning should overcome the sense of hunger, or disagreeableness of the temper of the air. Besides, how come they to steer their course aright to their several quarters, which before the compass was invented was hard for man himself to do, they being not able, as I noted before, to see them at that distance? Think we that the *quails,* for instance, could see quite across the *Mediterranean Sea?* And yet, it's clear, they fly out of Italy into Africa: lighting many times on ships in the midst of the sea, to rest themselves when tired and spent with flying. That they should thus shift places, is very convenient for them, and accordingly we see they do it; which seems to be impossible they should, unless themselves were endowed with reason, or directed and acted by a superior intelligent cause.

The like may be said of the migration of divers sorts of fishes. As for example; the *salmon,* which from the sea yearly ascends up a river sometimes 400 or 500 miles, only to cast their spawn, and secure it in banks of sand, for the preservation of it till the young be hatched or excluded, and then return to sea again. How these creatures when they have been wandering a long time in the wide ocean, should again find out and repair to the mouths of the same rivers, seems to me very strange, and hardly accountable, without recourse to instinct, and the direction of a superior cause. That birds, seeing they have no teeth for the mastification and preparation of their food, should for the more convenient comminution of it in their stomachs or gizzards, swallow down little pebble-stones, or other hard bodies, and because they are not all fit or proper for that use, should first try them in their bills, to feel whether they be rough or angular, for their turns; which if they find them not to be, they reject them. When these by the working of the stomach are worn smooth, or too small for their use, they avoid them by siege, and pick up others. That these are of great use to them for the grinding of their meat, there is no doubt. And I have observed in birds, that have been kept up in houses, where they could get no pebbles, the very yolks of their eggs have changed color, and become a great deal paler, than theirs who have had their liberty to go abroad.

Another observation I shall add concerning generation, which is of some moment, because it takes away some concessions of naturalists, that give countenance to the atheists' fictitious and ridiculous account of the first production of mankind, and other animals, *viz.* that all sorts of insects, yea, and some quadrupeds too, as frogs and mice, are produced spontaneously. My observation and affirmation is, that there is no such thing in nature, as equivocal or spontaneous generation, but that all animals, as well small as great, not excluding the vilest and most contemptible insect, are generated by animal parents of the same species with themselves; that noble Italian virtuoso, Francisco Redi having experimented that no putrified flesh (which one would think were the most likely of anything) will of itself, if all insects be carefully kept from it, produce any: the same experiment I remember Doctor Wilkins, late Bishop of Chester, told me had been made by some of the Royal Society. No instance against this opinion doth so much puzzle me, as worms bred in the intestines of man and other animals. But seeing the round worms do manifestly generate, and probably the other kinds too, it's likely they come originally from seed, which how it was brought into the guts, may afterwards possibly be discovered. Moreover, I am inclinable to believe, that all plants too, that themselves produce seed (which are all but some very imperfect ones, which scarce deserve the name of plants) come of seeds themselves. For that great naturalist Malpighius, to make experiment whether earth would of itself put forth plants, took some purposely digged out of a deep place, and put into a glass vessel, the top whereof he covered with Silk many times doubled and strained over it, which would admit the water and air to pass through, but exclude the least seed that might be wafted by the wind; the event was, that no plant at all sprang up in it. Nor need we wonder how in a ditch, bank or grass-plat newly digged, or in the fen-banks in the Isle of Ely, mustard should abundantly spring up, where in the memory of man none hath been known to grow, for it might come of seed which had lain there more than a man's age. Some of the ancients mentioning some seeds that retain their fecundity forty years. And I have found in a paper received from a friend, but whom I have forgotten, that melon seeds after thirty years, are best for raising of melons. As for the mustard that sprung up in the Isle of Ely, though there had never been any in that country, yet might it have brought down in the channels by the floods, and so being thrown up the banks, together with the earth, might germinate and grow there.

And indeed a spontaneous generation of animals and plants upon due examination will be found to be nothing less than a creation of them. For after the matter was made, and the sea and dry land separated, how is the creation of plants and animals described but by a commanding, that is, effectually causing the waters and earth to produce their several kinds without any seed? Now creation being the work of omnipotency, and incommunicable to any creature, it must be beyond the power of nature or natural agents, to produce things after that manner. And as for God Almighty, He is said to have rested from his work of creation after the seventh day. But if there be any spontaneous generation, there was nothing done at the creation, but what is daily done; for the earth and water produced animals then without seed, and so they do still.

JOHN RAY
[The Wisdom of God Manifest in the Works of His Creation (1691)]

A Sage Is Not Impressed;
Darwin's Grandfather Is

[Dr. Samuel Johnson had met Lord Monboddo and was moved only to a rotund pronouncement against him. On the other hand, Darwinism must have run in the Darwin family since Erasmus Darwin, the grandfather of

Charles, plumped unequivocally for the theory that all the animals, including man, are indeed of the same stock.]

⚘

Sir, it is all conjecture about a thing useless, even were it known to be true. Knowledge of all kinds is good; conjecture, as to things useful is good; but conjecture as to what it would be useless to know, such as whether men went upon all fours, is very idle.

JAMES BOSWELL
[*Life of Johnson* (1791)]

⚘

The Great Creator of All Things has infinitely developed the works of his hands, but has at the same time stamped a certain similitude on the features of nature that demonstrates to us, that *the* whole is one family of one parent.

ERASMUS DARWIN
[*Zoonomia; or the Laws of Organic Life* (1794)]

Born Again

[During the late eighteenth century the most widely read natural history was Oliver Goldsmith's Animated Nature, largely compiled from Buffon. Dr. Johnson said truly that Goldsmith "had the art of compiling" and that he would make the work "as interesting as a Persian tale"—despite the fact that, "if he could tell a horse from a cow," this was the extent of his knowledge of natural history. Here is his account of the metamorphosis of a butterfly, which is still pretty much of a mystery despite the fact that no wonder of insect life has been longer known.]

⚘

In proportion as the time approaches in which the caterpillar is to cast its old skin, its colours become more feeble, the skin seems to wither and grow dry, and in some measure resembles a leaf, when it is no longer supplied with moisture from the stock. At that time, the insect begins to find itself under a necessity of changing; and it is not effected without violent labour, and perhaps pain. A day or two before the critical hour approaches, the insect ceases to eat, loses its usual activity, and seems to rest immoveable. It seeks some place to remain in security; and no longer timorous, seems regardless even of the touch. It is now and then seen to bend itself and elevate its back; again it stretches to its utmost extent: it sometimes lifts up the head, and then lets it fall again; it sometimes waves it three or four times from side to side, and then remains in quiet. At length, some of the rings of its body, particularly the first and second, are seen to swell considerably, the old skin distends and bursts, till, by repeated swellings and contractions in every ring, the animal disengages itself, and creeps from its inconvenient covering.

How laborious soever this operation may be, it is performed in the space of a minute; and the animal, having thrown off its old skin, seems to enjoy new vigour, as well as acquired colouring and beauty. Sometimes it happens that it takes a new appearance, and colours very different from the old. Those that are hairy still preserve their covering; although their ancient skin seems not to have lost a single hair: every hair appears to have been drawn like a sword from the scabbard. However, the fact is, that a new crop of hair grows between the old skin and the new, and probably helps to throw off the external covering.

The caterpillar having in this manner continued for several days feeding, and at intervals casting its skin, begins at last to prepare for its change into an aurelia. It is most probable that, from the beginning, all the parts of the butterfly lay hid in this insect, in its reptile state; but it required time to bring them to perfection; and a large quantity of food, to enable the animal to undergo all the changes requisite for throwing off these skins, which seemed to clog the butterfly form. However, when the caterpillar has fed sufficiently, and the parts of the future butterfly have formed themselves beneath its skin, it is then time for it to make its first great and principal change into an aurelia, or a chrysalis, as some have chosen to call it; during which, as was observed, it seems to remain for several days, or even months, without life or motion.

Preparatory to this important change, the caterpillar most usually quits the plant, or the tree on which it fed: or at least attaches itself to the stalk or the stem, more gladly than the leaves. It forsakes its food, and prepares, by fasting, to undergo its transmutation. In this period, all the food it has taken is thoroughly digested; and it often voids even the internal membrane which lined its intestines.

Some of this tribe, at this period also, are seen entirely to change colour; and the vivacity of the tints, in all, seems faded. Those of them which are capable of spinning themselves a web, set about this operation; those which have already spun, await the change in the best manner they are able. The web or cone, with which some cover themselves, hides the aurelia contained within from the view; but in others, where it is more transparent, the caterpillar, when it has done spinning, strikes into it the claws of the two feet under the tail, and afterwards forces in the tail itself, by contracting those claws, and violently striking the feet one against the other. If, however, they be taken from their web at this time, they appear in a state of great languor; and, incapable of walking, remain on that spot where they are placed. In this condition they remain one or two days, preparing to change into an aurelia; somewhat in the manner they made preparations for changing their skin. They then appear with their bodies bent into a bow, which they now and then are seen to straighten: they make no use of their legs; but if they attempt to change place, do it by the contortions of their body. In proportion as their change into an aurelia approaches, their body becomes more and more bent; while their extensions and convulsive contractions become more frequent. The hinder end of the body is the part which the animal first disengages from its caterpillar skin; that part of the skin remains empty, while the body is drawn up contractedly towards the head. In the same manner they disengage themselves from the two succeeding rings; so that the animal is then lodged entirely in the fore part of its caterpillar covering: that half which is abandoned, remains flaccid and empty; while the fore part, on the contrary, is swollen and distended. The animal, having thus quitted the hinder part of its skin, to drive itself up into the fore part, still continues to heave and work as before; so that the skull is soon seen to burst into three pieces, and a longitudinal opening is made in the three first rings of the body, through which the insect thrusts forth its naked body with strong efforts. Thus at last it entirely gets free from its caterpillar skin, and for ever forsakes its most odious reptile form.

The caterpillar, thus stripped of its skin for the last time, is now become an aurelia; in which the parts of the future butterfly are all visible; but in so soft a state, that the smallest touch can discompose them. The animal is now become helpless and motionless; but only waits for the assistance of the air to dry up the moisture on its surface, and supply it with a crust capable of resisting external injuries. Immediately after being stripped of its caterpillar skin, it is of a green colour, especially in those parts which are distended by an extraordinary afflux of animal moisture; but in ten or twelve hours after being thus exposed, its parts harden, the air forms its external covering into a firm crust, and in about four and twenty hours the aurelia may be handled, without endangering the little animal that is thus left in so defenceless a situation. Such is the history of the little pod or cone that is found so common by every pathway, sticking to nettles, and sometimes shining like polished gold. From the beautiful and resplendent colour, with which it is thus sometimes adorned, some authors have called it a Chrysalis, implying a creature made of gold.

Such are the efforts by which these little animals prepare for a state of perfection; but their care is still greater to provide themselves a secure retreat, during this season of their imbecility. It would seem like erecting themselves a monument, where they were to rest secure, until nature had called them into a new and more improved existence. For this purpose, some spin themselves a cone or web, in which they lie secure till they have arrived at maturity: others, that cannot spin so copious a covering, suspend themselves by the tail, in some retreat where they are not likely to meet disturbances. Some mix sand with their gummy and moist webs, and thus make themselves a secure incrustation; while others, before their change, bury themselves in the ground, and thus avoid the numerous dangers that might attend them. One would imagine that they were conscious of the precise time of their continuance in their aurelia state; since their little sepulchres, with respect to the solidity of the building, are proportioned to such duration. Those that are to lie in that state of existence but a few days, make choice of some tender leaf, which they render still more pliant by diffusing a kind of glue upon it: the leaf thus gradually curls up, and withering as it infolds, the insect wraps itself within, as in a mantle, till the genial warmth of the sun enables it to struggle for new life, and burst from its confinement. Others, whose time of transformation is also near at hand, fasten their tails to a tree, or to the first worm-hole they meet in a beam, and wait in that defenceless situation. Such caterpillars, on the other hand, as are seen to lie several months in their aurelia state, act with much greater circumspection. Most of them mix their web with sand, and thus make themselves a strong covering: others build in wood, which serves them in the nature of a coffin. Such as have made the leaves of willows their favourite food, break the tender twigs of them first into small pieces, then pound them as it were to powder; and, by means of their glutinous silk, make a kind of paste, in which they wrap themselves up. Many are the forms which these animals assume in this helpless state; and it often happens, that the most deformed butterflies issue from the most beautiful aurelias.

In general, however, the aurelia takes the rude outline of the parts of the animal which is contained within it; but as to the various colours which it is seen to assume, they are rather the effect of accident; for the same species of insect does not at all times assume the same hue, when it becomes an aurelia. In some, the beautiful gold colour is at one time found; in others, it is wanting. This brilliant hue, which does not fall short of the best gilding, is formed in the same manner in which we see leather obtain a gold colour, though none of that metal ever enters into the tincture. It is only formed by a beautiful brown varnish, laid upon a white ground; and the white thus gleaming through the transparency of the brown, gives a charming golden yellow. These two colours are found, one over the other, in the aurelia of the little animal we are describing; and the whole appears gilded, without any real gilding.

The aurelia thus formed, and left to time to expand into a butterfly, in some measure resembles an animal in an egg, that is to wait for external warmth to hatch it into life and vigour. As the quantity of moisture, that is enclosed within the covering of the aurelia, continues to keep its body in the most tender state, so it is requisite that this humidity should be dried away, before the little butterfly can burst its prison. Many have been the experiments to prove that nature may in this respect be assisted by art; and that the life of the insect may be retarded or quickened, without doing it the smallest injury. For this purpose, it is only requisite to continue the insect in its aurelia state, by preventing the evaporation of its humidity; which will consequently add some days, nay weeks, to its life: on the other hand, by evaporating its moisture in a warm situation, the animal assumes its winged state before its usual time, and goes through the offices assigned its existence. To prove this, Mr. Réaumur enclosed the aurelia in a glass tube; and found the evaporated water, which exhaled from the body of the insect, collected in drops at the bottom of the tube: he covered the aurelia with varnish; and this making the evaporation more difficult and slow, the butterfly was two months longer than its natural term, in coming out of its case: he found, on the other hand, that by laying the animal in a warm room, he hastened the disclosure of the butterfly, and by keeping it in an ice-house, in the same manner he delayed it. Warmth acted, in this case, in a double capacity; invigorating the animal, and evaporating the moisture.

The aurelia, though it bears a different external appearance, nevertheless contains within it all the parts of the butterfly in perfect formation; and lying each in a very orderly manner, though in the smallest compass. These, however, are so fast and tender, that it is impossible to visit without discomposing them. When either by warmth, or increasing vigour, the parts have acquired the necessary force and solidity, the butterfly then seeks to disembarrass itself of those bands which kept it so long in confinement. Some insects continue under the form of an aurelia not above ten days; some twenty; some several months; and even for a year together.

The butterfly, however, does not continue so long under the form of an aurelia, as one would be apt to imagine. In general those caterpillars that provide themselves with cones, continue within them but a few days after the cone is completely finished. Some, however, remain buried in this artificial covering for eight or nine months, without taking the smallest sustenance during the whole time: and though in the caterpillar state no animals were so voracious, when thus transformed they appear a miracle of abstinence. In all, sooner or later, the butterfly bursts from its prison; not only that natural prison which is formed by the skin of the aurelia, but also from the artificial one of silk, or any other substance in which it has enclosed itself.

Thus, to use the words of Swammerdam, we see a little insignificant creature distinguished, in its last birth, with qualifications and ornaments, which man, during his stay upon earth, can never even hope to acquire. The butterfly, to enjoy life, needs no other food but the dews of heaven, and the honeyed juices which are distilled from every flower. The pageantry of princes cannot equal the ornaments with which it is invested; nor the rich colouring that embellishes its wings. The skies are the butterfly's proper habitation, and the air is its element: whilst man comes into the world naked, and often roves about without habitation or shelter; exposed on one hand to the heat of the sun, and, on the other to the damps and exhalations of the earth; both alike enemies of his happiness and existence. A strong proof that, while this little animal is raised to its greatest height, we are as yet in this world only candidates for perfection!

OLIVER GOLDSMITH
[*Animated Nature* (1774)]

Poor Relation

[Perhaps it all began with the disturbing fact that monkeys look too much like men for comfort and that men too often look (and too often act) like monkeys. Even Topsell resented the fact, for he wrote that "As the body of an ape is ridiculous by reason of an indecent likeness and imitation of man so is his soul and spirit." A century later the comic dramatist William Congreve expressed the same thought more flippantly: "I could never look long upon a monkey without very mortifying reflections: though I never heard anything to the contrary why that creature is not originally of a distinct species."

Had Congreve lived half a century later he might have heard just what he never had, for that learned and eccentric Scottish lawyer Lord Monboddo was widely ridiculed by his contemporaries when he undertook to prove that the orangutan was indeed of the same species as man.]

As I have so often mentioned this race of animals, I think it proper to give here a more particular account of them than I have hitherto done; being, according to my hypothesis, a barbarous nation, which has not yet learned the use of speech. This opinion, I know, will appear very singular to many, and will give offence to some, as highly derogatory, according to their notions, from the dignity of human nature. But as I do not write to flatter the vanity or prejudices of any man, I will fairly examine the question, and begin with stating the facts, as they are collected by Mr. Buffon, in his natural history, vol. 14. And, first, with respect to his body, there has been an accurate dissection made of it by two English anatomists, Mr. Tyson and Mr. Cooper; and from their observations, joined with some of his own, Mr. Buffon pronounces, that, as to his body, he is altogether man, both outside and inside, excepting some small variations, such as cannot make a specific difference betwixt the two animals, and I am persuaded are less considerable than are to be found betwixt individuals that are undoubtedly of the human species. And, more particularly, he has, says Mr. Buffon, the tongue, and the other organs of pro-nunciation, the same as those of man; and the brain is altogether of the same form and the same size. He and man are the only animals that have the viscera, such as the heart, the lungs, the liver, the stomach and intestines, exactly of the same structure; and they alone have buttocks and calfs of the leg, which make them more proper for walking upright, than any other animal. Then there is the same variety of size among them that is in our species; for some of them are from six to seven feet, and others of them do not exceed three feet. Of this last kind appears to have been the one dissected by the English anatomists, and in general all those that have ever been seen in Europe: so that, for anything we know, the great Orang Outang may be still more like men such as we. In short, according to Mr. Buffon, the Orang Outang resembles man more in the structure of his body, than he does even the apes and baboons, with whom he is commonly ranked; and therefore, says he, the Indians are excusable for having associated him with the human race, under the name of *Orang Outang,* which signifies, in their language, *a wild man.* As to the relations of travellers concerning this animal, I will begin with that of Bontius, who was first physician in Batavia, and has written a learned natural history of India, in which he relates, that he saw several Orang Ou-tangs, of both sexes, walking erect; and he particularly observed the female, that she showed signs of modesty, by hiding herself from men whom she did not know. And he adds, that she wept.

The substance of all these different relations is, that the Orang Outang is an animal of the human form, inside as well as outside: that he has the human intelligence, as much as can be expected in an animal living without civility or arts: that he has a disposition of mind, mild, docile, and humane: that he has the sentiments and affections peculiar to our species, such as the sense of modesty, of honor, and of justice; and likewise an attachment of love and friendship to one individual, so strong in some instances, that the one friend will not survive the other: that they live in society, and have some arts of life; for they build huts, and use an artical weapon for attack and defense, *viz.* a stick; which no animal, merely brute, is known to do. They show also counsel and design, by carrying off creatures of our species, for certain purposes, and keeping them for years together, without doing them any harm; which no brute creature was ever known to do. They appear likewise to have some kind of civility among them, and to practice certain rites, such as that of burying the dead.

It is from these facts that we are to judge, whether or not the Orang Outang belongs to our species. Mr. Buffon has decided that he does not. Mr. Rousseau inclines to a different opinion. The first seems to be sensible of the weight of the facts against him, and particularly what Bontius, the Batavian physician, relates. But Bontius, says he, has exaggerated. He was prejudiced; and, if we retrench from his narrative what he has said of the modesty of the Orang Outang female, there will remain nothing but an ape, of which we have more accurate descriptions from other authors. If we are in this way to treat the testimony of a learned physician and naturalist, I do not know how any fact of natural history can be proved. But why does he not reject, for the same reason, the authority of a countryman of his own, Mr. Noëlle, likewise a physician; and who reports what is still more extraordinary than what Bontius relates of this animal, and indeed incredible, upon the supposition of his being a monkey, not a man, namely, the learning to play very well upon the pipe, harp, and other instruments of music? Why not that of Mr. de la Broffe, likewise his countryman? Why not that of Henry Gross, our countryman? Why not that of Battel and Purchas, from whom he has taken his division of this species of animal into great and small, calling the great *Pongo,* and the small *Jocko?* Besides several others whom I have not mentioned, particularly, one Mr. Guat; who relates that he saw, in Java, and brought along with him in the ship, a female, whom he is pleased to call an ape; who showed the same marks of modesty that the female Orang Outang did, mentioned by Bontius, by covering with her hand what the ancients thought it was proper the goddess of love should conceal, in the same manner; and besides, performed several other human actions, such as, making her bed, covering herself with her bed-clothes, binding her head with a handkerchief, when she had a headache? If such actions as these, and others mentioned by other travellers, whom I have quoted, are not the result of human intelligence, I do not know how we are to discover it from actions: and if we do not believe facts proved by such a concurrence of testimony, not only of common travellers, but of learned physicians, I repeat it again, I do not know how any fact of natural history is to be proved.

JAMES BURNETT, LORD MONBODDO
[*Of the Origin and Progress of Language,* 2nd Edition (1774)]

The Watchmaker and the Watch

[No implication of Darwinism was more shocking to those who encountered it than its implied disposal of the "argument from design." It had long been held that the wonderful adaptations of the living world furnish abundant proof that it was planned by a creative intelligence. In Darwin's theory "design" becomes an illusion and, since the world created itself, the "argument from design" a fallacy. Perhaps the dispute is not as completely settled as science once professed to believe. Here, at any rate, is a classic statement of the "argument from design" as the eighteenth century formulated it.]

In crossing a heath, suppose I pitched my foot against a *stone,* and were asked how the stone came to be there; I might possibly answer, that, for anything I knew to the contrary, it had lain there forever: nor would it perhaps be very easy to show the absurdity of this answer. But suppose I had found a *watch* upon the ground, and it should be inquired how the watch happened to be in that place; I should hardly think of the answer which I had before given, that, for anything I knew, the watch might have always been there. Yet why should not this answer serve for the watch as well as for the stone? Why is it not as admissible in the second case, as in the first? For this reason, and for no other, *viz.* that, when we come to inspect the watch, we perceive (what we could not discover in the stone) that its several parts are framed and put together for a purpose, *e.g.* that they are so formed and adjusted as to produce motion, and that motion so regulated as to point out the hour of the day; that if the different parts had been differently shaped from what they are, of a different size from what they are, or placed after any other manner, or in any other order, than that in which they are placed, either no motion at all would have been carried on in the machine, or none which would have answered the use that is now served by it. To reckon up a few of the plainest of these parts, and of their offices, all tending to one result: We see a cylindrical box containing a coiled elastic spring, which, by its endeavor to relax itself, turns round the box. We next observe a flexible chain (artificially wrought for the sake of flexure) communicating the action of the spring from the box to the fusee. We then find a series of wheels, the teeth of which catch in, and apply to each other, conducting the motion from the fusee to the balance, and from the balance to the pointer; and at the same time, by the size and shape of those wheels, so regulating that motion, as to terminate in causing an index by an equable and measured progression, to pass over a given space in a given time. We take notice that the wheels are made of brass in order to keep them from rust; the springs of steel, no other metal being so elastic; that over the face of the watch there is placed a glass, a material employed in no other part of the work; but in the room of which, if there had been any other than a transparent substance, the hour could not be seen without opening the case. This mechanism being observed (it requires indeed an examination of the instrument, and perhaps some previous knowledge of the subject, to perceive and understand it; but being once, as we have said, observed and understood), the inference, we think, is inevitable; that the watch must have had a maker; that there must have existed, at sometime, and at some place or other, an artificer or artificers, who formed it for the purpose which we find it actually to answer; who comprehended its construction, and designed its use.

WILLIAM PALEY
[*Natural Theology* (1802)]

Charles Darwin Is Puzzled

[When the young Charles Darwin signed on as naturalist for the round-the-world voyage of her majesty's ship The Beagle he had never given much thought to any theory of evolution though such theories had been in many men's minds for a long time. The problem first began to concern him when he observed during the voyage that several of the Galápagos Islands were inhabited by both birds and tortoises significantly different from those to be found a short distance away. Was it reasonable to suppose that God had intentionally created unique species for these small, adjacent areas?]

I have not as yet noticed by far the most remarkable feature in the natural history of this archipelago; it is, that the different islands to a considerable extent are inhabited by a different set of beings. My attention was first called to this fact by the Vice-Governor, Mr. Lawson, declaring that the tortoises differed from the different islands, and that he could with certainty tell from which island any one was brought. I did not for some time pay sufficient attention to this statement, and I had already partially mingled together the collections from two of the islands. I never dreamed that islands, about 50 or 60 miles apart, and most of them in sight of each other, formed of precisely the same rocks, placed under a quite similar climate, rising to a nearly equal height, would have been differently tenanted; but we shall soon see that this is the case. It is the fate of most voyagers, no sooner to discover what is most interesting in any locality, than they are hurried from it; but I ought, perhaps, to be thankful that I obtained sufficient materials to establish this most remarkable fact in the distribution of organic beings.

The inhabitants, as I have said, state that they can distinguish the tortoises from the different islands; and that they differ not only in size, but in other characters. Captain Porter has described those from Charles and from the nearest island to it namely, Hood Island, as having their shells in front thick and turned up like a Spanish saddle, whilst the tortoises from James Island are rounder, blacker, and have a better taste when cooked. M. Bibron, moreover, informs me that he has seen what he considers two distinct species of tortoise from the Galápagos, but he does not know from which islands. The specimens that I brought from three islands were young ones: and probably owing to this cause neither Mr. Gray nor myself could find in them any specific differences. I have remarked that the marine Amblyrhynchus was larger at Albermarle Island than elsewhere; and M. Bibron informs me that he has seen two distinct aquatic species of this genus; so that the different islands probably have their representative species or races of the Amblyrhynchus, as well as of the tortoise. My attention was first thoroughly aroused, by comparing together the numerous specimens, shot by myself and several other parties on board, of the mocking-thrushes, when, to my astonishment, I discovered that all those from Charles Island belonged to one species (Mimus trifasciatus); all from Albermarle Island to M. parvulus; and all from James and Chatham Islands (between which two other islands are situated, as connecting links) belonged to M. melanotis. These two latter species are closely allied, and would by some ornithologists be considered as only well-marked races or varieties; but the Mimus trifasciatus is very distinct. Unfortunately most of the specimens of the finch tribe were mingled together; but I have strong reasons to suspect that some of the species of the sub-group Geospiza are confined to separate islands. If the different islands have their representatives of Geospiza, it may help to explain the singularly large number of the species of this sub-group in this one small archipelago, and as a probable consequence of their numbers, the perfectly graduated series in the size of their beaks. Two species of the sub-group Cactornis, and two of the Camarhynchus, were procured in the archipelago; and of the numerous specimens of these two sub-groups shot by four collectors at James Island, all were found to belong to one species of each; whereas the numerous specimens shot either on Chatham or Charles Island (for the two sets were mingled together) all belonged to the two other species: hence we may feel almost sure that these islands possess their respective species of these two sub-groups. In landshells this law of distribution does not appear to hold good. In my very small collection of insects, Mr. Waterhouse remarks, that of those which were ticketed with their locality, not one was common to any two of the islands.

The distribution of the tenants of this archipelago would not be nearly so wonderful, if, for instance, one island had a mocking-thrush, and a second island some other quite distinct genus;—if one island had its genus of lizard, and a second island another distinct genus, or none whatever;—or if the different islands were inhabited, not by representative species of the same genera of plants, but by totally different genera, as does to a certain extent hold good: for, to give one instance, a large berry-bearing tree at James Island has no representative species in Charles Island. But it is the circumstance, that several of the islands possess their own species of the tortoise, mocking-thrush, finches, and numerous plants, these species having the same general habits, occupying analogous situations, and obviously filling the same place in the natural economy of this archipelago, that strikes me with wonder. It may be suspected that some of these representative species, at least in the case of the tortoise and of some of the birds, may hereafter prove to be only well-marked races; but this would be of equally great interest to the philosophical naturalist. I have said that most of the islands are in sight of each other: I may specify that Charles Island is fifty miles from the nearest part of Chatham Island, and thirty-three miles from the nearest part of Albermarle Island. Chatham Island is sixty miles from the nearest part of James Island, but there are two intermediate islands between them which were not visited by me. James Island is only ten miles from the nearest part of Albemarle Island, but the two points where the collections were made are thirty-two miles apart. I must repeat, that neither the nature of the soil, nor height of the land, nor the climate, nor the general character of the associated beings, and therefore their action one on another, can differ much in the different islands. If there be any sensible difference in their climates, it must be between the Windward group (namely, Charles and Chatham Islands), and that to leeward; but there seems to be no corresponding difference in the productions of these two halves of the archipelago.

CHARLES DARWIN
[*The Voyage of* The Beagle (1839)]

The Darwinian Revolution

[*The seed of doubt planted in the Galápagos germinated slowly. Twenty years after the publication of the account just given, it bore fruit in* On The Origin of Species.

No previous proponent of any theory of evolution had offered a convincing "how" or "why" of the process. The possibility that "natural selection" operating in the course of a "struggle for survival" might be the answer occurred to Darwin while reading Malthus' Essay on Population. But he wanted facts and he kept his idea to himself until he had accumulated, during years of labor, what seemed to him convincing proof that "natural selection" not only might, but demonstrably did, explain evolution.

Here is the conclusion of his book in which he predicts that a whole new direction will be given to the study of natural history. Perhaps even he did not realize fully how far beyond the field of natural history his revolution would spread.]

⚘

When the views advanced by me in this volume, and by Mr. Wallace, or when analogous views on the origin of species are generally admitted, we can dimly foresee that there will be a considerable revolution in natural history. Systematists will be able to pursue their labours as at present; but they will not be incessantly haunted by the shadowy doubt whether this or that form be a true species. This, I feel sure and I speak after experience, will be no slight relief. The endless disputes whether or not some fifty species of British brambles are good species will cease. Systematists will have only to decide (not that this will be easy) whether any form be sufficiently constant and distinct from other forms, to be capable of definition; and if definable, whether the differences be sufficiently important to deserve a specific name. This latter point will become a far more essential consideration than it is at present; for differences, however slight, between any two forms, if not blended by intermediate gradations, are looked at by most naturalists as sufficient to raise both forms to the rank of species.

Hereafter we shall be compelled to acknowledge that the only distinction between species and well-marked varieties is, that the latter are known, or believed, to be connected at the present day by intermediate gradations whereas species were formerly thus connected. Hence, without rejecting the consideration of the present existence of intermediate gradations between any two forms, we shall be led to weigh more carefully and to value higher the actual amount of difference between them. It is quite possible that forms now generally acknowledged to be merely varieties may hereafter be thought worthy of specific names; and in this case scientific and common language will come into accordance. In short, we shall have to treat species in the same manner as those naturalists treat genera, who admit that genera are merely artificial combinations made for convenience. This may not be a cheering prospect; but we shall at least be freed from the vain search for the undiscovered and undiscoverable essence of the term species.

The other and more general departments of natural history will rise greatly in interest. The terms used by naturalists, of affinity, relationship, community of type, paternity, morphology, adaptive characters, rudimentary and aborted organs, &c., will cease to be metaphorical and will have a plain signification. When we no longer look at an organic being as a savage looks at a ship, as something wholly beyond his comprehension; when we regard every production of nature as one which has had a long history; when we contemplate every complex structure and instinct as the summing up of many contrivances, each useful to the possessor, in the same way as any great mechanical invention is the summing up of the labour, the experience, the reason, and even the blunders of numerous workmen; when we thus view each organic being, how far more interesting—I speak from experience—does the study of natural history become!

A grand and almost untrodden field of inquiry will be opened, on the causes and laws of variation, on correlation, on the effects of use and disuse, on the direct action of external conditions, and so forth. The study of domestic productions will rise immensely in value. A new variety raised by man will be a more important and interesting subject for study than one more species added to the infinitude of already recorded species. Our classifications will come to be, as far as they can be so made, genealogies; and will then truly give what may be called the plan of creation. The rules for classifying will no doubt become simpler when we have a definite object in view. We possess no pedigrees or armorial bearings; and we have to discover and trace the many diverging lines of descent in our natural genealogies, by characters of any kind which have long been inherited. Rudimentary organs will speak infallibly with respect to the nature of long-lost structures. Species and groups of species which are called aberrant, and which may fancifully be called living fossils, will aid us in forming a picture of the ancient forms of life. Embryology will often reveal to us the structure, in some degree obscured, of the prototypes of each great class.

When we can feel assured that all the individuals of the same species, and all the closely allied species of most genera, have within a not very remote period descended from one parent, and have migrated from some one birth-place; and when we better know the many means of migration, then, by the light which geology now throws, and will continue to throw, on former changes of climate and of the level of the land, we shall surely be enabled to trace in an admirable manner the former migrations of the inhabitants of the whole world. Even at present, by comparing the differences between the inhabitants of the sea on the opposite sides of a continent, and the nature of the various inhabitants on that continent, in relation to their apparent means of immigration, some light can be thrown on ancient geography. . . .

It is interesting to contemplate a tangled bank, clothed with many plants of many kinds, with birds singing on the bushes, with various insects flitting about, and with worms crawling through the damp earth, and to reflect that these elaborately constructed forms, so different from each other, and dependent upon each other in so complex a manner, have all been produced by laws acting around us. These laws, taken in the largest sense, being Growth with Reproduction; Inheritance which is almost implied by reproduction: Variability from the indirect and direct action of the conditions of life, and from use and disuse: a Ratio of Increase so high as to lead to a Struggle for Life, and as a consequence to Natural Selection, entailing Divergence of Character and the Extinction of less-improved forms. Thus, from the war of nature, from famine and death, the most exalted object which we are capable of conceiving, namely, the production of the higher animals, directly follows. There is grandeur in this view of life, with its several powers, having been originally breathed by the Creator into a few forms or into one; and that, whilst this planet has gone cycling on according to the fixed law of gravity, from so simple a beginning endless forms most beautiful and most wonderful have been, and are being evolved.

CHARLES DARWIN
[*On the Origin of Species* (1859)]

Not Quite Everyone Was Convinced

[No man between Copernicus and Darwin had so profound an effect as Darwin upon man's notion of his relation to the universe in which he finds himself. During the seventy-five years just past, there have been few competent biologists who were not evolutionists in some broad sense at least. For almost as long a time the strongest current of opinion has run in the direction to which Darwin's conclusions seemed to point: man is an animal, the animals were created by chance not by God, and the concept of purpose is merely a late human invention.

Yet it should not be forgotten that there were always a few who resisted these more remote conclusions. Some—Samuel Butler and Bernard Shaw especially—preferred the doctrine of that now generally despised pre-Darwinian evolutionist, Jean Lamarck, who had held that some continuing purpose had directed the course of evolution. But it is perhaps more significant as well as less often remembered that Alfred Russel Wallace, to whom the idea that natural selection might explain much of the process occurred at almost the same time that it occurred to Darwin, nevertheless refused to believe that it was sufficient to account wholly for the mind and nature of the human being. Here is part of his protest which Darwin regarded as little better than a betrayal of the cause he thought they had espoused together.]

In adopting the views of Mr. Darwin, Sir Charles Lyell carries them out to their legitimate results, and does not shrink from the logical necessity, of the derivation of man from the lower animals; and he has written a very interesting chapter on the "Origin and Distribution of Man." Into this subject, however, we cannot now enter, except to remark briefly on some aspects of the question which all who have hitherto written upon it seem to have neglected.

It would certainly appear in the highest degree improbable, that the whole animal kingdom from the lowest zoophytes up to the horse, the dog, and the ape, should have been developed by the simple action of natural laws, and that the animal man, so absolutely identical with them in all the main features and many of the details of his organization, should have been formed in some quite other unknown way. But if the researches of geologists and the investigations of anatomists should ever demonstrate that he was derived from the lower animals in the same way that they have been derived from each other, we shall not be thereby debarred from believing, or from proving, that his intellectual capacities and his moral nature were not wholly developed by the same process. Neither natural selection nor the more general theory of evolution can give any account whatever of the origin of sensational or conscious life. They may teach us how, by chemical, electrical, or higher natural laws, the organized body can be built up, can grow, can reproduce its like; but those laws and that growth cannot even be conceived as endowing the newly-arranged atoms with consciousness. But the moral and higher intellectual nature of man is as unique a phenomenon as was conscious life on its first appearance in the world, and the one is almost as difficult to conceive as originating by any law of evolution as the other. We may even go further, and maintain that there are certain purely physical characteristics of the human race which are not explicable on the theory of variation and survival of the fittest. The brain, the organs of speech, the hand, and the external form of man, offer some special difficulties in this respect, to which we will briefly direct attention.

In the brain of the lowest savages, and, as far as we yet know, of the pre-historic races, we have an organ so little inferior in size and complexity to that of the highest types (such as the average European), that we must believe it capable, under a similar process of gradual development during the space of two or three thousand years, of producing equal average results. But the mental requirements of the lowest savages, such as the Australians or the Andaman islanders, are very little above those of many animals. The higher moral faculties and those of pure intellect and refined emotion are useless to them, are rarely if ever manifested, and have no relation to their wants, desires, or well-being. How, then, was an organ developed so far beyond the needs of its possessor? Natural selection could only have endowed the savage with a brain a little superior to that of an ape, whereas he actually possesses one but very little inferior to that of the average members of our learned societies.

Again, what a wonderful organ is the hand of man, of what marvels of delicacy is it capable, and how greatly it assists in his education and mental development! The whole circle of the arts and sciences are ultimately dependent on our possession of this organ, without which we could hardly have become truly human. This hand is equally perfect in the lowest savage, but he has no need for so fine an instrument, and can no more fully utilize it than he could use without instruction a complete set of joiner's tools. But, stranger still, this marvellous instrument was foreshadowed and prepared in the Quadrumana; and any person, who will watch how one of these animals uses its hands, will at once perceive that it possesses an organ far beyond its needs. The separate fingers and the thumb are never fully utilised, and objects are grasped so clumsily, as to show that a much less specialised organ of prehension would have served its purpose quite as well; and if this be so, it could never have been produced through the agency of natural selection alone.

We have further to ask—How did man acquire his erect posture, his delicate yet expressive features, the marvellous beauty and symmetry of his whole external form;—a form which stands alone, in many respects more distinct from that of all the higher animals than they are from each other? Those who have lived much among savages know that even the lowest races of mankind, if healthy and well fed, exhibit the human form in its complete symmetry and perfection. They all have the soft smooth skin absolutely free from any hairy covering on the dorsal line, where all other mammalia from the Marsupials up to the Anthropoid apes have it most densely and strongly developed. What use can we conceive to have been derived from this exquisite beauty and symmetry and this smooth bare skin, both so very widely removed from his nearest allies? And if these modifications were of no physical use to him—or if, as appears almost certain in the case of the naked skin, they were at first a positive disadvantage—we know that they could not have been produced by natural selection. Yet we can well understand that both these characters were essential to the proper development of the perfect human being. The supreme beauty of our form and countenance had probably been the source of all our aesthetic ideas and emotions, which could hardly have arisen had we retained the shape and features of an erect gorilla; and our naked skin, necessitating the use of clothing, has at once stimulated our intellect, and by developing the feeling of personal modesty may have profoundly affected our moral nature.

The same line of argument may be used in connexion with the structural and mental organs of human speech, since that faculty can hardly have been physically useful to the lowest class of savages; and if not, the delicate arrangements of nerves and muscles for its production could not have been developed and coordinated by natural selection. This view is supported by the fact that, among the lowest savages with the least copious vocabularies, the capacity of uttering a variety of distinct articulate sounds, and of applying to them an almost infinite amount of modulation and inflection, is not in any way inferior to that of the higher races. An instrument has been developed in advance of the needs of its possessor.

This subject is a vast one, and would require volumes for its proper elucidation, but enough, we think, has now been said, to indicate the possibility of a new stand-point for those who cannot accept the theory of evolution as expressing the whole truth in regard to the origin of man. While admitting to the full extent the agency of the same great laws of organic development in the origin of the human race as in the origin of all organized beings, there yet seems to be evidence of a Power which has guided the action of those laws in definite directions and for special ends. And so far from this view being out of harmony with the teachings of science, it has a striking analogy with what is now taking place in the world, and is thus strictly uniformitarian in character. Man himself guides and modifies nature for special ends. The laws of evolution alone would perhaps never have produced a grain so well adapted to his uses as wheat; such fruits as the seedless banana, and the bread-fruit; such animals as the Guernsey milch-cow, or the London dray-horse. Yet these so closely resemble the unaided productions of nature, that we may well imagine a being who had mastered the laws of development of organic forms through past ages, refusing to believe that any new power had been concerned in their production, and scornfully rejecting the theory that in these few cases a distinct intelligence had directed the action of the laws of variation, multiplication, and survival, for his own purposes. We know, however, that this has been done; and we must therefore admit the possibility, that in the development of the human race, a Higher Intelligence has guided the same laws for nobler ends.

Such, we believe, is the direction in which we shall find the true reconciliation of Science with Theology on this most momentous problem. Let us fearlessly admit that the mind of man (itself the living proof of a supreme mind) is able to trace, and to a considerable extent has traced, the laws by means of which the organic no less than the inorganic world has been developed. But let us not shut our eyes to the evidence that an Overruling Intelligence has watched over the action of those laws, so directing variations and so determining their accumulation, as finally to produce an organization sufficiently perfect to admit of, and even to aid in, the indefinite advancement of our mental and moral nature.

ALFRED RUSSEL WALLACE
[In *The Quarterly Review* (April 1869)]

This Simian World

[Clarence Day indulged a fancy (see page 361); one of the most distinguished of recent American anthropologists considers more seriously the paradox that man, the most social of mammals, belongs to an order of animals less inclined than some others to social co-operation.]

Since humans are the most intelligent and also the most easily taught of animals, one would expect them to be the most highly individuated. No two persons are exactly alike in their physical and mental potentialities, and certainly no two individuals, even identical twins reared in the same family, have the same experiences. Human beings are thus potentially less alike than the individuals of any other species. It is most surprising, therefore, that they have chosen to live in closely organized groups whose members carry on a variety of specialized activities but are mutually interdependent for the satisfaction of practically all their fundamental needs. Many other mammalian species live in herds or packs, but the organization in these is minimal. The only division of activities is that devolving upon the two sexes by their different roles in connection with reproduction, while social control is a simple matter of the poorer fighters giving precedence to the better ones. To find anything which even remotely resembles the complexity of human societies, one must go to the social insects, such as the ants and the bees. Here the cooperation which is necessary for the survival of the community is assured by the physical specialization of the various groups of workers, fighters, and so forth, and by a high development of instincts. Since humans lack such instincts, it becomes necessary to subject them to an extraordinarily long and elaborate training if they are to function successfully as members of a society. We are, in fact, anthropoid apes trying to live like termites, and, as any philosophical observer can attest, not doing too well at it.

RALPH LINTON
[*The Tree of Culture* (1955)]

The Rebirth of Wonder

[Time brought many modifications of the Darwin theory, notably abandonment of the assumption that acquired characteristics can be inherited and stress upon the discovery of gene mutations of which no contemporary of

Darwin knew anything whatsoever. Nevertheless many—perhaps most—present-day biologists regard as foolish heresy any doubt that natural selection is sufficient to explain every aspect of evolution, including that of man and all his faculties. On the other hand, an increasing minority of scientists in and out of biology are confessing to an uneasy sense that some mystery remains. One of the most eloquent as well as one of the most tentative and modest statements of dissent comes from a distinguished contemporary anthropologist.]

All the way back into Cambrian time we know that sunlight fell, as it falls now, upon this planet. As Lyell taught, we can tell this by the eyes of fossil sea creatures such as the trilobites. We know that rain fell, as it falls now, upon wet beaches that had never known the step of man. We can read the scampering imprints of the raindrops upon the wet mud that has long since turned to stone. We can view the ripple marks in the sands of vanished coves. In all that time the ways of the inanimate world have not altered; storms and wind, sun and frost, have worked slowly upon the landscape. Mountains have risen and worn down, coast lines have altered. All that world has been the product of blind force and counterforce, the grinding of ice over stone, the pounding of pebbles in the mountain torrents—a workshop of a thousand hammers and shooting sparks in which no conscious hand was ever visible, today or yesterday.

Yet into this world of the machine—this mechanical disturbance surrounded by desert silences—a ghost has come, a ghost whose step must have been as light and imperceptible as the first scurry of a mouse in Cheops' tomb. Musing over the Archean strata, one can hear and see it in the subcellars of the mind itself, a little green in a fulminating spring, some strange objects floundering and helpless in the ooze on the tide line, something beating, beating, like a heart until a mounting thunder goes up through the towering strata, until no drum that ever was can produce its rhythm, until no mind can contain it, until it rises, wet and seaweed-crowned, an apparition from marsh and tide pool, gross with matter, gurgling and inarticulate, ape and man-ape, grisly and fang-scarred, until the thunder is in oneself and is passing—to the ages beyond—to a world unknown, yet forever being born.

"It is carbon," says one, as the music fades within his ear. "It is done with the amino acids," contributes another. "It rots and ebbs into the ground," growls a realist. "It began in the mud," criticizes a dreamer. "It endures pain," cries a sufferer. "It is evil," sighs a man of many disillusionments.

I have come to suspect that this long descent down the ladder of life, beautiful and instructive though it may be, will not lead us to the final secret. In fact I have ceased to believe in the final brew or the ultimate chemical. There is, I know, a kind of heresy, a shocking negation of our confidence in blue-steel microtomes and men in white in making such a statement. I would not be understood to speak ill of scientific effort, for in simple truth I would not be alive today except for the microscopes and the blue steel. It is only that somewhere among these seeds and beetle shells and abandoned grasshopper legs I find something that is not accounted for very clearly in the dissections to the ultimate virus or crystal or protein particle. Even if the secret is contained in these things, in other words, I do not think it will yield to the kind of analysis our science is capable of making.

If the day comes when the slime of the laboratory for the first time crawls under man's direction, we shall have great need of humbleness. It will be difficult for us to believe, in our pride of achievement, that the secret of life has slipped through our fingers and eludes us still. We will list all the chemicals and the reactions. The men who have become gods will pose austerely before the popping flashbulbs of news photographers, and there will be few to consider—so deep is the mind-set of an age—whether the desire to link life to matter may not have blinded us to the more remarkable characteristics of both.

I do not think, if someone finally twists the key successfully in the tiniest and most humble house of life, that many of these questions will be answered, or that the dark forces which create lights in the deep sea and living batteries in the waters of tropical swamps, or the dread cycles of parasites, or the most noble workings of the human brain, will be much if at all revealed. Rather, I would say that if "dead" matter has reared up this curious landscape of fiddling crickets, song sparrows, and wondering men, it must be plain even to the most devoted materialist that the matter of which he speaks contains amazing, if not dreadful powers, and may not impossibly be, as Hardy has suggested, "but one mask of many worn by the Great Face behind."

LOREN EISELEY
[*The Firmament of Time* (1960)]

SECTION SEVEN

DESTRUCTION AND CONSERVATION

Wherever Man has spread his dominion, scarcely any flight can save or any retreat harbour; wherever he comes, terror seems to follow, and all society ceases among the inferior tenants of the plain; their unity against him can afford them no protection, and their cunning is but weakness.

OLIVER GOLDSMITH
Animated Nature

It is really a pity the education of the human species did not develop in time to save from irremediable destruction so many species which the Creator placed on our earth to live beside man, not merely for beauty, but to fulfill a useful role for the economy of the whole. . . . Soon the horse and the pig on one hand and wheat and potatoes on the other will replace hundreds of thousands of animals and plants given us by God.

FATHER ARMAND DAVID
Diary

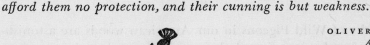

The sun, moon and stars would have disappeared long ago had they been within reach of predatory human hands.

HAVELOCK ELLIS
The Dance of Life

When I hear of the destruction of a species I feel as if all the works of some great writer had perished.

THEODORE ROOSEVELT
Letter to Frank M. Chapman, Feb. 16, 1899

For us of the minority, the opportunity to see wild geese is more important than television, and the chance to find a pasque-flower is a right as inalienable as free speech.

ALDO LEOPOLD
Sand County Almanac

And Then There Were None

[The last passenger pigeon died in a zoo in 1914; the last ivory-billed wood-pecker may or may not still be living; and there is no death so irretrievable as the death of a species. Audubon described both the pigeon and the wood-pecker some one hundred and twenty-five years ago when the former darkened the skies in incredible numbers.]

The multitudes of Wild Pigeons in our American woods are astonishing. Indeed, after having viewed them so often and under so many circumstances, I now feel inclined even to pause and reassure myself that what I am going to relate is fact. Yet I have seen it all, and in the company, too, of persons who like myself were struck with amazement.

In the autumn of 1813 I left my house at Henderson on the banks of the Ohio, on my way to Louisville ninety miles distant. In passing over the Kentucky barrens a few miles beyond Hardinsburg, I observed the Passenger Pigeons flying from northeast to southwest in greater numbers than I had ever seen them before, it seemed to me. Feeling an inclination to count the flocks that might pass within the reach of my eye in one hour, I dismounted, seated myself on an eminence, and began to mark a dot with my pencil for every flock that passed. In a short time, finding this task impracticable because the birds were pouring by in countless multitudes, I arose. But before I travelled on, I counted the dots that I had put down and found that one hundred and sixty flocks had been recorded in twenty-one minutes. I met still more, farther on. The air was literally filled with Pigeons, and the noon-day light was obscured as by an eclipse. The dung fell in spots not unlike melting flakes of snow; and the continuous buzz of wings tended to lull my senses.

While waiting for dinner at Young's Inn at the confluence of Salt River with the Ohio, I saw, at my leisure, immense legions still going by. Their front reached far beyond the Ohio on the west, and the beechwood forests directly east of me. Not a single bird alighted, for not a nut or acorn was that year to be seen in the neighborhood. Consequently they were flying so high that different attempts to reach them with a capital rifle proved ineffectual; nor did the reports disturb them in the least. I cannot describe to you the extreme beauty of their aerial evolutions when a Hawk chanced to press upon the rear of a flock. At once, like a torrent, and with a noise like thunder, they rushed in a compact mass, pressing upon each other towards the center. In these almost solid masses they darted forward in undulating and angular lines, descended to the earth and swept close over it with inconceivable velocity. Then they mounted perpendicularly so as to resemble a vast column, and, when high, they were seen wheeling and twisting within their continued lines, which resembled the coils of a gigantic serpent.

Before sunset I reached Louisville, fifty-five miles from Hardinsburg. The Pigeons were still passing in undiminished number. They continued to do so for three days in succession. The people were all in arms, and the banks of the Ohio were crowded with men and boys incessantly shooting at the pilgrims, which flew lower as they passed the river. Multitudes were thus destroyed. For a week or more, the population fed on no other flesh than that of Pigeons, and talked of nothing but Pigeons.

It is extremely interesting to see flock after flock performing exactly the same evolutions which a preceding flock has traced in the air. Thus should a Hawk charge on a group at a certain point, the angles, curves and undulations described by the birds in their efforts to escape the dreaded talons of the plunderer are undeviatingly followed by the next flock that comes up. Should the bystander happen to witness one of these affrays and be struck with the rapidity and elegance of the motions, and desire to see them repeated, his wishes will be gratified if he but remain in the same place until the next flock of Pigeons comes along.

As soon as the Pigeons discover a sufficiency of food to entice them to alight, they fly around in circles, reviewing the countryside below. During these evolutions the dense mass which they form presents a beautiful spectacle, as it changes its direction, turning from a glistening sheet of azure, as the backs of the birds come simultaneously into view, to a suddenly presented, rich deep purple. After that they pass lower, over the woods, and for a moment are lost among the foliage. Again they emerge and glide aloft. They may now alight, but the next moment take to wing as if suddenly alarmed, the flapping of their wings producing a noise like the roar of distant thunder, as they sweep through the forests to see if danger is near. However, hunger soon brings them to the ground. On alighting they industriously throw aside the withered leaves in quest of the fallen mast. The rear ranks continually rise, passing over the main body and alighting in front, and in such rapid succession that the whole flock seems still on the wing. The quantity of ground swept in this way is astonishing. So completely has it been cleared that the gleaner who might follow in the rear of the flock would find his labor completely lost. While feeding, their avidity is at times so great that, in attempting to swallow a large acorn or nut, they may be seen to gasp for a long while as if in the agonies of suffocation.

When the woods are filled with these Pigeons, they are killed in immense numbers, although no apparent diminution comes of it. About mid-day, after their repast is finished, they settle on the trees to enjoy rest and digest their food. On the ground and on the branches they walk with ease, frequently jerking their beautiful tails and moving their necks backward and forward in the most graceful manner. As the sun begins to sink beneath the horizon, they depart *en masse* for the roosting place which, not infrequently, is hundreds of miles away, a fact ascertained by persons who have kept track of their arrivals and departures.

Let us inspect their place of nightly rendezvous. One of these curious roosting places on the banks of the Green River in Kentucky I repeatedly visited. As always, it was in a part of the forest where the trees were huge and where there was little underbrush. I rode through it for more than forty miles, and on crossing it in different parts I found it rather more than three miles wide on average. My first view of it was at nearly two hours before sunset, about two weeks before the coming of the Pigeons. Few of these birds were then to be seen, but a great gathering of persons with horses and wagons, guns and ammunition had pitched camp on the edge of the forest.

Two farmers from the vicinity of Russellville, more than a hundred miles distant, had driven more than three hundred hogs to be fattened on the Pigeons they hoped to slaughter. Here and there, people were busy plucking and salting birds already killed, and they sat amid large piles of them. The dung lay several inches deep, covering the whole roosting place. I noticed that many trees two feet in diameter were broken off at no great distance from the ground; and the branches of many of the largest and tallest had given way. It was as if the forest had been swept by a tornado, proving to me that the number of birds must be immense beyond conception.

As the time of the arrival of the Passenger Pigeons approached, their foes anxiously prepared to receive them. Some persons were ready with iron pots containing sulphur, others with torches of pine knots; many had poles, and the rest, guns. The sun went down, yet not a Pigeon had arrived. However, everything was ready, and all eyes were fixed on the clear sky which could be glimpsed amid the tall tree-tops.

Suddenly a general cry burst forth, "Here they come!" The noise they made, even though still distant, reminded me of a hard gale at sea, passing through the rigging of a close-reefed vessel. As the birds arrived and passed over me, I felt a current of air that surprised me. Thousands of the Pigeons were soon knocked down by the pole-men, while more continued to pour in. The fires were lighted, then a magnificent, wonderful, and almost terrifying sight presented itself. The Pigeons, arriving by the thousands, alighted everywhere, one above another, until solid masses were formed on the branches all around. Here and there the perches gave way with a crash under the weight, and fell to the ground, destroying hundreds of birds beneath, and forcing down the dense groups of them with which every stick was loaded. The scene was one of uproar and confusion. I found it quite useless to speak, or even to shout, to those persons nearest to me. Even the gun reports were seldom heard, and I was made aware of the firing only by seeing the shooters reloading.

No one dared venture nearer the devastation. Meanwhile, the hogs had been penned up. The picking up of the dead and wounded birds was put off till morning. The Pigeons were constantly coming, and it was past midnight before I noticed any decrease in the number of those arriving. The uproar continued the whole night. I was anxious to know how far away the sound could be heard, so I sent off a man used to roaming the forest, who returned in two hours with the information that he had heard it distinctly three miles from the roosting place.

Towards the approach of day, the noise somewhat subsided. Long before I could distinguish them plainly, the Pigeons began to move off in a direction quite different from the one in which they flew when they arrived the evening before. By sunrise all that were able to fly had disappeared. The howling of the wolves now reached our ears, and the foxes, lynxes, cougars, bears, raccoons, opossums and polecats were sneaking off. Eagles and Hawks, accompanied by a crowd of Vultures, took their place and enjoyed their share of the spoils.

Then the authors of all this devastation began to move among the dead, the dying, and the mangled, picking up the Pigeons and piling them in heaps. When each man had as many as he could possibly dispose of, the hogs were let loose to feed on the remainder.

I have always imagined that there is something very closely allied to the style of the great Van Dyck's coloring in the plumage of the beautiful Ivory-Billed Woodpecker. I see this in its dark glossy body and tail. I see it, too, in the large, well-defined white markings of its wings, neck and bill, relieved by the rich carmine of the pendent crest of the male and the brilliant yellow of the eye. These have never failed to remind me of some of the boldest and noblest productions of that inimitable artist's pencil. So strongly, indeed, have these thoughts become fixed in my mind, on gradually more intimate acquaintance with this Woodpecker, that whenever I have observed one of these birds flying from tree to tree I have mentally exclaimed, "There goes a Van Dyck!" This notion may seem strange, perhaps ludicrous, but I relate it as a fact, whether or not it agrees with your own ideas after inspection of the portrait of this splendid species of the Woodpecker tribe in *The Birds of America*.

I have visited the favorite resort of the Ivory-Billed Woodpecker, those deep morasses overshadowed by millions of gigantic, dark, moss-covered cypresses which seem to admonish intruding man to pause and reflect on the many difficulties ahead. If he persists in venturing farther into these almost inaccessible recesses, he must follow for miles a tangle of massive trunks of fallen, decaying trees, huge projecting branches, and thousands of creeping and twining plants of numberless species! Would I could describe the dangerous nature of the ground, its oozing, spongy mire covered with a beautiful but treacherous carpet of the richest mosses, flags and water lilies. No sooner does this carpet feel the foot than it yields and endangers the very life of the adventurer as he approaches what he takes for a clearing, but which proves to be merely a lake of black muddy water. His ear is assailed by the dismal croaking of innumerable frogs, or the hissing of serpents, or the bellowing of alligators! Would that I could give you an idea of the sultry, pestiferous atmosphere that nearly suffocates the intruder during the noon-day heat of the dog-days in those gloomy and horrible swamps!

I have heard the amateur naturalist express astonishment that half-a-crown was asked by the person who had perhaps followed the bird through miles of such swamps, and, after procuring it, prepared its skin in the best manner, and carried it to a market thousands of miles distant from the spot where he obtained it. I must say this has grieved me as much as when I have heard some idle fop complain of the Louvre Gallery in Paris, where he had paid nothing to enter, or when I have listened to the same fatuous idler lamenting the loss of his shilling as he sauntered through the Exhibition Rooms of the Royal Academy of London, or any equally valuable repository of art.

But to return to the biography of the famed Ivory-Billed Woodpecker, the flight of this bird is graceful in the extreme, although seldom prolonged to more than a few hundred yards at a time, unless when the bird has to cross a large river. This it does in deep undulations, opening its wings to their full extent and nearly closing them to renew the propelling impulse. The flight from one tree to another is performed by a single sweep, even though the distance be as much as a thousand yards. The bird appears as if merely swinging itself in an elegantly curved line from the top of one tree to the top of another, exhibiting all the beauty of its plumage. It never utters a sound on the wing except during the mating season. But at all other times, after it has alighted, its remarkable voice is heard—at almost every leap which it makes, while ascending the upper trunk of a tree, or in its highest branches. Its notes are clear, loud and yet rather plaintive, and are heard at a considerable distance, perhaps half a mile. They resemble the false high note of a clarinet, usually repeated three times in succession, *pait, pait, pait*. They are heard so frequently that they lead to its destruction, which is aimed at, not because the species is a destroyer of trees but more because of its beauty. Its rich scalp attached to its upper mandible forms an ornament for the war-dress of most of our Indians, or for the shot-pouch of our squatters and hunters, by all of whom the bird is shot merely for that purpose. I have seen entire belts of Indian chiefs closely ornamented with the tufts and bills of this species, and have observed that a great value is frequently put upon them. Travellers of all nations are also fond of possessing the upper part of the head and the bill of the male. I have often remarked that on a steamboat's reaching what we call a wooding-place [where it stops to take on wood for fuel] the *strangers* were very apt to pay a quarter of a dollar for two or three heads of this Woodpecker.

The Ivory-Bill nestles earlier in spring than any others of its tribe. I have seen it boring a hole for that purpose in the beginning of March. The hole is, I believe, always made in the trunk of a live tree, generally an ash or a hackberry, at a great height. The birds pay much regard to the tree's location and to the slanting of its trunk, preferring retirement and wishing to protect the opening from access to running water during beating rainstorms. To prevent the latter, the hole is generally dug immediately under the junction of a large branch with the trunk. It is first bored horizontally for a few inches, then directly downwards, and not in a spiral manner as some people have imagined. This cavity is more or less deep, according to the circumstances; sometimes not more than ten inches, at other times nearly three feet downward into the core of the tree. I have been led to think that these differences result from the more or less immediate necessity under which the female may be of depositing her eggs. Again, I have thought that the older the Woodpecker is, the deeper it makes its hole. The nests average about seven inches in diameter within, but the entrance, which is perfectly round, is only just large enough to admit the bird.

Both birds work most assiduously at this excavation. One waits outside to encourage the other while it is engaged in digging, taking its place when it is fatigued. I have approached trees while these Woodpeckers were thus busily employed, and by resting my head against the bark I could easily distinguish every blow given by the bird. In two instances I observed that when the Woodpeckers saw me at the foot of the tree in which they were digging their nest, they abandoned it forever. The first brood, generally six eggs, are deposited on a few chips at the bottom of the hole, and are of a pure white color. About a fortnight before they venture to fly to any other tree, the young are seen creeping out of the hole. The second brood makes its appearance about the fifteenth of August. The Ivory-Bills raise no more than one brood each season in some places.

The young are at first the color of the female. Towards autumn their crests, which were wanting at first, nearly equal the mother's in size. This is particularly true of the first breed. The males have a slight line of red on the head by then, and do not attain their richness of plumage until spring, or their full size until the second year. Even then a difference may easily be seen between them and much older individuals.

Their food consists principally of beetles, larvae, and large grubs. I have seen this bird hang by its claws to the vines of ripe grapes, in the position so often assumed by a Titmouse, and reaching downwards help itself to a bunch of grapes with much apparent pleasure. It also feeds on persimmons and hackberries as soon as the fruit becomes quite mellow. It never attacks the corn, or the fruit of orchards, although it sometimes chips off the bark of the belted tress of the newly cleared plantations. It seldom comes near the ground, but prefers the tops of the tallest trees at all times. However, it will attack a half standing, broken shaft of a large dead and rotten tree in such a manner as nearly to demolish it in the course of a few days. I have seen the remains of some of these ancient monarchs of our forests so excavated, and in such a singular way, that the tottering fragments of the trunk appeared to be merely supported by the great pile of chips by which its base was surrounded. The strength of this Woodpecker is such that I have seen it detach pieces of bark seven or eight inches long with a single blow of its powerful bill. By beginning at the top branch of a dead tree, it will tear off the bark for twenty or thirty feet in a few hours, leaping downwards with its body in an upward position. All the while it tosses its head to right and left, or leans it against the bark to detect the spot where the grubs are concealed. Immediately afterward it renews its blows with fresh vigor, sounding its loud notes as if highly delighted.

This species generally moves in pairs after the young have left their parents. The female is always the most clamorous and the least shy. Their mutual attachment continues, I believe, throughout life. Except when digging a hole for nesting, these birds seldom if ever attack living trees for any other purpose than that of procuring food, in the process of which they destroy insects that would otherwise prove injurious to the trees.

I have frequently observed the male and female retire to rest for the night in the same hole where they had long before reared their young. This usually happens a short time before sunset.

The Ivory-Bill, when wounded and brought to the ground, immediately makes for the nearest tree, ascends it with great rapidity and perseverance, and squats and hides in the topmost branches. As it ascends it moves spirally round the tree, and utters its loud *pait, pait, pait,* at almost every hop, until it reaches a place where it feels itself safe. They sometimes cling to the bark with their claws so firmly as to remain cramped to the spot for several hours after death. To take them by the hand is a rather hazardous undertaking; they strike with great violence, and inflict very severe wounds with their bills and claws, which are extremely sharp and strong. On such occasions they utter a mournful and very piteous cry.

I have only to add that I found it very abundant along the finely wooded margins of that singular stream called "Buffalo Bayou" in Texas, where my expedition obtained several specimens.

JOHN JAMES AUDUBON
[Ornithological Biographies (1825)]

An Island Eden

[*Most animals do not fear man—just as mice do not fear the cat—until they get to know him. Charles Darwin was struck by this fact when he first visited an island where few men had ever been.*]

I will conclude my description of the natural history of these islands, by giving an account of the extreme tameness of the birds.

This disposition is common to all the terrestrial species; namely, to the mocking-thrushes, the finches, wrens, tyrant-flycatchers, the dove, and carrion-buzzard. All of them are often approached sufficiently near to be killed with a switch, and sometimes, as I myself tried, with a cap or hat. A gun is here almost superfluous; for with the muzzle I pushed a hawk off the branch of a tree. One day, whilst lying down, a mocking-thrush alighted on the edge of a pitcher, made of the shell of a tortoise, which I held in my hand, and began very quietly to sip the water; it allowed me to lift it from the ground whilst seated on the vessel: I often tried, and very nearly succeeded, in catching these birds by their legs. Formerly the birds appear to have been even tamer than at present. Cowley (in the year 1684) says that the "Turtle-doves were so tame, that they would often alight on our hats and arms, so as that we could take them alive; they not fearing man, until such time as some of our company did fire at them, whereby they were rendered more shy." Dampier also, in the same year, says that a man in a morning's walk might kill six or seven dozen of these doves. At present, although certainly very tame, they do not alight on people's arms, nor do they suffer themselves to be killed in such large numbers. It is surprising that they have not become wilder; for these islands during the last hundred and fifty years have been frequently visited by bucaniers and whalers; and the sailors, wandering through the wood in search of tortoises, always take cruel delight in knocking down the little birds.

These birds, although now still more persecuted, do not readily become wild. In Charles Island, which had then been colonized about six years, I saw a boy sitting by a well with a switch in his hand, with which he killed the doves and finches as they came to drink. He had already procured a little heap of them for his dinner; and he said that he had constantly been in the habit of waiting by this well for the same purpose. It would appear that the birds of this archipelago, not having as yet learnt that man is a more dangerous animal than the tortoise or the Amblyrhynchus, disregard him, in the same manner as in England shy birds, such as magpies, disregard the cows and horses grazing in our fields.

The Falkland Islands offer a second instance of birds with a similar disposition. The extraordinary tameness of the little Opetiorhynchus has been remarked by Pernety, Lesson, and other voyagers. It is not, however, peculiar to that bird: the Polyborus, snipe, upland and lowland goose, thrush, bunting, and even some true hawks, are all more or less tame. As the birds are so tame there, where foxes, hawks, and owls occur, we may infer that the absence of all rapacious animals at the Galapagos, is not the cause of their tameness here. The upland geese at the Falklands show, by the precaution they take in building on the islets, that they are aware of their danger from the foxes; but they are not by this rendered wild towards man. This tameness of the birds, especially of the waterfowl, is strongly contrasted with the habits of the same species in Tierra del Fuego, where for ages past they have been persecuted by the wild inhabitants. In the Falklands, the sportsman may sometimes kill more of the upland geese in one day than he can carry home; whereas in Tierra del Fuego it is nearly as difficult to kill one, as it is in England to shoot the common wild goose.

In the time of Pernety (1763), all the birds there appear to have been much tamer than at present; he states that the Opetiorhynchus would almost perch on his finger; and that with a wand he killed ten in half an hour. At that period the birds must have been about as tame as they now are at the Galapagos. They appear to have learnt caution more slowly at these latter islands than at the Falklands, where they have had proportionate means of experience; for besides frequent visits from vessels, those islands have been at intervals colonized during the entire period. Even formerly, when all the birds were so tame, it was impossible by Pernety's account to kill the black-necked swan—a bird of passage, which probably brought with it the wisdom learnt in foreign countries.

I may add that, according to Du Bois, all the birds at Bourbon in 1571-72, with the exception of the flamingoes and geese, were so extremely tame, that they could be caught by the hand, or killed in any number with a stick. Again, at Tristan d'Acunha in the Atlantic, Carmichael states that the only two land-birds, a thrush and a bunting, were "so tame as to suffer themselves to be caught with a hand-net." From these several facts we may, I think, conclude, first, that the wildness of birds with regard to man, is a particular instinct directed against *him,* and not dependent upon any general degree of caution arising from other sources of danger; secondly, that it is not acquired by individual birds in a short time, even when much persecuted; but that in the course of successive generations it becomes hereditary. With domesticated animals we are accustomed to see new mental habits or instincts acquired or rendered hereditary; but with animals in a state of nature, it must always be most difficult to discover instances of acquired hereditary knowledge. In regard to the wildness of birds towards man, there is no way of accounting for it, except as an inherited habit: comparatively few young birds, in any one year, have been injured by man in England, yet almost all, even nestlings, are afraid of him; many individuals, on the other hand, both at the Galapagos and at the Falklands, have been pursued and injured by man, yet have not learned a salutary dread of him. We may infer from these facts, what havoc the introduction of any new beast of prey must cause in a country, before the instincts of the indigenous inhabitants have become adapted to the stranger's craft or power.

CHARLES DARWIN
[*Voyage of* The Beagle (1840-1842)]

Progress in Concord

[*Slow attrition may be quite as effective as mass slaughter and the more or less law-abiding sportsman hunter in the long run less destructive than the trigger-happy to whom all animals that are not "game" are regarded as (in the traditional term of the English country gentleman) "vermin."*]

✍

In the fall the loon (*Colymbus glacialis*) came, as usual, to moult and bathe in the pond, making the woods ring with his wild laughter before I had risen. At rumor of his arrival all the Mill-dam sportsmen are on the alert, in gigs and on foot, two-by-two and three-by-three, with patent rifles and conical balls and spyglasses. They come rustling through the woods like autumn leaves, at least ten men to one loon. Some station themselves on this side of the pond, some on that, for the poor bird cannot be omnipresent; if he dive here he must come up there. But now the kind October wind rises, rustling the leaves and rippling the surface of the water, so that no loon can be heard or seen, though his foes sweep the pond with spyglasses, and make the woods resound with their discharges. The waves generously rise and dash angrily, taking sides with all waterfowl, and our sportsmen must beat a retreat to town and shop and unfinished jobs. But they were too often successful. When I went to get a pail of water early in the morning I frequently saw this stately bird sailing out of my cove within a few rods. If I endeavored to overtake him in a boat, in order to see how he would maneuver, he would dive and be completely lost, so that I did not discover him again, sometimes, till the latter part of the day. But I was more than a match for him on the surface. He commonly went off in a rain.

As I was paddling along the north shore one very calm October afternoon—for such days especially they settle on to the lakes, like the milkweed down—having looked in vain over the pond for a loon, suddenly one sailing out from the shore toward the middle a few rods in front of me set up his wild laugh and betrayed himself. I pursued with a paddle and he dived, but when he came up I was nearer than before. He dived again, but I miscalculated the direction he would take, and we were fifty rods apart when he came to the surface this time, for I had helped to widen the interval; and again he laughed long and loud, and with more reason than before. He maneuvered so cunningly that I could not get within half-a-dozen rods of him. Each time, when he came to the surface, turning his head this way and that, he coolly surveyed the water and the land, and apparently chose his course so that he might come up where there was the widest expanse of water and at the greatest distance from the boat. It was surprising how quickly he made up his mind and put his resolve into execution. He led me at once to the widest part of the pond, and could not be driven from it. While he was thinking one thing in his brain, I was endeavoring to divine his thought in mine. It was a pretty game, played on the smooth surface of the pond, a man against a loon. Suddenly your adversary's checker disappears beneath the board, and the problem is to place yours nearest to where his will appear again. Sometimes he would come up unexpectedly on the opposite side of me, having apparently passed directly under the boat. So long-winded was he and so unweariable, that when he had swum farthest he would immediately plunge again, nevertheless; and then no wit could divine where in the deep pond, beneath the smooth surface, he might be speeding his way like a fish, for he had time and ability to visit the bottom of the pond in its deepest part. It is said that loons have been caught in the New York lakes eighty feet beneath the surface, with hooks set for trout—though Walden is deeper than that. How surprised must the fishes be to see this ungainly visitor from another sphere speeding his way amid their schools! Yet he appeared to know his course as surely under water as on the surface, and swam much faster there. Once or twice I saw a ripple where he approached the surface, just put his head out to reconnoiter, and instantly dived again. I found that it was as well for me to rest on my oars and wait his reappearing, as to endeavor to calculate where he would rise; for again and again, when I was straining my eyes over the surface one way, I would suddenly be startled by his unearthly laugh behind me. But why, after displaying so much cunning, did he invariably betray himself the moment he came up, by that loud laugh? Did not his white breast enough betray him? He was indeed a silly loon, I thought. I could commonly hear the plash of the water when he came up, and so also detect him. But after an hour he seemed as fresh as ever, dived as willingly, and swam yet farther than at first. It was surprising to see how serenely he sailed off with unruffled breast when he came to the surface, doing all the work with his webbed feet beneath. His usual note was this demoniac laughter, yet somewhat like that of a waterfowl; but occasionally, when he had balked me most successfully and come up a long way off, he uttered a long-drawn unearthly howl, probably more like that of a wolf than any bird; as when a beast puts his muzzle to the ground and deliberately howls. This was his looning,—perhaps the wildest sound that is ever heard here, making the woods ring far and wide. I concluded that he laughed in derision of my efforts, confident of his own resources. Though the sky was by this time overcast, the pond was so smooth that I could see where he broke the surface when I did not hear him. His white breast, the stillness of the air, and the smoothness of the water were all against him. At length, having come up fifty rods off, he uttered one of those prolonged howls, as if calling on the god of loons to aid him, and immediately there came a wind from the east and rippled the surface, and filled the whole air with misty rain; and I was impressed as if it were the prayer of the loon answered, and his god was angry with me; and so I left him disappearing far away on the tumultuous surface.

This afternoon, being on Fair Haven Hill, I heard the sound of a saw, and soon after from the Cliff saw two men sawing down a noble pine beneath, about forty rods off. I resolved to watch it till it fell, the last of a dozen or more which were left when the forest was cut and for fifteen years have waved in solitary majesty over the sprout-land. I saw them like beavers or insects gnawing at the trunk of this noble tree, the diminutive manikins with their cross-cut saw which could scarcely span it. It towered up a hundred feet, as I afterward found by measurement, one of the tallest, probably, in the township and straight as an arrow, but slanting a little toward the hillside, its top seen against the frozen river and the hills of Conantum. I watch closely to see when it begins to move. Now the sawers stop, and with an ax open it a little on the side toward which it leans, that it may break the faster. And now their saw goes again. Now surely it is going; it is inclined one-quarter of the quadrant, and breathless, I expect its crashing fall. But no, I was mistaken; it has not moved an inch; it stands at the same angle as at first. It is fifteen minutes yet to its fall. Still its branches wave in the wind, as if it were destined to stand for a century, and the wind soughs through its needles as of yore; it is still a forest tree, the most majestic tree that waves over Musketaquid. The silvery sheen of the sunlight is reflected from its needles; it still affords an inaccessible crotch for the squirrel's nest; not a lichen has forsaken its mast-like stem, its raking mast—the hill is the hulk. Now, now's the moment! The manikins at its base are fleeing from their crime. They have dropped the guilty saw and ax. How slowly and majestically it starts! as if it were only swayed by a summer breeze, and would return without a sigh to its location in the air. And now it fans the hillside with its fall; and it lies down to its bed in the valley, from which it is never to rise, as softly as a feather, folding its green mantle about it like a warrior, as if, tired of standing, it embraced the earth with silent joy, returning its elements to the dust again.

I went down and measured it. It was about four feet in diameter where it was sawed, about one hundred feet long. Before I had reached it the axmen had already half divested it of its branches. Its gracefully spreading top was a perfect wreck on the hillside, as if it had been made of glass; and the tender cones of one year's growth upon its summit appealed in vain and too late to the mercy of the chopper. Already he has measured it with his axe, and marked off the mill-logs it will make. And the space it occupied in upper air is vacant for the next two centuries. It is lumber. He has laid waste the air. When the fish hawk in the spring revisits the banks of the Musketaquid, he will circle in vain to find his accustomed perch, and the hen-hawk will mourn for the pines lofty enough to protect her brood. A plant which it has taken two centuries to perfect, rising by slow stages into the heavens, has this afternoon ceased to exist. Its sapling top had expanded to this January thaw as the forerunner of summers to come. Why does not the village bell sound a knell? I hear no knell tolled. I see no procession of mourners in the streets, or the woodland aisles.

While the Republic has already acquired a history world-wide, America is still unsettled and unexplored. Like the English in New Holland, we live only on the shores of a continent even yet, and hardly know where the rivers come from which float our navy. The very timber and boards and shingles of which our houses are made grew but yesterday in a wilderness where the Indian still hunts and the moose runs wild. New York has her wilderness within her own borders; and though the sailors of Europe are familiar with the soundings of her Hudson, and Fulton long since invented the steamboat on its waters, an Indian is still necessary to guide her scientific men to its headwaters in the Adirondack country.

We have advanced by leaps to the Pacific, and left many a lesser Oregon and California unexplored behind us. Though the railroad and the telegraph have been established on the shores of Maine, the Indian still looks out from her interior mountains over all these to the sea. There stands the city of Bangor, fifty miles up the Penobscot, at the head of navigation for vessels of the largest class, the principal lumber depot on this continent, with a population of twelve thousand, like a star on the edge of night, still hewing at the forests of which it is built, already overflowing with the luxuries and refinement of Europe, and sending its vessels to Spain, to England, and to the West Indies for its groceries—and yet only a few axmen have gone "up river," into the howling wilderness which feeds it. The bear and deer are still found within its limits; and the moose, as he swims the Penobscot, is entangled amid its shipping, and taken by foreign sailors in its harbor. Twelve miles in the rear, twelve miles of railroad, are Orono and the Indian Island, the home of the Penobscot tribe; and then commence the bateau and the canoe, and the military road; and sixty miles above, the country is virtually unmapped and unexplored, and there still waves the virgin forest of the New World.

Maine, perhaps, will soon be where Massachusetts is. A good part of her territory is already as bare and commonplace as much of our neighborhood, and her villages generally are not so well shaded as ours.

And what are we coming to in our Middlesex towns? A bald, staring townhouse, or meetinghouse, and a bare liberty pole, as leafless as it is fruitless, for all I can see. We shall be obliged to import the timber for the last, hereafter, or splice such sticks as we have. And our ideas of liberty are equally mean with these. The very willow-rows lopped every three years for fuel or powder, and every sizable pine and oak, or other forest tree, cut down within the memory of man! As if individual speculators were to be allowed to export the clouds out of the sky, or the stars out of the firmament, one by one. We shall be reduced to gnaw the very crust of the earth for nutriment.

The kings of England formerly had their forests "to hold the king's game," for sport or food, sometimes destroying villages to create or extend them; and I think that they were impelled by a true instinct. Why should not we, who have renounced the king's authority, have our national preserves, where no villages need be destroyed, in which the bear and panther, and some even of the hunter race, may still exist, and not be "civilized off the face of the earth"—our forests, not to hold the king's game merely, but to hold and preserve the king himself also, the lord of creation—not for idle sport or food, but for inspiration and our own true recreation? Or shall we, like the villains, grub them all up, poaching on our own national domains?

HENRY DAVID THOREAU
[*Walden* (1854) and *Journal*, Jan. 29, 1860]

Genocide

[*Man may be more ruthless than many other creatures but he is far more efficient, and neither the instinct of an individual animal nor the slow adjustments of evolution can maintain the balance he shatters. Countless species had been wiped out in the old world before anyone took note; but Buffalo Bill (who* boasted that he had killed 4,280 buffalos in seventeen months) has left a narrative which shows what happened when modern man invaded a continent whose inhabitants had previously had to reckon with no member of the human species equipped with any weapon more efficient than the bow and arrow.]

Shortly after the adventures mentioned in the preceding chapter, I had my celebrated buffalo hunt with Billy Comstock, a noted scout, guide and interpreter, who was then chief of scouts at Fort Wallace, Kansas. Comstock had the reputation, for a long time, of being a most successful buffalo hunter, and the officers in particular, who had seen him kill buffaloes, were very desirous of backing him in a match against me. It was accordingly arranged that I should shoot him a buffalo-killing match, and the preliminaries were easily and satisfactorily agreed upon. We were to hunt one day of eight hours, beginning at eight o'clock in the morning, and closing at four o'clock in the afternoon. The wager was five hundred dollars a side, and the man who should kill the greater number of buffaloes from on horseback was to be declared the winner.

The hunt took place about twenty miles east of Sheridan, and as it had been pretty well advertised and noised abroad, a large crowd witnessed the interesting and exciting scene. An excursion party, mostly from St. Louis, consisting of about a hundred gentlemen and ladies, came out on a special train to view the sport, and among the number was my wife, with little baby Arta, who had come to remain with me for a while.

The buffaloes were quite plenty, and it was agreed that we should go into the same herd at the same time and "make a run," as we called it, each one killing as many as possible. A referee was to follow each of us on horseback when we entered the herd, and count the buffaloes killed by each man. The St. Louis excursionists, as well as the other spectators, rode out to the vicinity of the hunting grounds in wagons and on horseback, keeping well out of sight of the buffaloes, so as not to frighten them, until the time came for us to dash into the herd; when they were to come up as near as they pleased and witness the chase.

We were fortunate in the first run in getting good ground. Comstock was mounted on one of his favorite horses, while I rode old Brigham. I felt confident that I had the advantage of Comstock in two things —first, I had the best buffalo horse that ever made a track; and second, I was using what was known at that time as the needle-gun, a breech-loading Springfield rifle—calibre 50—it was my favorite old "Lucretia," which has already been introduced to the notice of the reader; while Comstock was armed with a Henry rifle, and although he could fire a few shots quicker than I could, yet I was pretty certain that it did not carry powder and lead enough to do execution equal to my calibre 50.

At last the time came to begin the match. Comstock and I dashed into a herd, followed by the referees. The buffaloes separated: Comstock took the left bunch and I the right. My great *forte* in killing buffaloes from horseback was to get them circling by riding my horse at the head of the herd, shooting the leaders, thus crowding their followers to the left, till they would finally circle round and round.

On this morning the buffaloes were very accommodating, and I soon had them running in a beautiful circle, when I dropped them thick and fast, until I had killed thirty-eight; which finished my run.

Comstock began shooting at the rear of the herd, which he was chasing, and they kept straight on. He succeeded, however, in killing twenty-three, but they were scattered over a distance of three miles, while mine lay close together. I had "nursed" my buffaloes, as a billiard-player does the balls when he makes a big run.

After the result of the first run had been duly announced, our St. Louis excursion friends—who had approached to the place where we had stopped—set out a lot of champagne, which they had brought with them, and which proved a good drink on a Kansas prairie, and a buffalo hunter was a good man to get away with it.

While taking a short rest, we suddenly spied another herd of buffaloes coming toward it. It was only a small drove, and we at once prepared to give the animals a lively reception. They proved to be a herd of cows and calves—which, by the way, are quicker in their movements than the bulls. We charged in among them, and I concluded my run with a score of eighteen, while Comstock killed fourteen. The score now stood fifty-six to thirty-seven, in my favor.

Again the excursion party approached, and once more the champagne was tapped. After we had eaten a lunch which was spread for us, we resumed the hunt. Striking out for a distance of three miles, we came up close to another herd. As I was so far ahead of my competitor in the number killed, I thought I could afford to give an extra exhibition of my skill. I had told the ladies that I would, on the next run, ride my horse without saddle or bridle. This had raised the excitement to fever heat among the excursionists, and I remember one fair lady who endeavored to prevail upon me not to attempt it.

"That's nothing at all," said I; "I have done it many a time, and old Brigham knows as well as I what I am doing, and sometimes a great deal better."

So, leaving my saddle and bridle with the wagons, we rode to the windward of the buffaloes, as usual, and when within a few hundred yards of them we dashed into the herd. I soon had thirteen laid out on the ground, the last one of which I had driven down close to the wagons, where the ladies were. It frightened some of the tender creatures to see the buffalo coming at full speed directly toward them; but when he had got within fifty yards of one of the wagons, I shot him dead in his tracks. This made my sixty-ninth buffalo, and finished my third and last run, Comstock having killed forty-six.

As it was now late in the afternoon, Comstock and his backers gave up the idea that he could beat me, and thereupon the referees declared me the winner of the match, as well as the champion buffalo-hunter of the plains.

BUFFALO BILL CODY
[*The Life of Buffalo Bill* (1879)]

One Bird Less on Martha's Vineyard

[Thoreau wondered that the village bell did not toll when a great tree was felled. He would have been pleased to know that the last heath hen on Martha's Vineyard got the following obituary.]

ᚖ

Now we know there are degrees even in death. All around us nature is full of casualties, but they do not interrupt the stream of life. When most living things die, they seem only to revert to the central theme of existence from which they were temporarily detached. There is a spirit of vitality everywhere which enfolds the dead with a countenance of consolation, and bestows upon the living races more than has been taken away. But to the heath hen something more than death has happened, or, rather, a different kind of death. There is no survivor, there is no future, there is no life to be recreated in this form again. We are looking upon the uttermost finality which can be written, glimpsing the darkness which will not know another ray of light. We are in touch with the reality of extinction.

It is written in scientific works that the heath hen had ceased long ago to be of economic importance, and that it could never have been of economic importance again. It follows, therefore, that preservation of this bird was a matter of sentiment alone, since between economic usefulness and sentiment our world knows no middle ground. The heath hen was a curious creature, an actor out of place, surviving beyond its appointed days, simply because there happened to be a bit of scenery fortuitously at hand for the playing of a last dramatic act and a sentimental epilogue. The bird we are speaking of was the prairie chicken of the east, and the contradiction in terms is clear, for where in the east is there a prairie, or any suitable environment for a bird not of the forest nor of the sea nor of the air, but of the open range? By chance there is a great plain on Martha's Vineyard, and despite the fact that the island is relatively small, it has never been considered amiss to speak of the vastness of this great plain of scrub oak, sweet fern, alder, blasted pine—and of the heath hen. Here, then, in sound of the roaring surf, amid such great and monotonous distances all encompassed in small space, the prairie chicken of the east lived a century beyond its time and then died, a single specimen making an end of the race, somewhere alone in the brush.

The heath hen failed to adapt to changing conditions and fell a victim to the laws of natural selection. This is a curious thing, for until the white men took over the land, the heath hen had achieved an admirable adaptation, embodying such fine distinctions of nature that scientists appreciate their nicety and would like to understand them better. Even if you knew where a heath hen was, against a background of twigs and brush, you could not see it unless it moved. Failed to adapt! Why, no creature was ever more at home, more nicely adjusted to place and time than the heath hen on the Vineyard plains! The whole trouble lay in the fact that the heath hen was a bird man could kill, and so it had to die. A wild bird in a thicket and a man in a house cannot be neighbors, for cats will be turned loose and forced to forage, fire will burn over the landscape time and time again, and there are even diseases of the domestic poultry yard to menace wild things.

In recent years an impression has gone forth that man has learned to withhold his hand and to let things about him grow and multiply. The gospel of conservation, it is said, has won the day. We know this is not true. May the death of the heath hen serve to bring us nearer a time of realization and fulfillment! Until now, saving only the imperious grace of economic importance and sometimes not even that, a creature that man could kill has had to die.

Is nothing to follow the extinction of this bird except one more lesson in conservation for school books, and a sentimental mourning? On the Vineyard, certainly, there is more. What an awe and fascination have been written into the theses of scientific men who came to observe the heath hen on the great plain! What accents of mystery, beauty and the eternal rites of life the heath hen, in spring, has given to this strange region! At first sight a visitor has thought the seemingly limitless mile of plain both dreary and uninteresting. But not for long. The most prosaic scientist, full of a passion for metric measurements of feathers or Latin labels, has lain among the black scrub oak in the white mists of a chill April morning, and has returned to write poetry. The meticulous observations and Latin terms appear modestly, softened by a cloak of mystery. We read of birds appearing "as if by magic." We are told that the call of the heath hen did not rise or fall, but "ended in the air like a Scotch ballad." And a naturalist who is also a writer has heard in the peeping of the pinkletinks the voice of Ariel, and in the witch dances and goblin cries of the heath hen the grosser spirits of the island.

And so it is that the extinction of the heath hen has taken away part of the magic of the Vineyard. This is the added loss of the island. There is a void in the April dawn, there is an expectancy unanswered, there is a tryst not kept. Not until the great plain has grown again a forest of tall pines and cedars, such as that which wooded the level acres a few centuries ago, will the loss of the heath hen be forgotten. One turns to Prospero's promise that he will abjure his charms:

". . . I'll break my staff,
Bury it certain fathoms in the earth,
And, deeper than did ever plummet sound,
I'll drown my book,"

So deeply, so irrevocably is part of the island's magic buried and drowned; so before our eyes is Prospero's promise perversely carried out.

ARTHUR BEETLE HOUGH
[*Vineyard Gazette* (April 21, 1933)]

No Use for a Gun

[*John Steinbeck accompanied the biologist Edward Ricketts (who was the original of one of his fictional characters) on an oceanographic expedition in the Gulf of California. An adventure on shore in the mountains of the Mexican peninsula gave him a chance to reflect upon the psychology of the hunters responsible for the threatened extinction of one of North America's most impressive animals.*]

When the dawn came, our Indians made coffee for us and we ate more of the lunch. Then, with some ceremony, the ranch-owner presented a Winchester .30-30 carbine with a broken stock to those Indians, and they set off straight up the mountainside. This, our first hunt for the *borrego,* or big-horn sheep, was the nicest hunting we have ever had. We did not raise a hand in our own service during the entire trip. Besides, we do not like to kill things—we do it when it is necessary, but we take no pleasure in it; and those fine Indians did it for us—the hunting, that is—while we sat beside the little waterfall and discussed many things with our hosts—how all Americans are rich and own new Fords; how there is no poverty in the United States and everyone sees a moving picture every night and is drunk as often as he wishes; how there are no political animosities; no need; no fear; no failure; no unemployment or hunger. It was a wonderful counrty we came from and our hosts knew all about it and told us. We could not spoil such a dream. After each one of his assurances we said, *"Cómo no?"* which is the most cautious understatement in the world, for *"Cómo no?"* means nothing at all. It is a polite filler between two statements from your companion. And we sat in that cool place and looked out over the hot desert country to the blue Gulf. In a couple of hours our Indians came back; they had no *borrego,* but one of them had a pocketful of droppings. It was time by now to start back to the boat. We intend to do all our future hunting in exactly this way. The ranch-owner said a little sadly, "If they had killed one we could have had our pictures taken with it," but except for that loss, there was no loss, for none of us likes to have the horns of dead animals around.

On the way back from the mountain one of the Indians offered us his pocketful of sheep droppings, and we accepted only a few because he did not have many and he probably had relatives who wanted them. We came back through heat and dryness to Puerto Escondido, and it seemed ridiculous to us that the *Western Flyer* had been there all the time. Our hosts had been kind to us and considerate as only Mexicans can be. Furthermore, they had taught us the best of all ways to go hunting, and we shall never use any other. We have, however, made one slight improvement on their method: we shall not take a gun, thereby obviating the last remote possibility of having the hunt cluttered up with game. We have never understood why men mount the heads of animals and hang them up to look down on their conquerors. Possibly it feels good to these men to be superior to animals, but it does seem that if they were sure of it they would not have to prove it. Often a man who is afraid must constantly demonstrate his courage and, in the case of the hunter, must keep a tangible record of his courage. For ourselves, we have had mounted in a small hardwood plaque one perfect *borrego* dropping. And where another man can say, "There was an animal, but because I am greater than he, he is dead and I am alive, and there is his head to prove it," we can say, "There was an animal, and for all we know there still is and here is the proof of it. He was very healthy when we last heard of him."

JOHN STEINBECK
[*Sea of Cortez* (1941)]

How to Become Extinct

[*The late Will Cuppy spoofed naturalists in a fashion which endeared him to all but the solemnest among them.* How to Become Extinct *is absurd only because the true facts are.*]

The last two Great Auks in the world were killed June 4, 1844, on the island of Eldey, off the coast of Iceland. The last Passenger Pigeon, an old female named Martha, died September 1, 1914, peacefully, at the Cincinnati Zoo. I became extinct on August 23, 1934. I forget where I was at the time, but I shall always remember the date.

The two Great Auks were hit on the head by Jon Brandsson and Sigurdr Islefsson, a couple of Icelandic fishermen who had come from Cape Reykjanes for the purpose. A companion, Ketil Ketilsson, looked around for another Great Auk but failed to find one, naturally, since the species had just become extinct. Vilhjalmur Hakônarsson, leader of the expedition, stayed in the boat.

The main reason why these particular fishermen went birding that day is part of history. It seems that bird lovers and bird experts everywhere were upset over the disappearance of the Great Auk from its accustomed haunts and its extreme rarity even in its last refuge, the little island of Eldey. Since there was grave danger that it would soon become entirely and irrevocably extinct—as dead as the Dodo, in fact—it looked as though something would have to be done and done quickly.

Well, something was done. As always, one man rose to the occasion. Mr. Carl Siemsen, a resident of Reykjavik and quite an ornithologist on his own, hired Jon and Sigurdr and the rest of the boys to row over to Eldey and kill all the Great Auks they could find, in order that they might be properly stuffed and placed in various museums for which he acted as agent and talent scout. And of course that was one way of handling the situation. It was pretty tough on the Auks, though, wasn't it?

I don't say the museum people themselves would have hit the Great Auks on the head, or even that they would have approved such an act. I do say that ornithologists as a class, so far as I have been able to observe them, generally from a safe distance, do seem to suffer from a touch of split personality when faced with a dwindling species of bird. They appear to be torn between a sincere desire to bring that bird back to par, at any cost to themselves and to certain well-to-do persons whose names they keep in a little black book, and an uncontrollable urge or compulsion to skin a few more specimens and put them in a showcase at the earliest possible moment. I don't pretend to follow their line of reasoning, if such it may be called. To do that you have to be a Ph.D. in birdology. It takes years of hard study and I guess you have to be that way in the first place.

Right here I might offer a word of advice to the Ivory-billed Woodpecker, now the rarest bird on the North American continent and one that is going to come in for more and more attention. Keep away from bird lovers, fellows, or you'll be standing on a little wooden pedestal with a label containing your full name in Latin: *Campephilus principalis.* People will be filing past admiring your glossy blue-black feathers, your white stripes and patches, your nasal plumes in front of lores, your bright red crest and your beady yellow eyes. You'll be in the limelight, but you won't know it. I don't want to alarm you fellows, but there are only about twenty of you alive as I write these lines, and there are more than two hundred of you in American museums and in collections owned by Ivory-billed Woodpecker enthusiasts. Get it?

Yes, I know that many ornithologists are gentle, harmless souls without a murderous thought in their whole field equipment. I should like to remind them, though, that even a bird has a nervous system, and I am thinking especially of the Roseate Spoonbill, one of our few native birds with a bill shaped like a soup ladle. It can't help the Roseate Spoonbill much to go chasing over hill and dale practically twenty-four hours a day, aiming binoculars at it from behind every bush—as if it didn't know you were there!—clicking your cameras, watching every move and that sort of thing. There must be Roseate Spoonbills who haven't had a decent night's rest in years. No sleep, no nothing. And you wonder why they're neurotic.

WILL CUPPY
[*How to Become Extinct* (1941)]

"How Careful of the Type She Seems..."

[The "*balance of nature*" *which permits one animal to prey upon another yet usually guarantees the survival of all is often extremely intricate, involving many different organisms. When a given area is isolated and small, it may be strikingly simple as it is on a small island in the Gulf of California. Here the gulls prey upon the terns but do not, as man so often does, exterminate the species they victimize.*]

On any forenoon during April, May, and June, the Heermann's Gulls blanket an area of the Gulf about 200 miles long, with Isla Raza at the center. They travel in bands of from 2 to 50 birds, and their focal points are the colony sites of pelicans, cormorants, and boobies. A few hours before dusk, however, the vagrant population diminishes as these birds that radiated from Raza at dawn start back to their tiny island home. Working toward this hub, singles converge with pairs, then with scores, and finally hundreds, until from an anchored boat the influx of birds makes Raza's coastline resemble a hive of swarming bees.

As each returning bird drops to a waiting mate on their chosen plot of ground, the beaks open and gull-talk pours out. The sounds and scenes of home-coming are everywhere, and the island roars with the combined vocal utterances of thousands of birds.

Each sweeping wing lowered toward the ground swirls a small cloud of dust. The dust raised by a single bird is insignificant, but across the mile-square island every foot of ground has its agitator, each contributing its share to the yellow plume of haze that marks from a distance this home of the Heermann's.

Aside from a few depressions that are occasionally flooded at night tide, every spot that could possibly accommodate a nest is utilized, and the nests are spaced about two feet apart. This distance seems to be just right. It permits sparring without interruption of incubation and with only a modicum of damage.

During most of the daylight hours, the nest is tended by only one adult, but occasionally the other partner may be seen sharing some of the duties. Family chores are performed only under difficulties as the territory is crowded, and every time the extra bird moves more than a few inches from its incubating mate, the bill of another setting gull forces battle. Every time the "outside" bird moves around, a brand new adversary, fresh and willing, attacks from the new direction. Hence on flat ground, these couples rarely stay together for more than a few minutes. However, when the nest has a rock or bush near by that affords the protection of elevation, both of the birds not infrequently remain in attendance.

Diligent search about mid-April will usually locate a few chicks hatched by the gulls that nested early on Raza. These young seek the shade of rocks or bushes immediately after hatching and crouch there, blending with the ground, awaiting food from the parents. Thus, if the eggs of several adjoining nests hatch simultaneously, a bare plot of ground is left unguarded. This situation sometimes permits the mixed colonies of Royal and Elegant Terns to establish a nesting foothold.

If one of these vacated spots is selected by the terns, a milling mass circles constantly above, and occasionally an individual nervously alights in the clearing. As more screeching birds fill the air, more drop to the ground; and with a few hours their bodies completely blanket the earth. Terns on the outskirts of the packed ring are pushed and shoved by those within and forced into fights with Heermann's Gulls that are trying to save their nests.

This battle of attrition continues throughout the daylight hours and probably throughout the night, with the nesting gulls destined to be evicted. By morning, tern eggs at eight-inch intervals dot the chosen plot, and by sheer numbers the new colony continues to encroach into more occupied gull territory.

Until the laying of the first tern eggs, border gulls have to fight their own battles against superior numbers without help from others of their own kind. But now things are changed. Tern eggs are also gull food. Selfishly inclined reinforcements flock to the area and patrol just out of reach of the nesting newcomers. An egg left uncovered for an instant is devoured by a waiting Heermann's Gull, and by nightfall only a handful of last night's eggs remain. The next morning brings a new crop, several times the original number; but even though the raids of patrolling gulls make inroads, it is evident that the pulsating colony is gaining a permanent foothold. Three weeks later this shimmering blanket of birds covers an acre or more, and eggs in the exact center commence to hatch. Each day thereafter, concentric rings of new young hatch out progressively farther from the center of the colony.

Any estimate of the number of eggs laid by the terns and utilized by the waiting Heerman's would run into the tens of thousands. During the nesting season of the terns, a major part of the gulls' diet consists of these eggs and, later, of young hatched from eggs that survived. The final chapter of this annual battle of Raza places the terns in another predicament, this time one that is hopeless. The original pioneers in the exact center of the colony eventually complete their home duties and, in vacating, leave an expanding bull's-eye of bare terrain. Gulls flock to this unprotected clearing and wage simultaneous attacks from without and within. The tern colony assumes the shape of a doughnut, then a bicycle tire, and finally fades into oblivion in a disappearing act so rapid that its original formation seems slow by comparison.

LEWIS WAYNE WALKER
[*Natural History* magazine (April, 1953)]

Conservation Is Not Enough

[It is an anthologist's privilege (immodest though it may make him) to include one piece of his own.]

🐎

Moralists often blame races and nations because they have never learned how to live and let live. In our time we seem to have been increasingly aware of how persistently and brutally they undertake to eliminate one another. But it is not only the members of his own kind that man seems to want to push off the earth. When he moves in, nearly everything else that lives suffers from his intrusion—sometimes because he wants the space it occupies and the food it eats, but often simply because when he sees a creature not of his kind or a man not of his race, his first impulse is "Kill it."

Even in the desert, where space is cheaper than in most places, the wild life grows scarcer and more secretive as the human population grows. The coyote howls farther and farther away. To almost everything except man, the smell of humanity is the most repulsive of all odors, the sight of man the most terrifying of all sights. Biologists call some animals *cryptozoic,* that is to say "leading hidden lives." As the human population increases, most animals develop cryptozoic habits; the deer is a good example of this development. Even now there are more wild animals around than we realize. They see us when we do not see them; and it is because they have seen us that we do not see them. Albert Schweitzer remarks somewhere that we owe kindness even to an insect, when we can afford to show it, just because we ought to do something to make up for all the cruelties, necessary as well as unnecessary, which we have inflicted upon almost the whole of animate creation.

Probably not one man in ten is capable of understanding such moral and aesthetic considerations, much less of permitting his conduct to be guided by them. But perhaps twice as many, though still far from a majority, are beginning to realize that the reckless devastation of the earth has practical consequences. They are beginning to hear at least about "conservation," even though they are not even dimly aware of any connection between it and a large morality and are very unlikely to suppose that it does or could mean anything more than looking after their own welfare.

Hardly more than two generations ago, Americans first woke up to the fact that their land was not inexhaustible. Every year since then, more and more has been said, and at least a little more has been done, about "conserving resources," about "rational use," and about such reconstruction as seemed possible. Scientists have studied the problem, public works have been undertaken, laws passed. Yet everybody knows that the using up still goes on, perhaps not so fast nor so recklessly as once it did, but still at a steady pace. And there is nowhere that it goes on more nakedly, more persistently, or with a fuller realization of what is happening than in the desert regions where the margin to be used up is narrower.

First, more and more cattle were set to grazing and overgrazing land from which the scanty rainfall now ran off even more rapidly than before. Then more outrageously, large areas of desert shrub were uprooted to plant cotton and other crops which were watered by wells tapping underground pools of water, now demonstrably shrinking fast because they represent years of accumulation which can be exhausted even more rapidly than an oil well. Everyone knows that this water supply will give out before long—very soon in fact, if the number of wells which draw on it continues to increase as it has been increasing. Soon dust bowls will be where was once a sparse but healthy desert; and man, having uprooted, slaughtered, or driven away everything which lived happily and normally there, will himself either abandon the country or die.

To the question of why men will do or are permitted to do such things, there are many replies. Some speak of population pressures, while others more bluntly discuss unconquerable human greed. Some despair; some hope that more education and more public works will, in the long run, prove effective. But is there, perhaps, something more, something different, which is indispensable? Is there some missing link in the chain of education, law and public works? Is there something lacking without which none of these is sufficient?

After a lifetime spent in forestry, wild-life management and conservation of one kind or another, after such a lifetime during which he nevertheless saw his country slip two steps backward for every one it took forward, the late Aldo Leopold pondered the question and came up with an unusual answer which many people would dismiss as "sentimental" and be surprised to hear from a "practical" scientific man. He published his article originally in the *Journal of Forestry,* but it was reprinted in the posthumous volume *A Sand County Almanac,* where it was given a seemingly neutral but actually very significant title, "The Land Ethic."

This is a subtle and original essay, full of ideas never so clearly expressed before, and seminal in the sense that each might easily grow into a separate treatise. Yet the conclusion reached can be simply stated. Something *is* lacking; and because of that lack, education, law and public works fail to accomplish what they hope to accomplish. Without it, the high-minded impulse to educate, to legislate and to manage becomes as sounding brass or a tinkling cymbal. And the main thing which is missing is love, some feeling for, as well as some understanding of, the inclusive community of rocks and soils, plants and animals, of which we are a part.

It is not, to put Mr. Leopold's thoughts in different words, enough to be enlightenedly selfish in our dealings with the land. That means, of course, that it is not enough for the farmer to want to get the most out of his farm or for the lumberer to get the most out of his forest without considering agriculture and wood production as a whole, both now and in the future. It also means more than that; and enlightened selfishness cannot be the occasion of that something else. This is partly because enlightened selfishness cannot possibly be extended to include remote posterity—to children perhaps and to grandchildren possibly, but not much beyond, because the very idea of "self" cannot be stretched much further, and some purely ethical considerations must operate if anything does. And even that is not all. The wisest, the most enlightened, the most remotely long-seeing exploitation of resources is not enough, for the simple reason that the whole concept of exploitation is so false and so limited that in the end it will defeat itself and the earth will have been plundered, no matter how scientifically and farseeingly the plundering has been done.

To live healthily and successfully on the land, we must also live with it. We must be part not only of the human community, but of the whole community; we must acknowledge some sort of oneness not only with our neighbors, our countrymen and our civilization, but also with the natural as well as the man-made community. Ours is not only "one world" in the sense usually implied by that term; it is also "one earth." And without some acknowledgment of that fact, men can no more live successfully than they can if they refuse to admit the political and economic interdependency of the various sections of the civilized world. It is not a sentimental but a grimly literal fact that unless we share this terrestrial globe with creatures other than ourselves, we shall not be able to live on it for long.

You may, if you like, think of this as a moral law. But if you are skeptical about moral laws, you cannot escape the fact that this has its factual, scientific aspect which the science of ecology is every day making clearer as it demonstrates those more and more remote inter-dependences which, no matter how remote they are, are crucial even for us.

Before even the most obvious aspects of the balance of nature had been recognized, a greedy, self-centered mankind naïvely divided plants into the useful and the useless. In the same way it divided animals into those which were either "domestic" on the one hand or "game" on the other, and those which were called "vermin" and ought to be destroyed. That was the day when extermination of whole species was taken as a matter of course and random introductions, which usually proved to be either complete failures or all too successful, were everywhere being made. Pretty soon, however, it became evident enough that to rid the world of vermin and to stock it with nothing but useful organisms was at least not a simple task if you assume that "useful" means simply "immediately useful to man."

Even to this day the ideal nevertheless remains the same for most people. They may know, or at least they may have been told, that what looks like the useless is often remotely but demonstrably essential. Out in this desert country they may see the land being rendered useless by overuse. They may have heard that when the mountain lion is killed off, the deer multiply; that when the deer multiply, the new growth of trees and shrubs is eaten away; and that when the hills are denuded, a farm or a section of grazing land many miles away is washed into gullies and made incapable of supporting either man or any other of the large animals. They may even have heard how the wonderful new insecticides proved so effective that fish and birds died of starvation; that on at least one Pacific island, insects had to be reintroduced to pollinate the crops; that when you almost completely kill off a destructive pest, you run the risk of starving out everything that preys upon it and thus run the risk that the pest itself will stage an overwhelming comeback because its natural enemies are no more. Yet, knowing all this and much more, their dream is still the dream that an earth for the use of man alone can be created if only we learn more and scheme more effectively. They still hope that nature's scheme of checks and balances, which provides for a varied population, in which she stubbornly refuses to scheme only from man's point of view and cherishes the weeds and vermin as persistently as she cherishes him, can be replaced by a scheme of his own devising. Ultimately he hopes he can beat the game. But the more the ecologist learns, the less likely it seems that man can in the long run do anything of the sort.

"Nature's social union" is not the purely gentle thing which Burns imagined. In fact it is a balance, with all the stress and conflict which the word implies, and not a "social union" at all. But it is, nevertheless, a workable, seesawing balance. And when it ceases to seesaw, there is trouble ahead for whatever is on the end that stays up.

For every creature there is a paradox at the heart of the necessary "struggle for existence" and the paradox is simply this: Neither man nor any other animal can afford to triumph in that struggle too completely. Unconditional surrender is a self-defeating formula—even in the war against insect pests. In nature as elsewhere, "to the victor belong the spoils"—but for a time only. When there are no more spoils to be consumed, the victor dies. That is believed by some to be what happened to the dominant carnivorous dinosaurs many millions of years ago. They became too dominant, and presently there was nothing left to dominate—or to eat. It is certainly what happens to other creatures like the too-protected deer who multiply so successfully that their herds can no longer be fed; or, more spectacularly, like the lemmings who head desperately toward a new area to be exploited and end in the cold waters of a northern sea because the new area does not exist.

What is commonly called "conservation" will not work in the long run, because it is not really conservation at all but rather, disguised by its elaborate scheming, a more knowledgeable variation of the old idea of a world for man's use only. That idea is unrealizable. But how can man be persuaded to cherish any other ideal unless he can learn to take some interest and some delight in the beauty and variety of the world for its own sake, unless he can see a "value" in a flower blooming or an animal at play, unless he can see some "use" in things not useful?

In our society we pride ourselves upon having reached a point where we condemn an individual whose whole aim in life is to acquire material wealth for himself. But his vulgarity is only one step removed from that of a society which takes no thought for anything except increasing the material wealth of the community. In his usual extravagant way, Thoreau once said: "This curious world which we inhabit is more wonderful than it is convenient; more beautiful than it is useful; it is more to be admired than it is to be used." Perhaps that "more" is beyond what most people could or perhaps ought to be convinced of. But without some realization that "this curious world" is at least beautiful as well as useful, conservation is doomed. We must live for something besides making a living. If we do not permit the earth to produce beauty and joy, it will in the end not produce food either.

Here practical considerations and those which are commonly called "moral," "aesthetic" and even "sentimental" join hands. Yet even the enlightened Department of Agriculture is so far from being fully enlightened that it encourages the farmer to forget that his land can ever produce anything except crops and is fanatical to the point of advising him how to build fences so that a field may be plowed to the last inch without leaving even a narrow margin within which one of the wild flowers—many of which agriculture has nearly rendered extinct— may continue to remind him that the world is beautiful as well as useful. And that brings us around to another of Aldo Leopold's seminal ideas:

> Conservation still proceeds at a snail's pace; . . . the usual answer . . . is "more conservation." . . . But is it certain that only the *volume* of education needs stepping up? Is something lacking in *content* as well? . . . It is inconceivable to me that an ethical relation to land can exist without love, respect and admiration for land, and a high regard for its value. By value, I of course mean something far broader than mere economic value; I mean value in the philosophcial sense.

Here in the West, as in the country at large, a war more or less concealed under the guise of a "conflict of interest" rages between the "practical" conservationist and the defenders of national parks, between cattlemen and lumberers on the one hand and "sentimentalists" on the other. The pressure to allow the hunter, the rancher or the woodcutter to invade the public domain is constant, and the plea is always that we should "use" what is assumed to be useless unless it is adding to material welfare. But unless somebody teaches love, there can be no ultimate protection to what is lusted after.

Any fully matured science of ecology will have to grapple with the fact that man, from the ecological point of view, is one of those animals which are in danger from a too successful participation in the struggle for existence. He has upset the balance of nature to a point where he has exterminated hundreds of other animals and has exhausted soils. Part of this he calls a demonstration of his intelligence and of the success which results from his use of it. Because of that intelligence he has learned how to exploit resources very thoroughly, and he is even beginning to learn how to redress the balance in certain minor ways. But he cannot keep indefinitely one step ahead of overcrowding and starvation; and from the standpoint of nature as a whole, he is both a threat to every other living thing and, therefore, a threat to himself also. If he were not so extravagantly successful, it would be better for nearly everything except man, and therefore possibly better in the longest run for him also. He has become the tyrant of the earth, the waster of its resources, the creator of the most prodigious imbalance in the natural order which has ever existed.

From a purely homocentric point of view, this may seem entirely proper. To most people it undoubtedly does. Is it not our proudest boast that we have learned how to "control nature"? Does not our dream of the future include a final emancipation from any dependence upon a natural balance and the substitution for it of some balance established by ourselves and in our exclusive interest? Is not that, in fact, what most people have in mind when they think of the final triumph of humanity?

Most would also go one step further and claim that we have every reason in experience to believe that this final triumph is possible. Has not all civilization been a closer and closer approach to it? Is not, indeed, the closeness of the approach the very measure of the degree of civilization? And if it is, then how can anyone even hint at the desirability of calling a halt? Could any halt possibly be called which would not be the beginning of a retreat back to the primitive?

Yet the fact remains that to all things there is a limit, that "progress" cannot continue indefinitely in one straight line. The growth of cities was, for instance, certainly essential to the development of civilization; but does that necessarily mean that cities should get greater and greater—that the bigger the city, the higher the civilization which it makes possible? Many would agree that it does not. Some might go on to suggest that the "control of nature" is itself something to which there are limits, that the control can never be absolute, that nature allows us only a certain length of rope, that in the long run it will appear that no complete emancipation from her rule is possible, that man's ability to "control nature" is something to which limits are set. If he insists upon trying to go beyond those limits, nature will have the last word.

The more completely we bring nature "under control," the more complicated our methods must become, the more disastrous the chain reaction set up by any failure of wisdom or watchfulness or technique. We are required to know more and more, and we are always threatened by the impossibility of achieving adequate knowledge, much less adequate wisdom and virtue.

Every increase in the complexity of organization has made the situation more precarious at the same time that it has increased our comfort, our wealth and our short-term safety. Until we learned to support a population far larger than we would have believed possible a century ago, there was no danger of general starvation, however disastrous and common local famines might have been. Although Malthus was certainly wrong in his estimates, it is by no means certain that he was wrong in his general principle. Until we increased the wealth of nations by linking them one with another, we were not exposed to the danger of a world-wide economic collapse. Until we learned how to "control" the atom, there was no danger that atomic phenomena would actually get out of control, and hence it is still not clear whether we are running the machines or the machines are running us. Thus we now have three tigers by the tail—the economic, the physical and the biological; and three tigers are three times as dangerous as one. We cannot let any of them go. But it is not certain that we can hang on to all of them indefinitely. Many a despot has discovered that it was just when his power seemed to have been made absolute that the revolution broke out. And it may be that just about three hundred years were necessary to expose the fallacy of the ideal born during the seventeenth century. Perhaps nature cannot really be controlled after all.

If one is prepared to admit that there is a limit to the extent to which we can exercise a biological control exclusively in our own interest, then it is certainly worth-while to ask how we might know when we are approaching that limit. It would, of course, be too easy to reply simply, "When man and society are obviously sick." Too many other explanations of the sickness can be given, and each can be made to seem more or less convincing; indeed, several of them may each be partially correct. But there is a criterion which it seems to me not wholly fanciful to apply. Might it not have something to do with nature's own great principle of "live and let live"? Might it not be that man's success as an organism is genuinely a success so long, but only so long, as it does not threaten the extinction of everything not useful to and absolutely controlled by him, so long as that success is not incompatible with the success of nature as the varied and free thing which she is, so long as, to some extent, man is prepared to share the earth with others?

And if by any chance that criterion is valid, then either one of two things is likely to happen. Either outraged nature will violently reassert herself and some catastrophe, perhaps the catastrophe brought about when more men are trying to live in our limited space than even their most advanced technology can make possible, will demonstrate the hollowness of man's supposed success; or man himself will learn in time to set a reasonable limit to his ambitions and accept the necessity of recognizing his position as that of the most highly evolved of living creatures, but not one which entitles him to assume that no others have a right to live unless they contribute directly to his material welfare.

But how can he learn to accept such a situation, to believe that it is right and proper, when the whole tendency of his thought and his interest carries him in a contrary direction? How can he learn to value and delight in a natural order larger than his own order? How can he come to accept, not sullenly but gladly, the necessity of sharing the earth?

As long ago as the seventeenth century—as long ago, that is, as the very time when the ambition to "control nature" in any large way was first coming to be formulated and embraced—a sort of answer to these questions was being given in theological terms. John Ray, one of the first great English biologists, formulated them in a book which was read for a hundred years; and they cut two ways, because what Ray had to say was directed against the egotism of man as expressed both by the old-fashioned theologians who thought that everything had been *made* for man's use and by the Baconians who assumed that he could at least *turn it* to that use.

"It is," Ray wrote, "a general received opinion, that all this visible world was created for Man; that Man is the End of Creation; as if there were no other end of any creature, but some way or other to be serviceable to man. . . . But though this be vulgarly received, yet wise men now-a-days think otherwise. Dr. Moore affirms, That creatures are made to enjoy themselves as well as to serve us." The greatest profit which we can get from the observation and study of other living things is, he went on to say, often not that we learn how to use them but that we may contemplate through them the wonders and the beauties of God's creation. What Ray was saying is precisely what Thoreau was restating in secularized form when he insisted that "this curious world which we inhabit . . . is more to be admired and enjoyed than it is to be used."

Since our age is not inclined to be interested in theological arguments, it is not likely to find Ray's exposition a sufficient reason for accepting gladly the continued existence on this earth of "useless" plants and animals occupying space which man might turn to his own immediate profit. He is more likely to make at least certain concessions in that direction as the result of absorbing what the ecologist has to say about the impossibility of maintaining a workable balance without a much more generous view of what is "useful" and what is not. But it is not certain that on that basis he will ever make quite enough concessions, and it *is* entirely certain that he will not make them happily, will not find life pleasanter just because he makes them, unless he can learn to love and to delight in the variety of nature.

JOSEPH WOOD KRUTCH
[*The Voice of the Desert* (1954)]

HEAD AND HEART

Come out here and behold a thousand painted butterflies and other beautiful insects which people the air; then go to the libraries and see what kind of prayer and glorification of God is there recorded. Massachusetts has published her report on "Insects Injurious to Vegetation," and our neighbours the "Noxious Insects of New York." . . . Though God may have pronounced his work good, we ask "Is it not poisonous?"

HENRY DAVID THOREAU
Journal, May 1, 1859

Christian theologians, many of them, confine Christianity to the human form of life. It does not seem to me correct. It lacks the essential universalization that I associate with Jesus.

ALBERT SCHWEITZER
Out of My Life and Thought

If you pick up a starving dog and make him prosperous, he will not bite you. This is the principal difference between a dog and a man.

MARK TWAIN
Pudd'nhead Wilson

Reflections on a Tortoise

["Nature writing" is perhaps principally a bookseller's term, but it does imply a real if rather vague distinction between biology or natural history on the one hand and, on the other, a genre which may include something of both yet is more intimate and more personal than either. It is often the work of amateurs rather than professionals though not necessarily, since the scientist who happens to "love nature" as well as study it has often adopted the manner when writing for a general public. Perhaps this suggests the most useful distinction: Pure science is concerned only with learning about the natural world; the nature writer is concerned also with learning from it. He does not, like some of the romantics, merely project himself upon clouds and mountains or read his own emotions into plants and animals. He must know facts and be loyal to them. But he does not stop there.

"Nature writing," clearly definable as such, is mostly the creation of the century just past. It may be in part a reaction against the chilliness of the Darwinian scheme. But the famous passages about a tortoise in Gilbert White's The History of Selborne are enough to demonstrate that emotional involvement as well as detached curiosity was sometimes communicated in writing long before Thoreau made such communication an outstanding characteristic of his literary work. White was an obscure country clergyman who corresponded with several other Englishmen of similar tastes and who published his letters only four years before his death. Soon they became, like Walton's Compleat Angler, a classic which seemed to defy classification.]

While I was in Sussex last autumn my residence was at the village near Lewes, from whence I had formerly the pleasure of writing to you. On the 1st of November I remarked that the old tortoise, formerly mentioned, began first to dig the ground, in order to the forming its hybernaculum, which it had fixed on just beside a great tuft of hepaticas. It scrapes out the ground with its fore-feet, and throws it up over its back with its hind; but the motion of its legs is ridiculously slow, little exceeding the hour-hand of a clock; and suitable to the composure of an animal said to be a whole month in performing one feat of copulation. Nothing can be more assiduous than this creature night and day in scooping the earth, and forcing its great body into the cavity; but as the noons of that season proved unusually warm and sunny, it was continually interrupted, and called forth by the heat in the middle of the day: and though I continued there till the 13th of November, yet the work remained unfinished. Harsher weather, and frosty mornings, would have quickened its operations. No part of its behaviour ever struck me more than the extreme timidity it always expresses with regard to rain; for though it has a shell that would secure it against the wheel of a loaded cart, yet does it discover as much solicitude about rain as a lady dressed in all her best attire, shuffling away on the first sprinklings, and running its head up in a corner. If attended to it becomes an excellent weather-glass: for as sure as it walks elate, and as it were on tiptoe, feeding with great earnestness in a morning, so sure will it rain before night. It is totally a diurnal animal, and never pretends to stir after it becomes dark. The tortoise, like other reptiles, has an arbitrary stomach as well as lungs; and can refrain from eating as well as breathing for a great part of the year. When first awakened it eats nothing; nor again in the autumn before it retires: through the height of the summer it feeds voraciously, devouring all the food that comes in its way. I was much taken with its sagacity in discerning those that do it kind offices; for as soon as the good old lady comes in sight who has waited on it for more than thirty years, it hobbles towards its benefactress with awkward alacrity; but remains inattentive to strangers. Thus not only "the ox knoweth its owner, and the ass his master's crib."

The old Sussex tortoise, that I have mentioned to you so often, is become my property. I dug it out of its winter dormitory in March last, when it was enough awakened to express its resentments by hissing; and packing it in a box with earth, carried it eighty miles in post-chaises. The rattle and hurry of the journey so perfectly roused it that, when I turned it out on a border, it walked twice down to the bottom of my garden; however, in the evening, the weather being cold, it buried itself in the loose mould, and continues still concealed.

As it will be under my eye, I shall now have an opportunity of enlarging my observations on its mode of life, and propensities; and perceive already that towards the time of coming forth, it opens a breathing-place in the ground near its head, requiring, I conclude, a freer respiration as it becomes more alive. This creature not only goes under the earth from the middle of November to the middle of April, but sleeps a great part of the summer; for it goes to bed in the longest days at four in the afternoon, and often does not stir in the morning till late. Besides, it retires to rest for every shower; and does not move at all on wet days.

When one reflects on the state of this strange being, it is a matter of wonder to find that Providence should bestow such a profusion of days, such a seeming waste of longevity, on a reptile that appears to relish it so little as to squander more than two-thirds of its existence in a joyless stupor, and be lost to all sensation for months together in the profoundest of slumbers.

While I was writing this letter, a moist and warm afternoon, with the thermometer at fifty, brought forth troops of shell-snails, and, at the same juncture, the tortoise heaved up the mould and put out his head; and the next morning came forth, as it were raised from the dead; and walked about till four in the afternoon. This was a curious coincidence! a very amusing occurrence! to see such a similarity of feelings between the two φερέοικοι! for so the Greeks call both the shell-snail and the tortoise.

Because we call "the old family tortoise" an abject reptile, we are too apt to undervalue his abilities, and depreciate his powers of instinct. Yet he is, as Mr. Pope says of his lord,

"— — — Much too wise to walk into a well:"

and has so much discernment as not to fall down a ha-ha: but to stop and withdraw from the brink with the readiest precaution.

Though he loves warm weather, he avoids the hot sun; because his thick shell when once heated, would, as the poet says of solid armour —"scald with safety." He therefore spends the more sultry hours under the umbrella of a large cabbage-leaf, or amidst the waving forests of an asparagus-bed.

But as he avoids heat in the summer, so, in the decline of the year, he improves the faint autumnal beams by getting within the reflection of a fruit-wall; and, though he never has read that planes inclining to the horizon receive a greater share of warmth, he inclines his shell, by tilting it against the wall, to collect and admit every feeble ray.

Pitiable seems the condition of this poor embarrassed reptile:

to be cased in a suit of ponderous armour which he cannot lay aside; to be imprisoned, as it were, within his own shell, must preclude, we should suppose, all activity and disposition for enterprise. Yet there is a season of the year (usually the beginning of June) when his exertions are remarkable. He then walks on tiptoe, and is stirring by five in the morning; and, traversing the garden, examines every wicket and interstice in the fences, through which he will escape if possible; and often has eluded the care of the gardener, and wandered to some distant field. The motives that impel him to undertake these rambles seem to be of the amorous kind: his fancy then becomes intent on sexual attachments, which transport him beyond his usual gravity, and induce him to forget for a time his ordinary solemn deportment.

There is a wonderful spirit of sociality in the brute creation, independent of sexual attachment. Of this the congregation of gregarious birds in the winter is a remarkable instance.

Many horses, though quiet with company, will not stay one minute in a field by themselves: the strongest fences cannot restrain them. My neighbour's horse will not only not stay by himself abroad, but he will not bear to be left alone in a strange stable without discovering the utmost impatience, and endeavouring to break the rack and manger with his fore-feet. He has been known to leap out at a stable-window, through which dung was thrown, after company; and yet in other respects is remarkably quiet. Oxen and cows will not fatten by themselves: but will neglect the finest pasture that is not recommended by society. It would be needless to add instances in sheep, which constantly flock together.

But this propensity seems not to be confined to animals of the same species; for we know a doe, still alive, that was brought up from a little fawn with a dairy of cows; with them it goes a-field, and with them it returns to the yard. The dogs of the house take no notice of this deer, being used to her; but, if strange dogs come by, a chase ensues; while the master smiles to see his favourite securely leading her pursuers over hedge, or gate, or stile, till she returns to the cows, who, with fierce lowings and menacing horns, drive the assailants quite out of the pasture.

Even great disparity of kind and size does not always prevent social advances and mutual fellowship. For a very intelligent and observant person has assured me that, in the former part of his life, keeping but one horse, he happened also on a time to have but one solitary hen. These two incongruous animals spent much of their time together in a lonely orchard, where they saw no creature but each other. By degrees an apparent regard began to take place between these two sequestered individuals. The fowl would approach the quadruped with notes of complacency, rubbing herself gently against his legs: while the horse would look down with satisfaction, and move with the greatest caution and circumspection, lest he should trample on his diminutive companion. Thus by mutual good offices, each seemed to console the vacant hours of the other: so that Milton, when he puts the following sentiment in the mouth of Adam, seems to be somewhat mistaken:—

"Much less can bird with beast, or fish will fowl,
So well converse, nor with the ox the ape."

We had in this village more than twenty years ago an idiot boy, whom I well remember, who, from a child, showed a strong propensity to bees; they were his food, his amusement, his sole object. And as people of this cast have seldom more than one point in view, so this lad exerted all his few faculties on this one pursuit. In the winter he dozed away his time, within his father's house, by the fireside, in a kind of torpid state, seldom departing from the chimney-corner; but in the summer he was all alert, and in quest of his game in the fields, and on sunny banks. Honey-bees, humble-bees, and wasps, were his prey wherever he found them: he had no apprehensions from their stings, but he would seize them *nudis manibus,* and at once disarm them of their weapons, and suck their bodies for the sake of their honey-bags. Sometimes he would fill his bosom between his shirt and his skin with a number of these captives; and sometimes would confine them in bottles. He was a very *Merops apiaster,* or bee-bird; and very injurious to men that kept bees: for he would slide into their bee-gardens, and, sitting down before the stools, would rap with his finger on the hives, and so take the bees as they came out. . . .

We have remarked in a former letter how much incongruous animals, in a lonely state, may be attached to each other from a spirit of sociality; in this it may not be amiss to recount a different motive which has been known to create as strange a fondness.

My friend had a little helpless leveret brought to him, which the servants fed with milk in a spoon, and about the same time his cat kittened and the young were despatched and buried. The hare was soon lost, and supposed to be gone the way of most fondlings, to be killed by some dog or cat. However, in about a fortnight, as the master was sitting in his garden in the dusk of the evening, he observed his cat, with tail erect, trotting towards him, and calling with little short inward notes of complacency, such as they use towards their kittens, and something gamboling after, which proved to be the leveret that the cat had supported with her milk, and continued to support with great affection.

Thus was a graminivorous animal nurtured by a carnivorous and predaceous one!

Why so cruel and sanguinary a beast as a cat, of the ferocious genus of *Feles,* the *Murium leo,* as Linnæus calls it, should be affected with any tenderness towards an animal which is its natural prey, is not so easy to determine.

This strange affection probably was occasioned by that desiderium, those tender maternal feelings, which the loss of her kittens had awakened in her breast; and by the complacency and ease she derived to herself from the procuring her teats to be drawn, which were too much distended with milk, till, from habit, she became as much delighted with this fondling as if it had been her real offspring.

This incident is no bad solution of that strange circumstance which grave historians as well as the poets assert, of exposed children being sometimes nurtured by female wild beasts that probably had lost their young. For it is not one whit more marvellous that Romulus and Remus, in their infant state, should be nursed by a she-wolf, than that a poor little suckling leveret should be fostered and cherished by a bloody grimalkin.

Or, as Christopher Pitt renders the Roman poet:—

"Here in a verdant cave's embowering shade,
The fostering wolf and martial twins were laid;
The indulgent mother, half reclined along,
Look'd fondly back, and formed them with her tongue."

Again a boy has taken three little squirrels in their nest, or drey, as it is called in these parts. These small creatures he put under the care of a cat who had lately lost her kittens, and finds that she nurses and suckles them with the same assiduity and affection as if they were her own offspring.

So many people went to see the little squirrels suckled by a cat, that the foster-mother became jealous of her charge, and in pain for their safety; and therefore hid them over the ceiling, where one died. This circumstance shows her affection for these fondlings, and that she supposes the squirrels to be her own young. Thus hens, when they have hatched ducklings, are equally attached to them, as if they were their own chickens.

GILBERT WHITE
[*The Natural History of Selborne* (1789)]

New England Birds

[Will Cuppy once remarked that the ability to tell one kind of sparrow from another "seems to be hereditary in certain old New England families." This, so the sober scientist would reply, is a case of cultural rather than genetic heredity. But be that as it may, no other section of the nation has produced so many ornithologists, amateur and quasi-professional. One of the earlier of such was a contemporary of Thoreau's of whom Thoreau said: "He is not alert enough. He wants stirring up with a pole. He should practice turning a series of somersaults rapidly, or jump up and see how many times he can strike his feet together before coming down." Perhaps. Nevertheless he was capable of a quiet charm which should have saved him from the almost total oblivion into which he has fallen.]

Birds acquire new habits as certain changes take place upon the surface of the country that create a necessity for using different modes of sheltering and protecting their young. Singing-birds frequent in greatest numbers our half-cultivated lands and the woods adjoining them. It may therefore be inferred that as the country grows older and is more extensively cleared and cultivated, the numbers of our songsters will increase, and it is not improbable that their vocal powers may improve. It may be true that for many years after the first settlement of this country there were but few singing-birds and that they have multiplied with the cultivation of the soil. At that time, though the same species existed here and were musical, their numbers were so small that they were not universally heard. Hence early travellers were led to believe that American birds were generally silent.

By a little observation we should soon be convinced that the primitive forest contains but few songsters. There you find crows, jays, woodpeckers, and other noisy birds in great numbers; and you occasionally hear the notes of the sylvias and solitary thrushes. But not until you are in the vicinity of farms and other cultivated lands are your ears saluted by a full band of feathered musicians. The bobolinks are not seen in a forest, and are unfrequent in the wild pastures or meadows which were their primitive resorts. At the present day they have left their early habitats, and seek the cultivated grass-lands, that afford them a more abundant supply of insect-food, with which they feed their young. They build upon the ground in the grass, and their nests are exposed in great numbers by the scythe of the mower, if he begins hay-making early in the season.

These birds, as well as robins, before America was settled by the Europeans, and when the greater part of the country was a wilderness, must have been comparatively few. Though the bobolink consumes great quantities of rice after the young are fledged and the whole family have departed, it is not the rice-fields which have made its species more numerous, but the increased abundance of insect food in the North, where they breed,—an increase consequent upon the increased amount of tillage. The robins are dependent entirely upon insect food, and must have multiplied in greater proportion than the bobolinks. There are probably thousands of both species at the present day to as many hundreds that existed at the discovery of America. Many other small birds, such as the song-sparrow and the linnet, have increased nearly in the same ratio with the progress of agriculture and the settlement of the country.

Domestication blunts the original instincts of animals and renders birds partially indifferent to colors. It changes their plumage as well as their instincts. In proportion to the length of time any species has been domesticated, it is unsafe to depend on the correctness of our observation of their instincts with respect to colors. All the gallinaceous birds, except the common hen, lay speckled eggs. It is probable that during the thousands of ages since the latter was domesticated her eggs have lost their original marking and have become white. As great a change has happened in their plumage, while the more recently domesticated birds, like the turkey and guinea-hen, retain more nearly their original markings. After domestication birds no longer require to be protected from the sight of their enemies by the hues of their plumage. Their natural predisposition to be marked only by a certain combination of hues is weakened. Being entirely in the power and under the protection of man, color is of no service to them, as in their natural and wild state.

Mr. S. P. Fowler communicated to the Essex Institute an essay containing some important facts concerning the changes in the habits of some of our own birds. He says: "The Baltimore oriole still constructs her nest after the old pattern, but has learned to weave it with materials furnished by civilization. I have a whole nest of this kind, made wholly from materials swept out of a milliner's shop, woven and interlaced with ribbons and laces, including a threaded needle." He has noticed for several years a change in the habits of our crow-black-birds, and thinks they are becoming domesticated, like the rooks of England. This change, in his opinion, has been produced by planting the white pine in cultivated grounds; for wherever a group of pines has attained the height of thirty feet, they are visited by these birds for breeding, even in proximity to our populous villages. He states that the purple finches have followed the evergreen trees that have been planted in our enclosures, though a few years since they were to be seen chiefly in our cedar groves. They have grown more numerous, and breed in his grounds on the branches of the spruce, feeding early in the season upon the flower-buds of the elm or upon those of the pear-tree.

From the same communication I gather the following facts, slightly abridging his statements. He remarks that the swallows have suffered more changes than any other birds in our vicinity. The barn-swallows long since left their ancient breeding-places, the overhanging cliffs of rocks, and have sought buildings erected by man; the chimney-swallow has deserted the hollow sycamore for some deserted chimney; and the cliff-swallow has left the shelving rock to seek shelter under the eaves of our roofs. The purple martin and white-bellied swallow have left the wilderness to find a home in our villages. The purple martins, during the last fifty years, have gradually diminished in Eastern Massachusetts. He thinks it equally certain that the barn-swallows are growing less numerous, and attributes their diminution to our modern tight barns. Chimney-swallows, on the other hand, have become more numerous. The opening of the Pacific Railroad, he thinks, will cause both plants and birds to follow its track.

WILSON FLAGG
[*Birds and Seasons of New England* (1875)]

Pigeons on the Grass

[*Of all the English literary naturalists, Richard Jefferies, self-educated son of a farmer, was the most completely a countryman. Yet, like W. H. Hudson, he could note that there is "wild life" in a metropolis.*]

The front of the British Museum stands in the sunlight clearly marked against the firm blue of the northern sky. The blue appears firm as if solid above the angle of the stonework, for while looking towards it—towards the north—the rays do not come through the azure, which is therefore colour without life. It seems nearer than the southern sky, it descends and forms a close background to the building; as you approach you seem to come nearer to the blue surface rising at its rear. The dark edges of sloping stone are distinct and separate, but not sharp; the hue of the stone is toned by time and weather, and is so indefinite as to have lost its hardness. Those small rounded bodies upon the cornice are pigeons resting in the sun, so motionless and neutral-tinted that they might be mistaken for some portion of the carving. A double gilt ring, a circle in a circle, at the feet of an allegorical figure gleams brightly against the dark surface. The sky already seems farther away seen between the boles of stone, perpetual shade dwells in their depth, but two or three of the pigeons fluttering down are searching for food on the sunlit gravel at the bottom of the steps. To them the building is merely a rock, pierced with convenient caverns; they use its exterior for their purpose, but penetrate no farther. With air and light, the sunlit gravel, the green lawn between it and the outer railings—with these they are concerned, and with these only. The heavy roll of the traffic in Oxford Street, audible here, is nothing to them; the struggle for money does not touch them, they let it go by. Nor the many minds searching and researching in the great Library, this mental toil is no more to them than the lading of the waggons in the street. Neither the tangible product nor the intellectual attainment is of any value—only the air and light. There are idols in the galleries within upon whose sculptured features the hot Eastern sun shone thousands of years since. They were made by human effort, however mistaken, and they were the outcome of human thought and handiwork. The doves fluttered about the temples in those days, full only of the air and light. They fluttered about the better temples of Greece and round the porticoes where philosophy was born. Still only the light, the sunlight, the air of heaven. We labour on and think, and carve our idols and the pen never ceases from its labour; but the lapse of the centuries has left us in the same place. The doves who have not laboured nor travailed in thought possess the sunlight. Is not theirs the preferable portion?

The shade deepens as I turn from the portico to the hall and vast domed house of books. The half-hearted light under the dome is stagnant and dead. For it is the nature of light to beat and throb; it has a pulse and undulation like the swing of the sea. Under the trees in the woodlands it vibrates and lives; on the hills there is a resonance of light. It beats against every leaf, and, thrown back, beats again; it is agitated with the motion of the grass blades; you can feel it ceaselessly streaming on your face. It is renewed and fresh every moment, and never twice do you see the same ray. Stayed and checked by the dome and book-built walls, the beams lose their elasticity, and the ripple ceases in the motionless pool. The eyes, responding, forget to turn quickly, and only partially see. Deeper thought and inspiration quit the heart, for they can only exist where the light vibrates and communicates its tone to the soul. If any imagine they shall find thought in many books, certainly they will be disappointed. Thought dwells by the stream and sea, by the hill and in the woodland, in the sunlight and free wind, where the wild dove haunts. Walls and roof shut it off as they shut off the undulation of light. The very lightning cannot penetrate here. A murkiness marks the coming of the cloud, and the dome becomes vague, but the fierce flash is shorn to a pale reflection, and the thunder is no more than the rolling of a heavier truck loaded with tomes. But in closing out the sky, with it is cut off all that the sky can tell you with its light, or in its passion of storm.

Sitting at these long desks and trying to read, I soon find that I have made a mistake; it is not here I shall find that which I seek. Yet the magic of books draws me here time after time, to be as often disappointed. Something in a book tempts the mind as pictures tempt the eye; the eye grows weary of pictures, but looks again. The mind wearies of books, yet cannot forget that once when they were first opened in youth they gave it hope of knowledge. Those first books exhausted, there is nothing left but words and covers. It seems as if all the books in the world—really books—can be bought for £10. Man's whole thought is purchasable at that small price, for the value of a watch, of a good dog. For the rest it is repetition and paraphrase. The grains of wheat were threshed out and garnered two thousand years since. Except the receipts of chemists, except specifications for the steam-engine, or the electric motor, there is nothing in these millions of books that was not known at the beginning of our era. Not a thought has been added. Continual threshing has widened out the heap of straw and spread it abroad, but it is empty. Nothing will ever be found in it. Those original grains of true thought were found beside the stream, the sea, in the sunlight, at the shady verge of woods. Let us leave this beating and turning-over of empty straw; let us return to the stream and the hills; let us ponder by night in view of the stars.

It is pleasant to go out again into the portico under the great columns. On the threshold I feel nearer knowledge than when within. The sun shines, and southwards above the houses there is a statue crowning the summit of some building. The figure is in the midst of the light; it stands out clear and white as if in Italy. The southern blue is luminous—the beams of light flow through it—the air is full of the undulation and life of light. There is rest in gazing at the sky: a sense that wisdom does exist and may be found, a hope returns that was taken away among the books. The green lawn is pleasant to look at, though it is mown so ruthlessly. If they would only let the grass spring up, there would be a thought somewhere entangled in the long blades as a dew-drop sparkles in their depths. Seats should be placed here, under the great columns or by the grass, so that one might enjoy the sunshine after books and watch the pigeons. They have no fear of the people, they come to my feet, but the noise of a door heavily swinging-to in the great building alarms them; they rise and float around, and return again. The sunlight casts a shadow of the pigeon's head and neck upon his shoulder; he turns his head, and the shadow of his beak falls on his breast. Iridescent gleams of bronze and green and blue play about his neck; blue predominates. His pink feet step so near, the red round his eye is visible. As he rises vertically, forcing his way in a straight line upwards, his wings almost meet above his back and again beneath the body; they are put forth to his full stroke. When his flight inclines and becomes gradually horizontal, the effort is less and the wing tips do not approach so closely.

They have not laboured in mental searching as we have; they have not wasted their time looking among empty straw for the grain that is not there. They have been in the sunlight. Since the days of ancient Greece the doves have remained in the sunshine; we who have laboured have found nothing. In the sunshine, by the shady verge of woods, by the sweet waters where the wild dove sips, there alone will thought be found.

RICHARD JEFFERIES

[*The Life of the Fields* (1884)]

Sociable Hermit

[*Probably no other American nature writer was known (at least by name) to so many of his contemporaries as John Burroughs. Perhaps just because he lacked both the bite of Thoreau and the wild aloofness of Muir he was sought out by such notables as Thomas Edison and Henry Ford and he became for them, as well as for that general public to whom they recommended him, a sort of semiofficial custodian of the "feeling for nature" which the Edisons and the Fords were too busy to cultivate for themselves.*]

The country is more of a wilderness, more of a wild solitude, in the winter than in the summer. The wild comes out. The urban, the cultivated, is hidden or negatived. You shall hardly know a good field from a poor, a meadow from a pasture, a park from a forest. Lines and boundaries are disregarded; gates and bar-ways are unclosed; man lets go his hold upon the earth; title-deeds are deep buried beneath the snow; the best-kept grounds relapse to a state of nature; under the pressure of the cold, all the wild creatures become outlaws, and roam abroad beyond their usual haunts. The partridge comes to the orchard for buds; the rabbit comes to the garden and lawn; the crows and jays come to the ash-heap and corn-crib, the snow buntings to the stack and to the barnyard; the sparrows pilfer from the domestic fowls; the pine grosbeak comes down from the north and shears your maples of their buds; the fox prowls about your premises at night; and the red squirrels find your grain in the barn or steal the butternuts from your attic. In fact, winter, like some great calamity, changes the status of most creatures and sets them adrift. Winter, like poverty, makes us acquainted with strange bedfellows.

For my part, my nearest approach to a strange bedfellow is the little gray rabbit that has taken up her abode under my study floor. As she spends the day here and is out larking at night, she is not much of a bedfellow, after all. It is probable that I disturb her slumbers more than she does mine. I think she is some support to me under there,—a silent, wide-eyed witness and backer; a type of the gentle and harmless in savage nature. She has no sagacity to give me or lend me, but that soft, nimble foot of hers, and that touch as of cotton wherever she goes, are worthy of emulation. I think I can feel her goodwill through the floor, and I hope she can mine. When I have a happy thought, I imagine her ears twitch, especially when I think of the sweet apple I will place by her doorway at night. I wonder if that fox chanced to catch a glimpse of her the other night when he stealthily leaped over the fence near by and walked along between the study and the house? How clearly one could read that it was not a little dog that had passed there! There was something furtive in the track; it shied off away from the house and around it, as if eying it suspiciously; and then it had the caution and deliberation of the fox,—bold, bold, but not too bold; wariness was in every footprint. If it had been a little dog that had chanced to wander that way, when he crossed my path he would have followed it up to the barn and have gone smelling around for a bone; but this sharp, cautious track held straight across all others, keeping five or six rods from the house, up the hill, across the highway toward a neighboring farmstead, with its nose in the air, and its eye and ear alert, so to speak.

A winter neighbor of mine, in whom I am interested, and who perhaps lends me his support after his kind, is a little red owl, whose retreat is in the heart of an old apple-tree just over the fence. Where he keeps himself in spring and summer, I do not know, but late every fall, and at intervals all winter, his hiding-place is discovered by the jays and nuthatches, and proclaimed from the treetops for the space of half an hour or so, with all the powers of voice they can command. Four times during one winter they called me out to behold this little ogre feigning sleep in his den, sometimes in one apple-tree, sometimes in another. Whenever I heard their cries, I knew my neighbor was being berated. The birds would take turns looking in upon him, and uttering their alarm-notes. Every jay within hearing would come to the spot, and at once approach the hole in the trunk or limb, and with a kind of breathless eagerness and excitement take a peep at the owl, and then join the outcry. When I approached they would hastily take a final look, and then withdraw and regard my movements intently. After accustoming my eye to the faint light of the cavity for a few moments, I could usually make out the owl at the bottom feigning sleep. Feigning, I say, because this is what he really did, as I first discovered one day when I cut into his retreat with the axe. The loud blows and the falling chips did not disturb him at all. When I reached in a stick and pulled him over on his side, leaving one of his wings spread out, he made no attempt to recover himself, but lay among the chips and fragments of decayed wood, like a part of themselves. Indeed, it took a sharp eye to distinguish him. Not till I had pulled him forth by one wing, rather rudely, did he abandon his trick of simulated sleep or death. Then, like a detected pickpocket, he was suddenly transformed into another creature. His eyes flew wide open, his talons clutched my finger, his ears were depressed, and every motion and look said, "Hands off, at your peril." Finding this game did not work, he soon began to "play 'possum" again. I put a cover over my study wood-box and kept him captive for a week. Look in upon him at any time, night or day, and he was apparently wrapped in the profoundest slumber; but the live mice which I put into his box from time to time found his sleep was easily broken; there would be a sudden rustle in the box, a faint squeak, and then silence. After a week of captivity I gave him his freedom in the full sunshine: no trouble for him to see which way and where to go.

Just at dusk in the winter nights, I often hear his soft *bur-r-r-r*, very pleasing and bell-like. What a furtive, woody sound it is in the winter stillness, so unlike the harsh scream of the hawk! But all the ways of the owl are ways of softness and duskiness. His wings are shod with silence, his plumage is edged with down.

Another owl neighbor of mine, with whom I pass the time of day more frequently than with the last, lives farther away. I pass his castle every night on my way to the post-office, and in winter, if the hour is late enough, am pretty sure to see him standing in his doorway, surveying the passers-by and the landscape through narrow slits in his eyes. For four successive winters now have I observed him. As the twilight begins to deepen, he rises up out of his cavity in the apple-tree, scarcely faster than the moon rises from behind the hill, and sits in the opening, completely framed by its outlines of gray bark and dead wood, and by his protective coloring virtually invisible to every eye that does not know he is there. Probably my own is the only eye that has ever penetrated his secret, and mine never would have done so had I not chanced on one occasion to see him leave his retreat and make a raid upon a shrike that was impaling a shrew-mouse upon a thorn in a neighboring tree, and which I was watching. Failing to get the mouse, the owl returned swiftly to his cavity, and ever since, while going that way, I have been on the lookout for him. Dozens of teams and foot-passengers pass him late in the day, but he regards them not, nor they him. When I come along and pause to salute him, he opens his eyes a little wider, and, appearing to recognize me, quickly shrinks and fades into the background of his door in a very weird and curious manner. When he is not at his outlook, or when he is, it requires the best powers of the eye to decide the point, as the empty cavity itself is almost an exact image of him. If the whole thing had been carefully studied, it could not have answered its purpose better. The owl stands quite perpendicular, presenting a front of light mottled gray; the eyes are closed to a mere slit, the ear-feathers depressed, the beak buried in the plumage, and the whole attitude is one of silent, motionless waiting and observation. If a mouse should be seen crossing the highway, or scudding over any exposed part of the snowy surface in the twilight, the owl would doubtless swoop down upon it. I think the owl has learned to distinguish me from the rest of the passers-by; at least, when I stop before him, and he sees himself observed, he backs down into his den, as I have said, in a very amusing manner. Whether bluebirds, nuthatches, and chickadees— birds that pass the night in cavities of trees—ever run into the clutches of the dozing owl, I should be glad to know. My impression is, however, that they seek out smaller cavities. An old willow by the roadside blew down one summer, and a decayed branch broke open, revealing a brood of half-fledged owls, and many feathers and quills of bluebirds, orioles, and other songsters, showing plainly enough why all birds fear and berate the owl. . . .

The only ones of my winter neighbors that actually rap at my door are the nuthatches and woodpeckers, and these do not know that it is my door. My retreat is covered with the bark of young chestnut-trees, and the birds, I suspect, mistake it for a huge stump that ought to hold fat grubs (there is not even a book-worm inside of it), and their loud rapping often makes me think I have a caller indeed. I place fragments of hickory-nuts in the interstices of the bark, and thus attract the nuthatches; a bone upon my window-sill attracts both nuthatches and the downy woodpecker. They peep in curiously through the window upon me, pecking away at my bone, too often a very poor one. A bone nailed to a tree a few feet in front of the window attracts crows as well as lesser birds. Even the slate-colored snowbird, a seed-eater, comes and nibbles it occasionally.

The bird that seems to consider he has the best right to the bone both upon the tree and upon the sill is the downy woodpecker, my favorite neighbor among the winter birds, to whom I will mainly devote the remainder of this chapter. His retreat is but a few paces from my own, in the decayed limb of an apple-tree which he excavated several autumns ago. I say "he" because the red plume on the top of his head proclaims the sex. It seems not to be generally known to our writers upon ornithology that certain of our woodpeckers—probably all the winter residents—each fall excavate a limb or the trunk of a tree in which to pass the winter, and that the cavity is abandoned in the spring, probably for a new one in which nidification takes place. So far as I have observed, these cavities are drilled out only by the males. Where the females take up their quarters I am not so well informed, though I suspect that they use the abandoned holes of the males of the previous year.

The particular woodpecker to which I refer drilled his first hole in my apple-tree one fall four or five years ago. This he occupied till the following spring, when he abandoned it. The next fall he began a hole in an adjoining limb, later than before, and when it was about half completed a female took possession of his old quarters. I am sorry to say that this seemed to enrage the male very much, and he persecuted the poor bird whenever she appeared upon the scene. He would fly at her spitefully and drive her off. One chilly November morning, as I passed under the tree, I heard the hammer of the little architect in his cavity, and at the same time saw the persecuted female sitting at the entrance of the other hole as if she would fain come out. She was actually shivering, probably from both fear and cold. I understood the situation at a glance; the bird was afraid to come forth and brave the anger of the male. Not till I had rapped smartly upon the limb with my stick did she come out and attempt to escape; but she had not gone ten feet from the tree before the male was in hot pursuit, and in a few moments had driven her back to the same tree, where she tried to avoid him among the branches. A few days after, he rid himself of his unwelcome neighbor in the following ingenious manner: he fairly scuttled the other cavity; he drilled a hole into the bottom of it that let in the light and the cold, and I saw the female there no more. I did not see him in the act of rendering this tenement uninhabitable; but one morning, behold it was punctured at the bottom, and the circumstances all seemed to point to him as the author of it. There is probably no gallantry among the birds except at the mating season. I have frequently seen the male woodpecker drive the female away from the bone upon the tree. When she hopped around to the other end and timidly nibbled it, he would presently dart spitefully at her. She would then take up her position in his rear and wait till he had finished his meal. The position of the female among the birds is very much the same as that of woman among savage tribes. Most of the drudgery of life falls upon her, and the leavings of the males are often her lot.

JOHN BURROUGHS
[*A Year in the Fields* (1896)]

Defenseless but Happy

[The life of Dallas Lore Sharp, by profession a teacher of English at Boston University, barely overlaps that of Wilson Flagg (see page 462). One of his essays, "Turtle Eggs for Agassiz," is a favorite of anthologists and makes his name at least not entirely forgotten. But he wrote rather voluminously and often with a charm somewhat more robust than that of Flagg.]

❦

In your woods walks did you ever notice a little furrow or tunnel through the underbrush, a tiny roadway in the briers and huckleberry-bushes? Did you ever try to follow this path to its beginning or end, wondering who traveled it? You have, doubtless. But the woods must be wild and the undergrowth thick and you must be as much at home among the trees as you are in your own dooryard, else this slight mark will make no impression upon you.

But enter any wild tract of wood or high swamp along the creek, and look sharp as you cut across the undergrowth. You will not go far before finding a narrow runway under your feet. It is about five inches wide, leading in no particular direction, and is evidently made by cutting off the small stems of vines and bushes at an inch or more from the ground. The work looks as if it had been laid out by rule and done with a sharp knife, it is so regular and clean.

This is a rabbit road. Follow it a few rods and you will find it crossed by another road, exactly similar. Take this new path now, and soon you are branching off, turning, and joining other roads. You are in rabbit-land, traveling its highways—the most complicated and entangling system of thoroughfares that was ever constructed. The individual roads are straight and plain enough, but at a glance one can see that the plan of the system is intended to bewilder and lead astray all who trespass here. Without a map and directions no one could hope to arrive at any definite point through such a snarl.

There often comes along with the circus a building called the "Moorish Maze," over whose entrance is this invitation:

COME IN AND GET LOST

This is what one reads at the cross-roads in rabbit-land. There are finger-boards and milestones along the way; but they point nowhere and mark no distances except to the rabbits.

An animal's strong points usually supplement each other; its well-developed powers are in line with its needs and mode of life. So, by the very demands of his peculiar life, the beaver has become chief among all the animal engineers, his specialty being dams. He can make a good slide for logging, but of the construction of speedways he knows absolutely nothing. The rabbit, on the other hand, is a runner. He can swim if he is obliged to. His interests, however, lie mostly in his heels, and hence in his highways. So Bunny has become an expert road-maker. He cannot build a house, nor dig even a respectable den; he is unable to climb, and his face is too flat for hole-gnawing: but turn him loose in a brambly, briery wilderness, and he will soon thread the trackless waste with a network of roads, and lay it open to his nimble feet as the sky lies open to the swallow's wings.

But how maddening these roads are to the dogs and foxes! In the first place, they have a peculiar way of beginning nowhere in particular, and vanishing all at once, in the same blind fashion. I am not sure that I ever found a satisfactory end to a rabbit's road—that is, a nest, a playground, or even a feeding-place. Old Calamity, the hound, is always tormented and undone whenever she runs afoul of a rabbit road.

She will start Bunny in the open field, and trail away after him in full tongue as fast as her fat bow-legs will carry her. The rabbit makes for the woods. Calamity is hot on his track, going down toward the creek. Suddenly she finds herself plunging along a rabbit road, breaking her way through by sheer force where the rabbit slipped along with perfect ease. She is following the path now rather than the scent, and, all at once, discovers that she is off the trail. She turns and goes back. Yes, here the rabbit made a sharp break to the right by a side-path; the track is fresh and warm, and the old hound sings in her eager delight. On she goes with more haste, running the path again instead of the trail, and—there is no path! It is gone. This bothers the old dog; but her nose is keen and she has picked up the course again. Here it goes into another road. She gives tongue again, and rushes on, when —*Wow!* she has plunged into a thick and thorny tangle of greenbrier.

That is where the torment comes in. These roads have a habit of taking in the brier-patches. Calamity will go round a patch if she can; she will work her way through if she must—but it is at the cost of bloody ears and a thousand smarting pricks. Bunny, meantime, is watching just inside the next brier-patch, counting the digs of his clumsy pursuer.

I suppose that this "blind alley" kind of road is due to the fact that the rabbits have no regular homes. They make a nest for the young; but they never have dens, like minks and coons. In New England they often live in holes and among the crannies of the stone walls; and there, as far as I have seen, they rarely or never make roads. Farther south, where the winters are less severe, they dig no holes, for they prefer an open, even an exposed, bed to any sort of shelter.

Shelters are dangerous. Bunny cannot back into a burrow and bare his teeth to his enemy; he is not a fighter. He can run, and he knows it; legs are his salvation, and he must have room to limber them. If he has to fight, then give him the open, not a hole; for it is to be a kangaroo kicking match, and a large ring is needed. He had as well surrender himself at once as to run into a hole that has only one opening.

At one time my home was separated from the woods by only a clover-field. This clover-field was a favorite feeding-ground for the rabbits of the vicinity. Here, in the early evening, they would gather to feed and frolic; and, not content with clover, they sometimes went into the garden for a dessert of growing corn and young cabbage.

Take a moonlight night in autumn and hide in the edge of

these woods. There is to be a rabbit party in the clover-field. The grass has long been cut and the field is clean and shining; but still there is plenty to eat. The rabbits from both sides of the woods are coming. The full moon rises above the trees, and the cottontails start over. Now, of course, they use the paths which they cut so carefully the longest possible way round. They hop leisurely along, stopping now and then to nibble the sassafras bark or to get a bit of wintergreen, even quitting the path, here and there, for a berry or a bunch of sweet wood-grass.

"Stop a moment; this won't do! Here is a side-path where the briers have grown three inches since they were last cut off. This path must be cleared out at once," and the old buck falls to cutting. By the time he has finished the path a dozen rabbits have assembled in the clover-field. When he appears there is a *thump,* and all look up; some one runs to greet the new-comer; they touch whiskers and smell, then turn to their eating.

The feast is finished, and the games are on. Four or five rabbits have come together for a turn at hop-skip-and-jump. And such hop-skip-and-jump! They are professionals at this sport, every one of them. There is not a rabbit in the game that cannot leap five times higher than he can reach on his tiptoes, and hop a clean ten feet.

Over and over they go, bounding and bouncing, snapping from their marvelous hind legs as if shot from a spring-trap. It is the greatest jumping exhibition that you will ever see. To have such legs as these is the next best thing to having wings.

Right in the thick of the fun sounds a sharp *thump! thump!* Every rabbit "freezes." It is the stamp of an old buck, the call, *Danger! danger!* He has heard a twig break in the woods, or has seen a soft, shadowy thing cross the moon.

As motionless as stumps squat the rabbits, stiff with the tense-ness of every ready muscle. They listen. But it was only a dropping nut or a restless bird; and the play continues.

They are chasing each other over the grass in a game of tag. There go two, round and round, tagging and re-tagging, first one being "it" and then the other. Their circle widens all the time and draws nearer to the woods. This time round they will touch the bush behind which we are watching. Here they come—there they go; they will leap the log yonder. Flash! squeak! scurry; Not a rabbit in the field! Yes; one rabbit—the limp, lifeless one hanging over the neck of that fox trotting off yonder in the shadows, along the border of the woods!

The picnic is over for this night, and it will be some time before the cottontails so far forget themselves as to play in this place again.

It is small wonder that animals do not laugh. They have so little play. The savage seldom laughs, for he hunts and is hunted like a wild animal, and is allowed so scant opportunity to be off guard that he cannot develop the power to laugh. Much more is this true of the animals. From the day an animal is born, instinct and training are bent toward the circumvention of enemies. There is no time to play, no chance, no cause for laughter.

The little brown rabbit has least reason of all to be glad. He is utterly inoffensive, the enemy of none, but the victim of many. Before he knows his mother he understands the meaning of *Be ready! Watch!* He drinks these words in with his milk. The winds whisper them; the birds call them; every leaf, every twig, every shadow and sound, says: *Be ready! Watch!* Life is but a series of escapes, little else than vigilance and flight. He must sleep with eyes open, feed with ears up, move with muffled feet, and, at short stages, he must stop, rise on his long hind legs, and listen and look. If he ever forgets, if he pauses one moment for a wordless, noiseless game with his fellows, he dies. For safety's sake he lives alone; but even a rabbit has fits of sociability, and gives way at times to his feelings. The owl and the fox know this, and they watch the open glades and field-edges. They must surprise him.

The barred owl is quick at dodging, but Bunny is quicker. It is the owl's soft, shadow-silent wings that are dreaded. They spirit him through the dusk like a huge moth, wavering and aimless, with dangling dragon-claws. But his drop is swift and certain, and the grip of those loosely hanging legs is the very grip of death. There is no terror like the ghost-terror of the owl.

DALLAS LORE SHARP
[*Wild Life Near Home* (1901)]

The Love Life of the Bee

[No other modern literary naturalist is so controversial as Maurice Maeterlinck, whose boldly mystical interpretations have offended many as dangerously "unscientific." On the other hand, he has been defended by other of-

ficial scientists who have seen in his sense of wonder something essential but lacking in the merely matter-of-fact accounts of technical specialists. Perhaps the most famous of his descriptions is that of the nuptial flight of the bee.]

Prodigious nuptials these, the most fairylike that can be conceived, azure and tragic, raised high above life by the impetus of desire; imperishable and terrible, unique and bewildering, solitary and infinite. An admirable ecstasy, wherein death supervening in all that our sphere has of most limpid and loveliest, in virginial, limitless space, stamps the instant of happiness in the sublime transparence of the great sky; purifying in that immaculate light the something of wretchedness that always hovers around love, rendering the kiss one that can never be forgotten; and, content this time with moderate tithe, proceeding herself, with hands that are almost maternal, to introduce and unite, in one body, for a long and inseparable future, two little fragile lives.

Profound truth has not this poetry, but possesses another that we are less apt to grasp, which, however, we should end, perhaps, by understanding and loving. Nature has not gone out of her way to provide these two "abbreviated atoms," as Pascal would call them, with a resplendent marriage, or an ideal moment of love.

Around the virgin queen, and dwelling with her in the hive, are hundreds of exuberant males, forever drunk on honey; the sole reason for their existence being one act of love. But, notwithstanding the incessant contact of two desires that elsewhere invariably triumph over every obstacle, the union never takes place in the hive, nor has it been possible to bring about the impregnation of a captive queen. While she lives in their midst the lovers about her know not what she is. They seek her in space, in the remote depths of the horizon, never suspecting that they have but this moment quitted her, have shared the same comb with her, have brushed against her, perhaps, in the eagerness of their departure. One might almost believe that those wonderful eyes of theirs, that cover their head as though with a glittering helmet, do not recognise or desire her save when she soars in the blue. Each day, from noon till three, when the sun shines resplendent, this plumed horde sallies forth in search of the bride, who is indeed more royal, more difficult of conquest, than the most inaccessible princess of fairy legend; for twenty or thirty tribes will hasten from all the neighbouring cities, her court thus consisting of more than ten thousand suitors; and from these ten thousand one alone will be chosen for the unique kiss of an instant that shall wed him to death no less

than to happiness; while the others will fly helplessly round the intertwined pair, and soon will perish without ever again beholding this prodigious and fatal apparition.

Very few, I imagine, have profaned the secret of the queen-bee's wedding, which comes to pass in the infinite, radiant circles of a beautiful sky. But we are able to witness the hesitating departure of the bride-elect and the murderous return of the bride.

However great her impatience, she will yet choose her day and her hour, and linger in the shadow of the portal till a marvellous morning fling open wide the nuptial spaces in the depths of the great azure vault. She loves the moment when drops of dew still moisten the leaves and the flowers, when the last fragrance of dying dawn still wrestles with burning day, like a maiden caught in the arms of a heavy warrior; when through the silence of approaching noon is heard, once and again, a transparent cry that has lingered from sunrise.

Then she appears on the threshold—in the midst of indifferent foragers, if she have left sisters in the hive; or surrounded by a delirious throng of workers, should it be impossible to fill her place.

She starts her flight backwards; returns twice or thrice to the alighting-board; and then, having definitely fixed in her mind the exact situation and aspect of the kingdom she has never yet seen from without, she departs like an arrow to the zenith of the blue. She soars to a height, a luminous zone, that other bees attain at no period of their life. Far away, caressing their idleness in the midst of the flowers, the males have beheld the apparition, have breathed the magnetic perfume that spreads from group to group till every apiary near is instinct with it. Immediately crowds collect, and follow her into the sea of gladness, whose limpid boundaries ever recede. She, drunk with her wings, obeying the magnificent law of the race that chooses her lover, and enacts that the strongest alone shall attain her in the solitude of the ether, she rises still; and, for the first time in her life, the blue morning air rushes into her stigmata, singing its song, like the blood of heaven, in the myriad tubes of the tracheal sacs, nourished on space, that fill the centre of her body. She rises still. A region must be found unhaunted by birds, that else might profane the mystery. She rises still; and already the ill-assorted troop below are dwindling and falling asunder. The feeble, infirm, the aged, unwelcome, ill-fed, who have flown from inactive or impoverished cities, these renounce the pursuit and disappear in the void. Only a small, indefatigable cluster remain, suspended in infinite opal. She summons her wings for one final effort; and now the chosen of incomprehensible forces has reached her, has seized her, and bounding aloft with united impetus, the ascending spiral of their intertwined flight whirls for one second in the hostile madness of love.

Let us return to the tragic nuptials of the queen. Here it is evidently nature's wish, in the interests of crossed fertilisation, that the union of the drone and the queen-bee should be possible only in the open sky. But her desires blend network-fashion, and her most valued laws have to pass through the meshes of other laws, which, in their turn, the moment after, are compelled to pass through the first.

In the sky she has planted so many dangers—cold winds, storm-currents, birds, insects, drops of water, all of which also obey invincible laws—that she must of necessity arrange for this union to be as brief as possible. It is so, thanks to the startlingly sudden death of the male. One embrace suffices; the rest all enacts itself in the very flanks of the bride.

She descends to the hive, trailing behind her, like an oriflamme, the unfolded entrails of her lover. Some writers pretend that the bees manifest great joy at this return so big with promise—Büchner, among others, giving a detailed account of it. I have many a time lain in wait for the queen-bee's return, and I confess that I have never noticed any unusual emotion except in the case of a young queen who had gone forth at the head of a swarm, and represented the unique hope of a newly founded and still empty city. In that instance the workers were all wildly excited, and rushed to meet her. But as a rule they appear to forget her, even though the future of their city will often be no less imperilled. They act with consistent prudence in all things, till the moment when they authorise the massacre of the rival queens. That point reached, their instinct halts; and there is, as it were, a gap in their foresight.—They appear to be wholly indifferent. They raise their heads; recognise, probably, the murderous tokens of impregnation; but, still mistrustful, manifest none of the gladness our expectation had pictured. Being positive in their ways, and slow at illusion, they probably need further proofs before permitting themselves to rejoice. Why endeavour to render too logical, or too human, the feelings of little creatures so different from ourselves? Neither among the bees nor among any other animals that have a ray of our intellect, do things happen with the precision our books record. Too many circumstances remain unknown to us. Why try to depict the bees as more perfect than they are, by saying that which is not? Those who would deem them more interesting did they resemble ourselves, have not yet truly realised what it is that should awaken the interest of a sincere mind.

The aim of the observer is not to surprise, but to comprehend; and to point out the gaps existing in an intellect, and the signs of a cerebral organisation different from our own, is more curious by far than the relating of mere marvels concerning it.

But this indifference is not shared by all; and when the breathless queen has reached the alighting-board, some groups will form and accompany her into the hive; where the sun, hero of every festivity in which the bees take part, is entering with little timid steps, and bathing in azure and shadow the waxen walls and curtains of honey. Nor does the new bride, indeed, show more concern than her people, there being not room for many emotions in her narrow, barbarous, practical brain. She has but one thought, which is to rid herself as quickly as possible of the embarrassing souvenirs her consort has left her, whereby her movements are hampered. She seats herself on the threshold, and carefully strips off the useless organs, that are borne far away by the workers; for the male has given her all he possessed, and much more than she requires. She retains only, in her spermatheca, the seminal liquid where millions of germs are floating, which, until her last day, will issue one by one, as the eggs pass by, and in the obscurity of her body accomplish the mysterious union of the male and female element, whence the worker-bees are born.

MAURICE MAETERLINCK
[*The Life of the Bee,* translated by Alfred Sutro (1901)]

Là Ci Darem La Mano

[*Jean Henri Fabre was not the first great observer of insect behavior—his fellow countryman René Réaumur had preceded him by a century. But Fabre, a literary craftsman as well as an almost superhumanly patient observer, was the first to find a large public for dramatic accounts of the strange ways of those generally despised creatures. A determined anti-evolutionist, he insisted that the wonders performed by blind instinct could only be explained on the assumption that God, having refused insects all intelligence, had given them instead the fixed habits they needed. One of the most famous of his set pieces describes the courtship of scorpions, which, though not technically insects, are even more ancient and primitive.]*

25th April, 1904.—Hullo! What is this, something I have not yet seen? My eyes, ever on the watch, look upon the affair for the first time. Two Scorpions face each other, with claws outstretched and fingers clasped. It is a question of a friendly grasp of the hand and not the prelude to a battle, for the two partners are behaving to each other in the most peaceful way. There is one of either sex. One is paunchy and browner than the other: this is the female; the other is comparatively slim and pale: this is the male. With their tails prettily curled, the couple stroll with measured steps along the pane. The male is ahead and walks backwards, without jolt or jerk, without any resistance to overcome. The female follows obediently, clasped by her finger-tips and face to face with her leader.

The stroll is interrupted by halts that do not affect the method of conjunction; it is resumed, now here, now there, from end to end of the enclosure. Nothing shows the object which the strollers have in view. They loiter, they dawdle, they most certainly exchange ogling glances. Even so in my village, on Sundays, after vespers, do the youth of both sexes saunter along the hedges, every Jack with his Jill.

Often they tack about. It is always the male who decides which fresh direction the pair shall take. Without releasing her hands, he turns gracefully to the left or right about and places himself side by side with his companion. Then, for a moment, with tail laid flat, he strokes her spine. The other stands motionless, impassive.

For over an hour, without tiring, I watch these interminable comings and goings. A part of the household lends me its eyes in the presence of the strange sight which no one in the world has yet seen, at least with a vision capable of observing. In spite of the lateness of the hour, which upsets all our habits, our attention is concentrated and no essential thing escapes us.

At last, about ten o'clock, something happens. The male has hit upon a potsherd whose shelter seems to suit him. He releases his companion with one hand, with one alone, and continuing to hold her with the other, he scratches with his legs and sweeps with his tail. A grotto opens. He enters and, slowly, without violence, drags the patient Scorpioness after him. Soon both have disappeared. A plug of sand closes the dwelling. The couple are at home.

To disturb them would be a blunder: I should be interfering too soon, at an inopportune moment, if I tried at once to see what was happening below. The preliminary stages may last for the best part of the night; and it does not do for me, who have turned eighty, to sit up so late. I feel my legs giving way; and my eyes seem full of sand.

All night long I dream of Scorpions. They crawl under my bed-clothes, they pass over my face; and I am not particularly excited, so many curious things do I see in my imagination. The next morning, at daybreak, I lift the stoneware. The female is alone. Of the male there is no trace, either in the home or in the neighbourhood. First disappointment, to be followed by many others.

10th May.—It is nearly seven o'clock in the evening; the sky is overcast with signs of an approaching shower. Under one of the potsherds is a motionless couple, face to face, with linked fingers. Cautiously I raise the potsherd and leave the occupants uncovered, so as to study the consequences of the interview at my ease. The darkness of the night falls and nothing, it seems to me, will disturb the calm of the home deprived of its roof. A sharp shower compels me to retire. They, under the lid of the cage, have no need to take shelter against the rain. What will they do, left to their business as they are but deprived of a canopy to their alcove?

An hour later, the rain ceases and I return to my Scorpions. They are gone. They have taken up their abode under a neighbouring tile. Still with their fingers linked, the female is outside and the male indoors, preparing the home. At intervals of minutes, the members of my family relieve one another, so as not to lose the exact moment of the pairing, which appears to be imminent. Wasted pains: at eight o'clock, it being now quite dark, the couple, dissatisfied with the spot, set out on a fresh ramble, hand in hand, and go prospecting elsewhere. The male, walking backwards, leads the way, chooses the dwelling as he pleases; the female follows with docility. It is an exact repetition of what I saw on the 25th of April.

At last a tile is found to suit them. The male goes in first but this time neither hand releases his companion for a moment. The nuptial chamber is prepared with a few sweeps of the tail. Gently drawn towards him, the Scorpioness enters in the wake of her guide.

I visit them a couple of hours later, thinking that I've given them time enough to finish their preparations. I lift the potsherd. They are there in the same posture, face to face and hand in hand. I shall see no more to-day.

The next day, nothing new either. Each sits confronting the

other, meditatively. Without stirring a limb, the gossips, holding each other by the finger-tips, continue their endless interview under the tile. In the evening, at sunset, after sitting linked together for four-and-twenty hours, the couple separate. He goes away from the tile, she remains; and matters have not advanced by an inch.

This observation gives us two facts to remember. After the stroll to celebrate the betrothal, the couple need the mystery and quiet of a shelter. Never would the nuptials be consummated in the open air, amid the bustling crowd, in sight of all. Remove the roof of the house, by night or day, with all possible discretion; and the husband and wife, who seem absorbed in meditation, march off in search of another spot. Also, the sojourn under the cover of a stone is a long one: we have just seen it spun out to twenty-four hours and even then without a decisive result.

12th May.—What will this evening's sitting teach us? The weather is calm and hot, favourable to nocturnal pastimes. A couple has been formed: how things began I do not know. This time the male is greatly inferior to his corpulent mate. Nevertheless, the skinny wight performs his duty gallantly. Walking backwards, according to rule, with his tail rolled trumpetwise, he marches the fat Scorpioness around the glass ramparts. After one circuit follows another, sometimes in the same, sometimes in the opposite direction.

Pauses are frequent. Then the foreheads touch, bend a little to left and right, as if the two were whispering in each other's ears. The little fore-legs flutter in feverish caresses. What are they saying to each other? How shall we translate their silent epithalamium into words?

The whole household turns out to see this curious team, which our presence in no way disturbs. The pair are pronounced to be "pretty"; and the expression is not exaggerated. Semitranslucent and shining in the light of the lantern, they seem carved out of a block of amber. Their arms outstretched, their tails rolled into graceful spirals, they wander on with a slow movement and with measured tread.

Nothing puts them out. Should some vagabond, taking the evening air and keeping to the wall like themselves, meet them on their way, he stands aside—for he understands these delicate matters—and leaves them a free passage. Lastly, the shelter of a tile receives the strolling pair, the male entering first and backwards: that goes without saying. It is nine o'clock.

The idyll of the evening is followed, during the night, by a hideous tragedy. Next morning, we find the Scorpioness under the potsherd of the previous day. The little male is by her side, but slain, and more or less devoured. He lacks the head, a claw, a pair of legs. I place the corpse in the open, on the threshold of the home. All day long, the recluse does not touch it. When night returns, she goes out and, meeting the deceased on her passage, carries him off to a distance to give him a decent funeral, that is to finish eating him.

This act of cannibalism agrees with what the open-air colony showed me last year. From time to time, I would find, under the stones, a pot-bellied female making a comfortable ritual meal off her companion of the night. I suspected that the male, if he did not break loose in time, once his functions were fulfilled, was devoured, wholly or partly, according to the matron's appetite. I now have the certain proof before my eyes. Yesterday, I saw the couple enter their home after their usual preliminary, the stroll; and, this morning, under the same tile, at the moment of my visit, the bride is consuming her mate.

Well, one supposes that the poor wretch has attained his ends. Were he still necessary to the race, he would not be eaten yet. The couple before us have therefore been quick about the business, whereas, I see that others fail to finish after provocations and contemplations exceeding in duration the time which it takes the hour-hand to go twice around the clock. Circumstances impossible to state with precision—the condition of the atmosphere perhaps, the electric tension, the temperature, the individual ardour of the couple—to a large extent accelerate or delay the finale of the pairing; and this constitutes a serious difficulty for the observer anxious to seize the exact moment whereat the as yet uncertain function of the combs might be revealed.

JEAN HENRI FABRE
[*The Life of the Scorpions*, translated by Alexander Teixerra de Mattos (1923)]

The Rapture of the Bird

[Some ornithologists are so fanatically committed to "objectivity" and "behaviorism" that they not only doubt the happiness of a singing bird (which is their privilege) but sometimes deny categorically that it is capable of any such emotion (which *is* surely an unprovable dogma). *A good corrective is the fine essay by Sir Julian Huxley whom no one ever accused of "sentimentality."*]

❧

"O Nightingale, thou surely art
A creature of a fiery heart."
                                —W. WORDSWORTH

"The inferior animals, when the conditions of life are favourable, are subject to periodical fits of gladness, affecting them powerfully and standing out in vivid contrast to their ordinary temper. . . . Birds are more subject to this universal joyous instinct than mammals, and . . . as they are much freer than mammals, more buoyant and graceful in action, more loquacious, and have voices so much finer, their gladness shows itself in a greater variety of ways, with more regular and beautiful motions, and with melody."
                                —W. H. HUDSON

"How do you know but ev'ry Bird that cuts the airy way
Is an immense world of delight, clos'd by your senses five?"
                                —BLAKE

"Ils n'ont pas de cerveau—ils n'ont que de l'âme." A dog was being described, with all his emotion, his apparent passion to make himself understood, his failure to reach comprehension; and that was how the French man of letters summed up the brute creation—*"pas de cerveau —que de l'âme."*

Nor is it a paradox: it is a half-truth that is more than half true —more true at least than its converse, which many hold.

There is a large school to-day who assert that animals are "mere machines." Machines they may be: it is the qualification which does not fit. I suppose that by saying "mere" machines it is meant to imply that they have the soulless, steely quality of a machine which goes when it is set going, stops when another lever is turned, acts only in obedience to outer stimuli, and is in fact unemotional—a bundle of operations without any quality meriting the name of a self.

It is true that the further we push our analysis of animal behaviour, the more we find it composed of a series of automatisms, the more we see it rigorously determined by combination of inner constitution and outer circumstance, the more we have cause to deny to animals the possession of anything deserving the name of reason, ideals, or abstract thought. The more, in fact, do they appear to us as mechanisms (which is a much better word than machines, since this latter carries with it definite connotations of metal or wood, electricity or steam). They are mechanisms, because their mode of operation is regular; but they differ from any other type of mechanism known to us in that their working is—to put it in the most non-committal way—accompanied by emotion. It is, to be sure, a combination of emotion with reason that we attribute to a soul; but none the less, in popular parlance at least, the emotional side is predominant, and pure reason is set over against the emotional content which gives soul its essence.

Birds in general are stupid, in the sense of being little able to meet unforeseen emergencies; but their lives are often emotional, and their emotions are richly and finely expressed. I have for years been interested in observing the courtship and the relations of the sexes in birds, and have in my head a number of pictures of their notable and dramatic moments. These seem to me to illustrate so well the emotional furnishing of birds, and to provide such a number of windows into that strange thing we call a bird's mind, that I shall simply set some of them down as they come to me.

First, then, the coastal plain of Louisiana; a pond, made and kept as a sanctuary by that public-spirited bird-lover Mr. E. A. McIlhenny, filled with noisy crowds of Egrets and little egret-like Herons. These, in great flocks, fly back across the "Mexique Bay" in the spring months from their winter quarters in South America. Arrived in Louisiana, they feed and roost in flocks for a time, but gradually split up into pairs. Each pair, detaching themselves from the flocks, choose a nesting-site (by joint deliberation) among the willows and maples of the breeding pond. And then follows a curious phenomenon. Instead of proceeding at once to biological business in the shape of nest-building and egg-laying, they indulge in what can only be styled a honeymoon. For three or four days both members of the pair are always on the chosen spot, save for the necessary visits which they alternately pay to the distant feeding grounds. When both are there, they will spend hours at a time sitting quite still, just touching one another. Generally the hen sits on a lower branch resting her head against the cock bird's flanks; they look for all the world like one of those inarticulate but happy couples upon a bench in the park in spring. Now and again, however, this passivity of sentiment gives place to wild excitement. Upon some unascertainable cause the two birds raise their necks and wings, and, with loud cries, intertwine their necks. This is so remarkable a sight that the first time I witnessed it I did not fully credit it, and only after it had happened before my eyes on three or four separate occasions was I forced to admit it as a regular occurrence in their lives. The long necks are so flexible that they can and do make a complete single turn round each other—a real true-lover's-knot! This once accomplished, each bird then —most wonderful of all—runs its beak quickly and amorously through the just raised aigrettes of the other, again and again, nibbling and clappering them from base to tip. Of this I can only say that it seemed to bring such a pitch of emotion that I could have wished to be a Heron that I might experience it. This over, they would untwist their necks and subside once more into their usual quieter sentimentality.

This, alas! I never saw with the less common little White Egrets, but with the Louisiana Heron (which should, strictly speaking, be called an egret too); but since every other action of the two species is (in all save a few minor details) the same, I assume that the flashing white, as well as the slate and vinous and grey birds, behave thus.

SIR JULIAN HUXLEY
[*Essays of a Biologist* (1923)]

He Made So Many of Them

[*It has been said that God must love the bugs because he made so many of them—which he certainly did or, to speak in round numbers, seven hundred thousand named species as well as thousands no one has yet got around to naming. Even a casual bird watcher may be familiar with every bird likely to be seen in his state, and an expert able to recognize any one to be found in*

North America or Europe. An entomologist, on the other hand, could not possibly know by sight all of even the commoner insects to be found within a radius of a few miles of his home. Here one of the best contemporary nature writers has a little fun with another of the same.]

ఉ

Edwin Way Teale joined us on occasions and we were delighted to have with us a man who knew so much about insects. On day in late August he set out with us to see what land birds were already on the southward migration through our territory, but we cut in on him with queries on insect life. Every time Mr. Teale began to focus his field glasses on a bird or bent over to have a look at a flower, one of us would shove an insect under his nose and demand its name, home address, general business activities and life history. He was watching a dozen or so Bobolinks in their yellow-brown Autumn traveling costumes swing down in the cat-tails of the swamp when the Medical Student nudged him and dropped on the palm of his hand some insignificant slug, larva, or caterpillar that he had gleaned from a bit of shrubbery.

"What is it?" asked the Medical Student.

"I don't know," said the insect expert with a shrug of his shoulders. "I'd have to look it up."

A few minutes later, when Mr. Teale was slipping around a tree trunk to watch a dazzling male Wood Duck that was swimming about the lazy stream in the center of the swamp, I found an inane-looking caterpillar slithering along a leaf and presented it to him for identification.

"Just a caterpillar," he said coldly. "Might be any of two hundred species."

He went off in chase of a small bird that was skulking low in the alders. It turned out to be a Swamp Sparrow. Then he investigated a slight movement in the cat-tails and found it to be a Long-billed Marsh Wren. A wasp alighted close at hand and we heckled him about it.

"Genus *Polistes*," he said, and gave an exhibition that almost unnerved us. He stuck his finger in the wasp's face—practically gave it a poke on the nose. The wasp clung to his finger as we looked on in horror.

"Notice its white face?" said Mr. Teale coolly. "All those with white faces are males and have no stings."

A man must be sure of his facts before he tries stunts like that. We were much impressed and didn't bother the insect expert for fully fifteen minutes. Indeed, it was the long-suffering entomologist who brought up the matter of insect study a little further along the trail. We were walking up a dirt path through a grove when Mr. Teale stopped and said as he pointed downward:

"Here's an Ant-lion's excavation. Let's dig him out."

We looked where he was pointing and saw, on the hard ground, a little funnel-shaped pit about an inch across and a half inch deep. Mr. Teale took a twig and began to pry into the bottom of the pit. In a few seconds he reached down and picked up an insect, saying as he did so:

"Here's the old boy now."

It was a brownish-gray insect with what looked like black incurved horns but were really sharp grasping jaws. It's with these pincer-like jaws that the Ant-lion grabs the ants that tumble into its pit. After we had looked over this curious insect, Mr. Teale put it back on the ground and said:

"Watch it dig itself backward into the ground and then start turning to make its pit."

Just as the insect expert had predicted, the amazing Ant-lion began to disappear by the stern. In half a minute it was out of sight and we could see the pit begin to take shape through the subterranean turning movements of the pit builder. Some yards ahead on the same path Mr. Teale discovered another Ant-lion's pit and, when we bent over to inspect it, we saw that there was an unfortunate ant at the bottom in the jaws of the owner and operator of the death trap. And to think that such an ugly larva as the Ant-lion turns into a beautiful flying insect with lacy wings! Truly the insect world makes the human world seem dull and stodgy.

We bored Mr. Teale with tales of the biggest thing in the insect line in our territory, the Cicada-killers that look like grandfather wasps and might be put on the game-bird list if they were any larger. They are sometimes called "Digger Wasps" because they have underground burrows in which they place their eggs and the food supply—the Cicadas they kill—for the larvae when they hatch. Our colony—it's something like a rabbit warren—is located between the ties of a siding on the railroad track that borders the swamp. The burrows run under the ties for the most part, though I have seen burrows in pastures and orchards that were simply holes in the ground with no rock or timber as partial protection or support.

The Cicada-killers are most noticeable in the Summer when they are flying around in search of their prey. They are big enough to frighten the ordinary citizen, but Mr. Teale comforted us with the information that they are not given to attacking innocent taxpayers but concentrate on Cicadas—called "Locusts" by all except entomologists —that they stalk by sound. When they hear a Cicada give off the rattling buzz that constitutes its "song," they go after it. Since the victims are about the same size as the killers, it's interesting to watch the big wasp handle the problem of transporting the body to the burying ground and pack it down the hole. The Cicada-killer lays an egg on the leg of its victim, and the egg, on the word of Mr. Teale, hatches in three days. The grub feeds on the body of the Cicada for about ten days and then spins a cocoon of silk and earth in which it spends the Winter, emerging as an adult wasp the following Spring.

The story of the Cicada-killer carried us to higher ground where I asked Mr. Teale to identify some odd insects that were sitting length-wise on the twigs of a Wafer-ash sapling.

"These are Tree-hoppers, sometimes called Brownie Bugs," said Mr. Teale. "This species is *Echenopa binotata*."

We all thanked him because we had seen the insects on that same tree year after year and we never saw them anywhere else in the neighborhood. It was a puzzle to us and we were grateful that Mr. Teale had named him. We allowed him a few minutes to enjoy the birds and flowers around us, and then the Medical Student came up with a little green crawling thing and asked:

"What species please?"

"You flatter me," said the entomologist wearily. "It's a caterpillar. Beyond that, it might be anything. Let me remind you gentlemen that there are 625,000 species of insects known to science and I don't carry them all in my head."

That ended our first lesson. Of course, we never have stopped bothering Mr. Teale about insects. We do it *viva voce* and by correspondence. I wrote him proudly that a lady had brought to the house what she said was a "bug" in a little box and I identified it for her. She said it had "great big eyes like the wolf in *Little Red Ridinghood* and it bounced off its back with a click," whereby I suspected that it was one of the "Click Beetles" and, through a reference book, identified it as the Eyed Elator (*Alaus oculatus*), so named because of black spots ringed with white to look like comparatively gigantic eyes up forward, the true eyes being much smaller and less noticeable.

Mr. Teale gave me a passing mark on that test, but more often I gave him cause for hearty laughter at my mistakes in insect identification. I humbly admit my vast ignorance in that field. Insects are marvelous, but there are too many of them. It isn't a difficult matter to track down the species of any mammal, bird, tree or flower that may be found in our territory, but the insects are overwhelming. At least, we find them so. We stop to admire beautiful insects when we see them on our walks but, except for a few common species that everybody can name, if we want to know more about them we take the matter up with some insect expert—like Edwin Way Teale.

JOHN KIERAN
[*Footnotes on Nature* (1947)]

Jungle Night

[*To most visitors from temperate climes the frenzied pace and crowded exuberance of the jungle is both fascinating and terrible. Here a Central American night is described by two well-known naturalists.*]

After seven o'clock the night activities of jungle animals were in full swing. Now the climbing creatures had fewer enemies, and they traveled aloft to gather nuts and fruits. Occasionally an owl sailed by, but no eagles, falcons, or hawks disturbed the foraging of monkeys and honeybears (kinkajous).

Like the tree porcupines, the silky anteaters ripping open termite nests (and the opossums, monkeys, and honeybears) have a fifth hand to help them hold their place—a long prehensile tail which can be curled around a branch.

Slower-moving foliage-eaters clamber about in the tree tops. Giant lizards—the green iguanas—stretch their six-foot length over the firm jungle covering of interlacing vines, to munch on buds and fresh leaves. Each is ready at a moment's notice to leap from the tree and crash to the ground. There the lizard scampers off, or, falling in any shallow waterway, hides in the bottom, waiting for a pursuer to give up the chase.

By contrast, the sloths feeding in the treetops cling to the branches below, from which they are suspended by hooked claws. These slowest of all mammals prefer the broad, many-fingered foliage of the *Cecropia,* a member of the mulberry family common throughout the American tropics but found nowhere else. Apparently their thick matted fur protects them from the hordes of small brown ants which make homes far from the ground in the hollow stems of this tree and attack any intruder.

On the soil far below the sloths, larger ants forage ceaselessly all day. Systematically they explore every log and leaf and cranny, seizing any form of living meat—whether mouse or bird, lizard or frog, grasshopper or spider. They tear apart each victim and distribute its remains as loads of flesh to be carried back along the column—nourishment to be shared with the brood of young carried by still other members of the colony. These are the dreaded army ants—the American *Eciton*—which resemble in their habits the driver ants of tropical Africa. But like old-time armies which fought by day and slept at night, these terrors of the rain forest respond to a silent, military tattoo at sunset. The columns cease their advance. The marching order is reversed. From everywhere the ants converge on a central rendezvous. And as the light fails, some inaudible signal leads these insects to climb a low bush or some strong liana to a point several feet above the ground. There they mass themselves into a tremendous quivering ball. Until daybreak this bivouac will cling together as a unit, ready to unfold, when morning comes, into a dozen raiding parties and a wholesale transportation system.

Other ants parade up and down a variety of trees. In the night they are safe from ant shrikes, honeycreepers, and other insect-eating birds. Sauba ants, known also as parasol or umbrella ants, climb to reach fresh foliage, choosing chiefly trees which are exceptional in the tropics in having small, thin leaves. Each half-inch ant employs one of its sidewise-working slender jaws to saw off an arc of leaf blade, handling the knife edge with the precision of a surgeon. Dexterous movements of all six legs transfer the fragment to the paired jaws, and the insect marches off with its booty held above its back like a green sail. Often whole petals are carried along in this fashion.

As the stevedores plod down the tree, they blunder every few steps into eager ants returning for another load. The two-way column wanders along the ground, converging with other living streams upon an irregular mound many feet across—the granular earth excavated from deep subterranean burrows. Down the many doorways the insects descend to transfer their burdens to still smaller sisters who drag the booty to chambers as large as bushel baskets. There the small ants mince the leaf pieces into a pulp.

Sauba ants are the agriculturalists of the tropical jungle. "In addition, they are the greatest defoliators known, their ravages far exceeding those of other famous leaf destroyers such as the Japanese beetle and the gypsy moth." All of their activities lead to the building of vast compost heaps in which strands of a particular kind of fungus grow. So far as is known the sauba ants eat nothing but this fungus, and they alone have the secret of its culture. When a young queen ant starts out to found a fresh colony, she carries with her a pellet of the fungus and tends it carefully until her first brood of young emerge.

Fortunately the sauba ants do not bite, and an explorer of the jungle night who stands unwittingly across their trail suffers no ill effects. By day their paths are clearly visible—little avenues four to seven inches broad, kept remarkably clear of sticks and stones, patted firm by myriad marching feet.

Far more irregular and plastic are the tracks of wild pigs—peccaries—whose sharp toes dig into the wet earth, and whose noses root vigorously in search of hidden food.

During nights in January, February, and early March these and other animals are particularly active under the spreading branches of great almendro trees. At this season the flattened elliptical nuts are ripening—each about two inches long and one inch wide. The brown outer covering has a slightly sweetish taste and is attractive to racoon-like coatis and to howler monkeys by day, to honeybears by night. Inside the skin, however, is a layer hard as stone, protecting the almond-shaped inner kernel for which the tree is named—even though it is a member of the pea family. The honeybears and monkeys pick the fruit, eat off the outer coat, and drop the shell-bound kernels. Waiting for this bounty, on the ground below are herds of white-lipped peccaries. A man needs a sledge-hammer to break the covering. Rabbit-like agoutis and squirrels gnaw through the hard shell. "The peccary, on the other hand, cracks the nut along the lateral seam that divides it into halves, a tribute to the hardness of his teeth and the power of his jaws."

Of all the known terrors in a jungle night, none compares with a herd of white-lipped peccaries. High boots and loose trousers can be worn as protection against poisonous snakes, and antivenins are available if one is bitten in spite of precautions. But "in the presence of a large herd of peccaries all of which rush viciously to the attack, a man, no matter how carefully chosen his arsenal, would have just about as much chance of coming off unscathed as a lightning beetle attacked by a regiment of army ants." Their armament is a pair of razor-sharp tusks in each jaw—weapons with which they slash an enemy to pieces.

These white-lipped wild pigs are frequently nocturnal and travel several abreast in bands of fifty to a hundred. Each adult animal weighs about a hundred pounds, and can demonstrate remarkable speed in either escape or attack. They are far more formidable than the collared peccaries which often scavenge the same jungle. The collared pigs are a third smaller, less odoriferous, form bands of eight or ten, and trot through the rain forest in single file. Tapir and deer, which pay no attention to the collared peccary, usually desert a region as soon as a band of white-lips moves in. Man must travel carefully in their neighborhood for, although they usually run off to avoid a meeting, they sometimes choose to charge, and do so with a terrifying clattering of teeth like "hundreds of castanets." The only haven from attack is in a tree. And smooth, branchless jungle trees are notoriously hard to climb.

The nearness of white-lipped peccaries is usually obvious to one's nose, since their musk is powerful and clings to the ground in the hot-house air of a jungle night. Eyes, however, seem more reliable. If for no other reason, the most stout-hearted night explorer of a jungle trail may be reluctant to turn off his flashlight and depend alone on his nose and ears. Often the patch of brightened area seems all too small. A soft-treading puma or a spotted jaguar could easily be preparing to pounce from the blind rear. A constrictor snake might be looped from the next low limb—a thirty-foot anaconda or a twelve-foot boa. How many six-inch tarantulas are waiting along the trail, crouching at the mouths of their down-slanted burrows?

These animals seldom attack a man, but in the pitch blackness of the rain forest, statistics offer a puny shield! Although we knew how acoustically dead the tropical woodland was, it seemed that our stumbling steps must alert every creature within a radius of a mile. Perhaps it would be better to sit quietly on an ant-free log, and wait for some animal to become curious enough to approach. Then right behind us a limb would crash, tearing leaves from branches and branches from trees. Fungus and termites had done their work, digesting dead wood and returning part of a tree to its mother earth.

On one night, our confidence high, we sat resolutely on a stump with flashlights off, listening to the squeaks and twitterings in the foliage high overhead. Suddenly, something snorted and brushed an outstretched foot. Startled, we pressed our lamp switches and found ourselves facing a pair of quarter-ton tapirs. They were as startled as we.

Down the trail they bolted, snorting, their broad backs wet and glistening. This largest animal native to Central and South America is a relative of the rhinoceros, but its flexible nose extends three or four inches as a soft proboscis which can be moved in all directions. Normally it hangs down over the mouth "like a drooping eyelid," but when frightened, the myopic mammal twists it from side to side and up and down, snorting and sniffing, apparently deciding which way to dash next.

Night still affords advantages not offered by day. For we barely glimpsed the brown bird which quietly vacated a pendant nest hung on the tip of a low palm leaf. Was it the large hummingbird known as a "Nicaraguan hermit"? In the dim afternoon light filtering through the ocean of leaves above us, no markings seemed distinctive as she flew. Yet after dark, when we returned, the mother sat as for her portrait, with only a bright eye cocked in our direction. We made a photograph of her from a distance of no more than ten feet. The flash bulb blazed, the shutter clicked, but the Nicaraguan hermit moved not a single feather. Whether in jungle or temperate forest, birds are reluctant to leave their nests at night, and pictures of them incubating their eggs are particularly easy to get.

Any field trip in the jungle night involves calculated hazards. If we dozed while sitting without a light, a hungry vampire might take advantage. We would miss seeing the specialist at work—opening a painless wound with razor-sharp teeth, and lapping the blood without disturbing the sleeper. A light will fend them off and so will movement. So long as we moved along the trail or kept a lamp burning, we had no need to fear them. Nor, in the wilder jungles of Guiana, was Beebe "conscious of the bloody fang, the poison tooth, of the wilderness. The peace of this jungle at night was the same peace as that of the trees in our city parks."

Even with a reliable flashlamp and no rain, events in a jungle night can be unpredictable. We found a brook less precipitous than most—one with permanent pools which cascaded gently down a slope. Time and again we visited the place a few hours after sunset, to watch the fresh-water shrimp sculling around, their big stalked eyes aglow with a reddish fire. If we stood downstream and held the light low, they would approach us, burning brilliantly by reflected eyeshine. On one of these occasions, while we were concentrating on shrimp, a wild yell cut through the darkness—probably the death scream of a coati which had been pounced upon by a jungle cat. Instantly the birds above awoke and began to clamor. In the topmost boughs a troupe of howler monkeys took up the cry with a crescendo of coughing barks that merged into one appalling roar, an "endless earth-shaking moan, followed by a quick series of grunts like staccato thunder." How many of the monkey tribe contributed to the hullabaloo we could not tell. But Bates, who commented on how much the howlers "deepened the feeling of solitude which crept on as darkness closed around us," was indulging in British understatement when he wrote that it is "a most fearful and harrowing noise, under which it is difficult to keep up one's buoyancy of spirit."

The chorusing of howler monkeys can begin at any time of night. Usually they are heard by day. A thunderstorm will start them, and the claps of exploding air are dimmed by the primate cries. "If contests were held among the beasts of the world to determine the one with the most powerful voice, the howling monkey would certainly be acclaimed champion on every occasion—the roar of the lion, the howl of the wolf, even the wail of a banshee dwindling to a mere whisper beside the efforts of the great, bearded vocalist of South [and Central] American forests." Yet this is the sound of a jungle dawn. There is no cheerful chirruping of robins, as on a temperate lawn, welcoming the new day. Night surrenders above a tropical forest to the reverberating jeers and hoots of this Stentor among mammals—to a skirl of defiance which ends human sleep more effectively than any alarm clock.

LOURUS J. AND MARGERY J. MILNE
[*The World of Night* (1956)]

The Newest Marvels of the Bee

[*The life of the bee has been wondered at since classical times, but it is only within the decade that the most wonderful of all its techniques has been known.*]

⚜

We were watching a bee arrive at a willow tassel at the foot of my meadow and perform an outlandish acrobatic act. Wait a few minutes and you will see eight or ten more bees arrive to load up on tassels that dangle all over the same tree. The length of time from the disappearance of the first bee to the arrival of the others depends on the distance to the hive; you might wait ten minutes or an hour. Later, these will be followed by more and more, steadily drifting in individually, until many are diving, splashing, and packing pollen among the tassels on the same tree. The new arrivals are all from the same hive as the first bee. They were not led to the spot personally yet here they are, and somehow the first one must have told the others about it.

This is true. It did tell the others back at the hive in a conversation so remarkable that the man who proved it exclaimed in his report, "No competent scientist *ought* to believe these things!" It took superpatience, ingenuity, and years of experimenting for Karl von Frisch to breach the barrier of understanding between himself and these marvelous little creatures.

You dissolve powdered artists' pigments in alcohol and shellac and apply the mixture to the bee with the smallest camel's-hair brush from which all but three hairs are plucked. With this you can stick a speck of color to a bee that dries instantly. Yellow, red, or green spots are then applied to front or rear of chest or abdomen, and if you have a system in which location and color represent numerals you can give thousands of bees identification tags with their own numbers.

This was the first step toward tuning in on bee conversations and discovering how one bee tells others that it has found pollen and in what direction to go for a wealth of the golden grains. Information is spelled out for compass course, distance, the exact kind of flower, and the abundance of pollen or nectar that is waiting to be plundered on that very day. The place where the willow tassel was discovered is pin-pointed in the outdoors so precisely that the others can go straight to the spot and load up.

The human animal also attaches instinctive meanings to words and colors. This is the art of the orator, the expression of music, and the suggestions of odors. Brain washers have discovered the sinister power of changing instinctive meanings through sheer repetition. So far as we know, there are no brain washers in the bee world, where every bee through generations of undeviating stereotypy agrees on the exact meaning of color, signs, odor, language. After all, this is true of every animal —the dog digging for a bone, the lofty giraffe reaching up at the fluttering green leaves against the blue sky, the whale opening its mouth wide as it rushes through a krill-filled sea. The secret signs are always there and understood by the particular animal who must use them to live.

The bee message is conveyed with two kinds of dancing—a figure eight and a wig-wag dance.

The figure eight is used only for pollen or nectar in nearby flowers. Bees fly so fast and examine so much area with their thousands of telescopes sweeping an arc of 270 degrees that it is unnecessary to waste time giving a compass course when the source of pollen or nectar is within 150 feet of the hive. In this case a space is cleared in the crowd of bees on the surface of the comb, and here the bee who made the original discovery runs around in the figure eight, circling to the left and then to the right. Excited bees crowd up, touch the performer with antennae to pick up the fragrance of the flower from the hairs on its body, and as soon as the scent is obtained off they go.

They fly in expanding circles around the hive, keeping within 150 feet, and soon pick up the exact scent which they are carrying around with them. The first bees back with a load perform the figure eight for other excited bees awaiting their turn to touch the dancers, and these pick up the odor for identifying the right flowers and are off. The figure-eight dance says, "Plenty all around, fellows. Go and get it!"

The wig-wag dance is for long-distance trips. The dancer runs straight forward, turns to the right, goes about to the starting point, runs straight forward again on the same path, turns to the left, goes about, repeats. This action right and left is emphasized by the wig-wagging of the dancer's abdomen. The performance electrifies the audience.

The straight line of the wig-wag dance gives the compass direction for the flowers to be visited. You and I might think that it would be very difficult to point out a direction with a line on a vertical wall, as on the face of a honeycomb which stands vertically in a hive. But the bee solves this mathematical problem easily by using gravity as a compass.

The straight line of the bee dance is at an exact angle to a plumb line, and that angle is the same as the angle which a bee is to fly in relation to the direction of the sun. If the flower with ripe pollen is directly into the sun from the hive, the wig-wag dance will have its center line straight up and down. "The place is in the same direction as the sun!" Or if the bee line of the wig-wag dance points straight down, "The place lies directly away from the sun!"

Shadows pivot all day long, changing every minute with the revolution of the earth, and so also does the line of the bee dance change its angle from the vertical, paced with the sun moving across the sky!

A curious man thought he would fool the bees by laying a comb flat, with its face horizontal, so it would be impossible for the bee to use the straight line of gravity for its compass. With scarcely a pause, the bee ran forward along the line, headed straight toward the flower burgeoning with pollen out yonder. When it must run on a horizontal surface the bee no longer changes the line of the wig-wag dance with the angle of the sun but points directly at the target.

Bees measure distance in flying-time—the way airlines measure distance these days—and the wig-wag dancer tells the distance by the speed of its run-around. Nine circles in fifteen seconds, says that the flowers are 330 feet from the hive; four and one half circles, five eighths of a mile; two circles in fifteen seconds, three and seven tenths of a mile. You take it from there and see how bees talk to each other. Then try to imagine where their protoplasm learned all this.

In the figure-eight dance, where distance doesn't matter, the bee lays the facts on the table by doing its figure eights faster and with more energy if there is lots of pollen or nectar; slowly, halfheartedly, if they are in limited supply. When the dance is energetic more bees hie forth to find the flowers. Only a few go forth if the dance is halfhearted, and the others seem to figure that it isn't worth the trouble as they will probably find the supply exhausted before they get there.

Both the distance and the abundance of the booty are spoken of in the wig-wag dance. The rate of speed of circling right and left calls the flying time exactly, while the vigor or languor of abdomen wagging spells out a plentiful or limited supply. This steps up the efficiency of the business of the hive, especially when a number of bees that have been exploring the landscape in various directions return about the same time. Then the one that shouts the loudest—that is to say, dances most energetically—dispatches the most bees to its flowers. The bee we were watching on the burgeoning willow tassel must have put on a furious performance back at the hive.

Spotting the particular kind of flower recommended by the returning scout is important to bees because they like to stick to one kind of pollen or one kind of nectar each day. Without clear information about the particular flower which a bee has been told to collect from, it could arrive at the right location only to find many kinds of flowers blooming there. On the twenty-first of June, the Festival of the Summer Solstice, I have counted forty-seven species of flowers blooming in a compact area. Little and big flowers are sprinkled like confetti over the ground. But the bees go straight to their work on the flowers which they have been told to collect from on that day because each carries in the eighth segment of its antenna a sample of that flower's odor picked up from the scout's hair.

Even a bee can miss its scent cue if it has to depend entirely on odor picked up from the hairs of a scout's body. Delicate scents are snatched from the hairs when they are exposed in a rush of fresh air over a long distance. So insurance is provided. The long-distance searcher, instead of letting the others pick up the scent by touching a hair, will hand over a particle of pollen dust or droplet of nectar which it has held in its mouth out of the wind all the way back. The recipient takes this particle in its mouth and thus carries on its trip a package of odor.

The recent translation of bee talk has been a great surprise. Nothing like it has ever been discovered among insects, birds, fishes, or animals, but it makes you wonder whether members of all the tribes of the Animal Kingdom may not be talking to one another all the time. And who can say that the plants may not talk among themselves just because they do not have nerve systems? The communication used by the bee in haranguing its fellows and giving them clear instructions is very different from the conventional communications of other animals with sight, sound, and odor. We have all been ordered around in unmistakable terms by birds, snakes, dogs, or skunk. But that is just saying *shoo!*

A rhinoceros talks that way to other rhinoceroses when he stakes out his territory with no-trespassing signs by using piles of dung as surveyor's stakes. Crows squawk harshly to announce the discovery of carrion to other crows. As for the universal subject of mating, birds unfurl brightly colored feathers, fireflies flash lights, paradise fishes blow bubbles, the blue-behinded ape shows a blue behind to entice a pursuer, swans whistle, and the howler monkey howls. All this is on-the-spot, impulse communication and cannot be compared with the bee's announcements of news headlines concerning fortuitous situations that lie ahead.

What the bees do as soon as they have received the information is as incredible as the bee talk. Every airport serviceman knows that running out of fuel brings a crash landing. Bees never crash land. The flying distance, which takes account of head winds that call for more fuel or tail winds that call for less, is brought back by the scout and known in advance. Whereupon the bee, before it takes off, somehow calculates the precise amount of fuel it will need and then helps itself from the hi-octane honey tanks of the hive, sucking up more honey for a long flight, less for a short flight, or only a pinhead speck of honey, which will give enough mileage if the flowers are in the immediate vicinity. For a quarter of a mile another half pinhead is added. And if the orders are to fly to a flower a mile away the bee, before starting, will suck three pinhead specks into its honey sac.

Despite this careful weighing of the situation, followed by intelligent action, the bee is truly a puppet in an inflexible commune. Bees are never so lazy that they visit flowers closer rather than farther if the word is that the farther place has more booty. They never refuse to work, never sulk, never talk back. They are the most efficient and hard-working living machines on earth. And these furry little ovals smaller than the tip of your little finger are sparked by microscopic knots of nerves which can calculate a situation.

Before taking off, not only does this creature carefully measure the fuel needed to reach the flower but it also measures it for the *kind* of trip this is going to be. Let me explain.

Nectar is a potential fuel. It is watered-down honey which, mixed with certain chemicals in the bee's head, can be used for fuel in a pinch —not hi-octane, such as the fully processed honey in the storage cells of the comb, but a satisfactory low-grade fuel. Thus the bee avoids wasting one fraction of a pinhead speck of the precious processed honey belonging to the commune by taking only enough for the outward trip to the flower, if it has been told that it is to collect nectar at the goal, or both pollen and nectar. It knows that there is a fuel pump at the other end, so that it can get nectar at the destination to convert into fuel to use on the return trip.

As a flying boxcar a bee has an impossible load factor. A load of pollen on its hind legs plus nectar in its stomach equal to its body weight must be lifted into the air and transported. Full baskets of pollen are about one third of its body weight, and two thirds are the honey fuel and pay load nectar in its honey sacs. The bees that came to the willow tassel, which delivers pollen only, from three or four miles away, must have started with full tanks of honey in order to have enough fuel to get there *and back* with a pollen load.

The question as to whether the mission is for pollen only, nectar only, or both, was answered by the dancer when it handed over the minute parcel of nectar or a grain of pollen, as though they are keys to the flower. The arresting point of the story is the way the bee acts for maximum efficiency—that is, maximum pay load. Knowing that honey taken for fuel from hive supplies is a loss to the hive, he acts to keep its fuel to a minimum and repay it with a profit on its return.

Bees also make decisions after arriving on the scene. They pause as though taking a fraction of a second to think; they hover, they look, they touch and smell with antennae, they taste with their feet, and then take appropriate action. On-the-spot decisions such as this are common with all sorts of animals. It is the decisions that bees make *before* they go forth that are so extraordinary.

We have already dredged out of the bee's weird world another case of decision that makes us wonder whether a bee can think. It takes something out of the ordinary course of events to summon a male into being. It is up to the queen herself to "decide" when to have the males around. She carries a bag of sperms with a valve that opens and closes to let the sperms out one at a time to fertilize each egg as it comes parading down the assembly line that is inside her. This smooth-running mechanism makes it possible for her to people the hive at the rate of one or two thousand babies per day. But the internal valve is under her control and cannot operate automatically according to outside conditions such as temperature or moisture, but only according to the emotions of the queen. If she elects not to open the valve and an egg slips by without being united to a sperm—the result is a male!

The queen's intention in this matter is unpredictable. She may permit one egg in five hundred to go unsparked and bring forth a male, or again she may choose to conjure up several dozen males in quick succession. In this respect the queen is a female of moods.

Scientists, naturally, recoil at the idea that insects are capable of voluntary acts involving intelligence, and it is interesting to find a profound statement of the late Frank E. Lutz, Curator of Insects at the American Museum of Natural History, about the praxis of this queen who can abolish or summon up males at will: "If a queen bee has to think about the sex of her offspring every time she lays one or two thousand eggs a day, in addition to thinking about all the other things that concern her, she must do a lot of thinking."

Of course we are always ready to defend intelligence as our prerogative, but isn't it a question of semantics? If intelligence is a relative word for a phenomenon of life in the way that voice or mobility is relative, we can be comforted that our intelligence is superior for us and their intelligence is superior for them. Both ours and theirs have qualities of intuition, genius, faculty for doing the right thing at the right time, keen senses to guide impulses. Beyond this there are two kinds of intelligence—that of action and that of thought. Our intelligence has special qualities of wisdom and understanding (or can have)—and above all imagination. Imagination is our mind's dominant power.

Bee intelligence is limited to the bee world. I suppose they never suspect that any other kind of animal lives on earth. Although referred to as the only domesticated insects, I believe that they are not the least bit tamed and that man channels this wild power to his desires only because bees can perform the miracle of changing sap into honey.

RUTHERFORD PLATT
[The River of Life (1956)]

About the Editor

As scholar, teacher, critic, naturalist and author, Joseph Wood Krutch has had a long and distinguished career. Born in Knoxville, Tennessee, in 1893, he moved to New York soon after graduation from the University of Tennessee and obtained his doctorate at Columbia University. He was Drama Critic for *The Nation* from 1924 to 1952, and Professor of Dramatic Literature at Columbia for more than ten years. Since 1952, he has resided in Tucson, Arizona.

Mr. Krutch is the author of more than twenty books and editor of seven other volumes. His early works are on literary or philosophical subjects; one of the most important is his analysis of the tragic dilemmas of today, *The Modern Temper*. Later in life, his youthful interest in natural history was revived and he came to believe that "the best context for human life is that provided by other living things—not machines." His most recent books on nature are *The Gardener's World*, an anthology, and *The Forgotten Peninsula*, a study of Lower California. Innumerable articles have appeared under his name in such magazines as *The Atlantic Monthly, Harper's, The American Scholar, Saturday Review*. He is a member of the American Academy of Arts and Sciences, the American Academy of Arts and Letters and the American Philosophical Society.